ROOTS

OF BEHAVIOR

Genetics, Instinct, and Socialization in Animal Behavior

ROOTS
OF BEHAVIOR

Genetics, Instinct, and Socialization

in Animal Behavior

BY THIRTY-ONE AUTHORS

EDITED BY EUGENE L. BLISS, M.D.

Associate Professor, Department of Psychiatry
University of Utah College of Medicine, Salt Lake City

(Facsimile Reprint of the 1962 Edition)

HAFNER PUBLISHING COMPANY

NEW YORK   LONDON

1968

Originally published 1962

Reprinted 1969

REPRINTED BY ARRANGEMENT

Printed and Published by

HAFNER PUBLISHING COMPANY, INC.
31 East 10th Street
New York, N. Y. 10003

CONTENTS

PART III / EARLY EXPERIENCE

PART IV / SOCIAL BEHAVIOR

CONTRIBUTORS

STUART A. ALTMANN, Ph.D.
Assistant Professor of Zoology, University of Alberta, Edmonton, Alberta, Canada

JAN H. BRUELL, Ph.D.
Associate Professor of Psychology, Western Reserve University, Cleveland

JOHN B. CALHOUN, Ph.D.
Laboratory of Psychology, National Institute of Mental Health, Bethesda

C. RAY CARPENTER, Ph.D.
Professor of Psychology and Director, Division of Academic Research and Services, The Pennsylvania State University, University Park

LINCOLN D. CLARK, M.D.
Associate Professor of Psychiatry, University of Utah College of Medicine, Salt Lake City; Scientific Associate, Roscoe B. Jackson Memorial Laboratory, Bar Harbor, Maine

NICHOLAS E. COLLIAS, Ph.D.
Associate Professor of Zoology, University of California, Los Angeles

DAVID E. DAVIS, Ph.D.
Professor of Zoology, The Pennsylvania State University, University Park

VICTOR H. DENENBERG, Ph.D.
Associate Professor of Psychology, Purdue University, Lafayette, Indiana

V. G. DETHIER, Ph.D.
Professor of Zoology and Psychology, The University of Pennsylvania, Philadelphia

WILLIAM C. DILGER, Ph.D.
Director of Research, Laboratory of Ornithology, Cornell University, Ithaca, New York

JOHN L. FULLER, Ph.D.
Senior Staff Scientist, Roscoe B. Jackson Memorial Laboratory, Bar Harbor, Maine

ROBERT W. GOY, Ph.D.
Assistant Professor of Anatomy, The University of Kansas, Lawrence

HARRY F. HARLOW, Ph.D.
Professor of Psychology, University of Wisconsin, Madison

ECKHARD H. HESS, Ph.D.
Professor of Psychology, The University of Chicago, Chicago

JERRY HIRSCH, Ph.D.
Fellow, Center for Advanced Study in the Behavioral Sciences, Stanford, California

JACQUELINE S. JAKWAY, Ph.D.
U.S. Department of Health, Education, and Welfare; Public Health Service Research Fellow, Department of Veterinary Science, University of Nebraska, Lincoln

DANIEL S. LEHRMAN, Ph.D.
Professor of Psychology and Director, Institute of Animal Behavior, Rutgers University, Newark, New Jersey

SEYMOUR LEVINE, Ph.D.
Fellow, Foundations Fund for Research in Psychiatry, Department of Neuroendo-crinology, Institute of Psychiatry, Maudsley Hospital, London

GERALD E. McCLEARN, Ph.D.
Assistant Professor, Department of Psychology, The University of California, Berkeley

DAVID A. RODGERS, Ph.D.
U.S. Department of Health, Education, and Welfare; Public Health Service Research Fellow, Department of Psychology, University of California, Los Angeles

JAY S. ROSENBLATT, Ph.D.
The American Museum of Natural History and Institute of Animal Behavior, Rutgers University, Newark, New Jersey

SHERMAN ROSS, Ph.D.
Executive Secretary, Education and Training Board, American Psychological Associa-tion, Washington, D.C.

PAUL B. SAWIN, Sc.D.
Staff Scientist, Roscoe B. Jackson Memorial Laboratory, Bar Harbor, Maine

T. C. SCHNEIRLA, Sc.D.
Curator, Department of Animal Behavior, The American Museum of Natural History; Adjunct Professor of Psychology, New York University Graduate School, New York

JOHN P. SCOTT, Ph.D.
Senior Staff Scientist, Roscoe B. Jackson Memorial Laboratory, Bar Harbor, Maine

EVELYN SHAW, Ph.D.
Research Associate, Department of Animal Behavior, The American Museum of Natural History, New York

ETHEL TOBACH, Ph.D.
Research Fellow, The American Museum of Natural History, New York

GERALD TURKEWITZ
Research Assistant, The American Museum of Natural History, New York

MARCUS B. WALLER, Ph.D.
Associate Staff Scientist, Roscoe B. Jackson Memorial Laboratory, Bar Harbor, Maine; USPH Postdoctoral Fellow, Department of Pharmacology, Harvard Medical School, Boston

WILLIAM C. YOUNG, Ph.D.
Professor of Anatomy, The University of Kansas, Lawrence

M. X. ZARROW, Ph.D.
Professor of Zoology, Department of Biological Sciences, Purdue University, Lafayette, Indiana

PREFACE

Few men are privileged to make the great discovery. Only an Archimedes, a Harvey, a Mendel, or an Einstein discerns a principle that transforms man's thinking. There is an elegance and a simplicity in the big theory; and in the history of science an organizing concept such as gravitation, the unconscious, or the chemical bond has given new meaning to old information and direction to inquiry.

But the glamour of the great discovery is preceded by the collection of humdrum facts; lacking these, few syntheses are possible. Observations must be made, and they are limited by techniques currently available. Bacteria are more easily observed under a microscope than with the naked eye, and emotions are evanescent and elusive unless captured and measured. The ancient Greeks knew that when a piece of amber was rubbed with wool or fur it had the power to attract light objects such as a feather or bits of straw. They even postulated a crude atomic theory. But progress was slow in the understanding of the electron until the cathode tube was invented. Then it became possible to examine the concept of an electron. Its mass and charge could be measured, and an intuitive or vague insight was transformed into a more precise understanding.

By the same token, the study of man's nature and its aberrations lags for the lack of suitable tools to investigate them. The questions are there, and many can be asked; but reliable, precise techniques must be devised before creditable information can be gathered. Psychiatry is awash with concepts and theories. Unfortunately, many are untestable, and few have been rigorously confirmed. The overriding importance of early experience is postulated. Dreams are respected as the royal road to the unconscious. The mother-child relationship is extolled, and heredity or a disturbed parental-child matrix is incriminated in schizophrenia. In the welter of confusing opinion, dogmatism and nihilism coexist. One is tempted to accept the "truth"—for certainty is reassuring—or, despairing, one may reject the entire field as hopelessly befuddled.

The notion for this symposium arose from such ruminations. Each year, the Research Committee of the American Psychiatric Association sponsors a symposium on some currently important topic at the annual meeting of the American Association for the Advancement of Science. The editor was given this responsibility and elected to organize a meeting devoted to animal behavior, not because the ultimate answers to man's behavior were evident in contemporary work in this field, but because the area offered *new techniques* to study the problems of behavior. It can be argued that man is not a fruit fly, a rat, or a monkey, and who is to deny the obvious? But the genetics of simple behavior can be explored in the fruit fly, and a monkey neonate can be isolated and mothered by a manikin. The sequence of the mother-child relationship can be disturbed in the rabbit, or alcoholic preference can be studied in strains of teetotaling mice. Techniques, though limited and not always applicable to man, are available to investigate a wide variety of behavioral puzzles. At the least, variables can be better controlled; and social, endocrinological, and even surgical modifications can be introduced to gain greater understanding. This is clearly only one of many ways through which man's nature will eventually be revealed, but it appears to be a potentially productive one—and one that should be made better known to many working in related areas. The fact that fighting behavior is best facilitated and perpetuated by combat success in rats may not explain a patient's behavior, but it and other observations may focus the clinician's as well as the investigator's attention on such critical variables.

The book, like the symposium, represents a cross section of activity in the field. It has been organized into four parts. Papers clearly overlap, and the categories, although artificial, may have usefulness since they do correspond to current areas of conceptualization and thinking.

Part I is concerned with the genetics of behavior, an area where systematic inquiry is developing. It is evident that people—being a heterologous population—differ amongst themselves, as do different strains of mice or fruit flies. Some men are tall, others short; some are intelligent, some less well endowed. It would seem that the genetic differences implied by such casual observations must also be true for many parameters of behavior, but the psychiatrist, as yet, can ill define them. He mentions differences in energy levels, ego strengths, or instinctual urges, but finds it impossible to be more specific or to delineate the contributions of the genes and the environment. There is evidence that schizophrenia and manic-depressive psychosis are gene-linked, but the precise nature of the connection is totally unknown. It is a long way from the desoxyribonucleic acids in the gene to the synthesis of proteins, and then eventually to behavioral tendencies that predispose, under appropriate circumstances, to schizophrenia. But this is the dim sequence that must some day be clarified.

Far from this goal are the studies of the birds, *Drosophila*, insects, and mice, but they suggest the beginning of some understanding. Certainly the biochemist has learned much about human metabolism from microorganisms, and we are vastly indebted to the rat for his contribution to our knowledge of mammalian nutrition. It now appears that our less privileged friends may help us to understand better the contribution of genes to behavior. Already initial steps have been taken to define the role of inheritance in such diverse behavior as alcoholic consumption, sex, exploratory behavior, problem solving, and geotropism, to cite only a few.

Part II is devoted to analysis of drive states and instinctual behavior. The problems of sexuality and aggression are carefully scrutinized, since work in both of these areas has been particularly intensive and rewarding. Certainly, papers on the physiology and psychology of alimentation and water intake would have been appropriate, as well as a discussion of such basic drives as exploration. Much work has been done in these fields, and articles and reviews are available. But these deficiencies are compensated, in part, by elegant analyses of maternal and affectional behavior in animals. There is at least the clue that in the monkey physical contact between mother and child is a critical need and that a strange offspring may be reared if this relationship is neglected.

Part III deals with the early socialization of animals, or early experience, and is introduced by a careful analysis of the problem. Attention is directed to the relevance of the sequence or schedule of experience as it intermingles with emerging biological changes. Several studies emphasize the vicissitudes of the initial social bonds, for there seems to be a period of varying length, depending upon the animal, when fear is in abeyance. During this time, the neonate attaches to his mother and, for that matter, to many other substitutes that may be experimentally introduced. One of the intriguing aspects of this period is the time-limited quality that varies from species to species. In man, undoubtedly, the period is much longer; but man, like the chick or puppy, may also have critical periods when he becomes socially imprinted as a *Homo sapiens*. The process of learning who he is and what behavior is appropriate is far more complex in man; but, notwithstanding, the studies of animals imply a specificity in the process that can be studied and understood. Finally, there is even the suggestion that changes in early experience may lead to structural and physiological alterations in the organism.

Part IV is devoted to studies of animals as members of groups and societies. The exploration of individual behavior is perplexing and difficult enough, but the variables are compounded when aggregrates are investigated. The several papers in this part illustrate both the naturalistic and more restricted experimental approaches to these problems. The relevance of dominance, territoriality, and family organization is described, amplifying discussions in previous papers. The problem of population and its controls is explored, and factors predisposing to social disintegration are suggested. This is but a limited sample of work in this area, but it does illustrate both the problems and possibilities for imaginative inquiry offered by these techniques.

The volume, like any collection of papers by different authors, lacks the evenness of style to be found in a textbook by one author; however, it hopefully offers some guide to current research and suggests that complex behavioral problems can be delimited and clarified in animals.

The contributors and I express our gratitude to the many colleagues who gave valuable assistance in the preparation of this manuscript or permitted quotation of passages from their publications.

E. L. B.

Salt Lake City

PART I

GENETICS OF BEHAVIOR

1

INDIVIDUAL DIFFERENCES IN BEHAVIOR AND THEIR GENETIC BASIS

Jerry Hirsch

It has been said that the ultimate task of science is to account for variation; where there are no variations there is nothing to be explained. The scientific study of behavior involves the analysis of variation and covariation along four dimensions which may be labeled response, stimulus, time, and individuals. Variations along the response dimension are studied as a function of variations along the other three; i.e., behavior shows (1) temporal variations or differences in response over time; (2) stimulus response covariations or response differences related to stimulus differences; and (3) individual variations or differences in response from one individual to another.

The phenomena called conditioning, learning, maturation, fatigue, adaptation, and sensitization are examples in which for a given individual under constant stimulus conditions a response changes over time. Tropisms, taxes, preferences, and all of the classical psychophysical relations provide examples in which for a given individual at a given time the response depends upon the stimulus presented. In all behavior under a given set of stimulus con-

ditions over a given time interval the individual members of a population may differ in the way that they respond.

The interindividual or phenotypic (P) variance in behavior can be partitioned into components

$$\sigma_P{}^2 = \sigma_G{}^2 + \sigma_E{}^2 + \sigma_I{}^2$$

assignable to heredity (G), environment (E), and their interaction (I). In this chapter I shall be concerned with the analysis of $\sigma_G{}^2$, the genetic variance. First, however, I shall briefly review some of the problems that arise in the analysis of the total, or phenotypic, variance, $\sigma_P{}^2$.

In the analysis of the phenotypic variance, $\sigma_P{}^2$, the last term of the equation, $\sigma_I{}^2$, is critical for the interpretation of the other two. When the interaction is zero, $\sigma_I{}^2 = 0$, the relation of the genetical and environmental components to the total phenotypic variance is additive and easily understandable. When the interaction is not zero, $\sigma_I{}^2 \neq 0$, the interpretation of how both hereditary and environmental factors combine to produce individual differences (IDs) may be difficult, especially in cases of rank reversal (Lerner, 1958, p. 44); e.g., it is common knowledge in farming that a certain strain of corn will give a

This work was supported by Grant No. G8998 from the National Science Foundation.

3

good yield in Texas and a bad yield in Kansas. With respect to behavior, interaction implies that the same method of training may be good for one individual and bad for another. Sometimes a transformation of scale can eliminate or reduce troublesome interactions.

SCALE

Variations take one of two forms, discontinuous or continuous. When variation is discontinuous the individuals are assignable to one or another of a comparatively few classes, as in the case of sex, blood type, political party, passing or failing a test item, etc. Measurement in this case consists of counting the frequency with which individuals are assigned to the separate classes.

When variation is continuous, the number of classes to which individuals can be assigned according to the grade of expression of a trait is limited only by the sensitivity of the method of measurement. Each observation is unique or potentially so. Without regular discontinuities there are no natural means of grouping observations into frequencies, and each datum has significance as a measurement of a different grade of expression of a trait. Hence it is necessary to use statistical quantities like means and variances to replace frequencies in describing continuous variations.

The validity of statistical description, however, is bound by the scale on which the measurements are taken. A change of scale, for example by a logarithmic transformation, will change the values of the descriptive statistics. Furthermore, it will change them unequally for measurements of different magnitude. Clearly, then, the first step in describing continuous variation is the choice of an appropriate scale of measurement. Unfortunately, the solution

to this question appears to be quite complicated:

The scales of the instruments which we employ in measuring our plants and animals are those which experience has shown to be convenient to us. We have no reason whatsoever to suppose that they are specially appropriate to the representation of the characters of living organisms for the purposes of genetical analysis. Nor have we any reason to believe that a single scale can reflect equally the idiosyncrasies of all the genes affecting a given character. We cannot even assume without evidence that a scale appropriate to the representation of variation of a character in one set of individuals under one set of conditions will be equally appropriate to the representation of that same character either in a different set of individuals, which may be heterogenic for different genes, or under different conditions. It may, therefore, never be possible to construct an a priori scale for the representation of variation in a character. Certainly with only our present knowledge of gene action, the construction of such a scale is impossible. Observations already available, such as those of Powers (1941), serve merely to emphasize this conclusion (Mather, 1949, p. 39).

For the purposes of the analysis of behavior in terms of either environmental factors or genetical factors, or both, the most satisfactory scale is one on which these factors are as nearly additive as possible. While there has been some discussion of this problem in the literature of both psychology and genetics (Mather, 1949; Mueller, 1949; Wright, 1952), to date far too little attention has been paid to it in actual experimental analyses. In the discussion that follows, therefore, I shall review some of the findings on IDs in behavior and their genetic basis without entering any further into this matter. I do not mean to imply that it is unimportant. Quite the contrary, this discussion assumes that the appropriate scales will ultimately be found.

THE GENETICS OF VARIABILITY

The appearance, structure, physiology, and behavior of any plant or animal, i.e., its phenotype, are determined by the interaction of its genotype with its environment. This section (from Hirsch, 1961) reviews the genetic mechanisms which contribute to produce genotypic variability.

Every member of a cross-fertilizing, sexually reproducing species possesses a diploid, or paired, set of chromosomes. All the species whose behavior is discussed in this volume are sexually dimorphic. The genetic basis of the dimorphism in a normal chromosome set lies in the difference between the presence of an homologous pair of sex chromosomes, e.g., XX in the human female, and an unequal pair of sex chromosomes, e.g., XY in the human male. Sexual dimorphism guarantees that any population will be variable to the extent of at least two classes. Whether or not sex or other genotypic differences are involved in any particular behavior remains an empirical question to be investigated separately for every behavior. It cannot be settled a priori by assumptions about uniformity.

The nonsex chromosomes are called autosomes. Every autosome is normally represented by an homologous pair having identical genetic loci. The alternative forms of a gene which may occupy a locus are termed alleles. If at a particular locus an individual has received identical alleles from both parents the individual is said to be homozygous for that gene. If, however, the members of an allelic pair differ with respect to their characteristics, the individual is said to be heterozygous for that gene. The process by which the structure of a gene changes from one allelic form to another is called mutation.

When a gene is represented in the gene pool of a population by two allelic forms, the population will be genotypically polymorphic to the extent of at least three classes. That is, individuals may be homozygous for either of the two alleles or heterozygous for their combination.

The study of populations has revealed that often series of alleles exist for a given locus. Well-known examples are the three (actually more) alleles at the ABO-blood locus in man and the dozen or more alleles at the white-eye locus in *Drosophila*. A 3-allele system like ABO generates 6 genotypic classes, and a 12-allele system generates 78 genotypic classes. In general, where there are n alleles there will be $n(n+1)/2$ genotypic classes in a population. Furthermore, according to Mendel's principle of segregation, the integrity of the individual alleles is preserved during the course of the temporary genotypic associations into which they enter in any generation. In a large random-mating population, therefore, all classes may be expected to recur every generation.

According to Mendel's principle of independent assortment, nonhomologous chromosomes are randomly distributed to the gametes. Also, because of the many genes which exist as multiple allelic series, and for other reasons, homologous chromosomes are rarely, if ever, completely homozygous. This means that the gametes produced by an organism will contain a large variety of genomes, i.e., haploid chromosome sets. For example, if we represent the three chromosome pairs of *Drosophila willistoni* by Aa, Bb, Cc, then gametogenesis in this species will produce eight alternative types of gametes: ABC, abc, ABc, AbC, Abc, aBC, aBc, abC. In general, n pairs of chromosomes produce 2^n alternative gametic genomes. Since man has 23 pairs of chromosomes a human produces gametes with any of 2^{23} alternative genomes. The chances that two nonidentical-twin siblings will be genetically identical are extremely small since the gamete contributed by each parent is chosen from 2^{23} or 8,388,608 alternatives. Hence the probability that the second offspring born to the same parents will have the identical genotype as their first offspring is $(1/2^{23})^2$ or less than one chance in over 64 trillion! The probability that two unrelated individuals will share the same genotype is effectively zero.

So far, the discussion has assumed the integrity of the individual chromosome from one generation to the next. Variability has been attributed to the exceedingly large number of possible combinations of integral chromosome units. Careful study of many species has revealed that under normal conditions chromosomes rarely maintain their integrity over several generations. In the course of meiosis, chromosomes break, exchange parts, and then recombine —a process known as crossing-over. Thus the argument for the genotypic uniqueness of the individual members of a population becomes even more compelling.

In speaking of genes on chromosomes, the analogy of beads on a string is frequently employed. That analogy can be very misleading if it is taken to imply that alleles, which are recognized by their effects, always have the same effect irrespective of their neighbors. The term position effect refers to the fact that sometimes the action of a gene is conditioned by the character of its neighbors on the chromosome.

Sometimes when a chromosome breaks and recombines, the detached segment, before recombining, reorients by 180°, thus reversing the order of the genes on the temporarily dissociated part with respect to the rest of the chromosome. When, as normally happens, recombination occurs with one of the homologues from which it was detached, the reconstituted chromosome is said to contain an inversion. Occasionally, a detached part of one chromosome becomes attached to another chromosome. When that happens the newly constituted chromosome is said to contain a translocation. If the detached part combines with the homologous chromosome without an exchange occurring, the homologue to which it has been added is said to contain a duplication. A chromosome with a part missing is said to contain a deficiency.

Deficiencies, duplications, inversions, and translocations are "aberrations" which involve segments of chromosomes but not entire chromosomes. Sometimes one or more chromosomes will be either deficient from or added to the normal chromosome complement. This is known as aneuploidy. Individuals with entire genomes in multiples greater than two are known as polyploid.

In spite of the many mechanisms producing variability which have been reviewed, it is nevertheless possible by inbreeding to produce homozygosity at many loci and thus achieve a limited degree of uniformity in a population. Every population, however, contains many alleles which when homozygous vary in effect from mildly deleterious to lethal. This condition sets a limit to the amount of uniformity that inbreeding can achieve.

There is still another mechanism which provides nature with insurance against genetic uniformity: gene interaction. The phenotypic expression of many genes is conditioned by the genetic background in which they occur. That is, their phenotypic expression depends upon which alleles of other genes are present and also sometimes upon which combinations of alleles of other genes are present. Since it appears that total uniformity is unattainable, genetic backgrounds will vary, and gene interaction will guarantee polymorphism.

Thus it can be seen that the materials on which a science of behavior must make its observations are intrinsically variable. The basic mechanisms producing this variety are gene mutation and genetic recombination.

INDIVIDUAL DIFFERENCES IN BEHAVIOR

Experimental psychology's treatment of IDs has been the analogue of Hamlet's dilemma: "To be or not to be . . . ?" James McKeen Cattell studied them, Watson buried them, Tolman understood them, Tryon emphasized their importance, Hull minimized their significance for theory, Hunter was perplexed by them, Skinner and his disciples have been maneuvered by them into an intellectual cul-de-sac, and the formal model builders have chosen to commit an elementary fallacy rather than acknowledge them. As McGill (1957, p. 1) describes the situation, for the most part "Experimental psychologists . . . ignore individual differences almost as an item of faith."

The case against IDs is verbal and dates back at least to Locke's *tabula rasa* pronouncement. The case for them comes from the data.

Watson (1924, p. 104) issued his famous dictum which effectively became an axiom of experimental psychology:

Give me a dozen healthy infants, well formed, and my own specified world to bring them up in, and I'll guarantee to take anyone at random and train him to become any type of specialist I might select—doctor, lawyer, artist, merchant-chief, and yes, even beggar and thief, regardless of his talents, penchants, tendencies, abilities, vocations, and race of his ancestors.

Tolman (1932, p. 390) understood and clearly stated the nature of the task facing a science of behavior:

. . . it may . . . be . . . that when . . . the investigation and control of individual differences shall have progressed . . . farther . . . the various actions . . . of the different "stimulus" laws will prove to be modified accordingly as different degrees of capacity are present. . . . there will have to be a much closer give and take . . . between a doctrine and description of capacities and a doctrine and description of the "normal" stimulus-response processes.

However, he never went beyond this statement of the problem.

Hull (1945, p. 56) also understood the problem:

There is much reason to believe . . . that even if organisms could be subjected to identical conditions from the moment of conception great differences would be displayed in the behavior of different species as a whole and in the behavior of the individual organisms of each species.

He believed he could resolve the difficulties these differences create by assuming that a constant in his equations would dispose of them.

Hunter (1952, p. 169) acknowledged at the end of his career that he had seen the problem IDs create for theory:

The wide scatter about the mean performance in learning experiments . . . poses a serious problem . . . which is . . . neglected in favor of an effort to secure some sort of data on the relationship between specified variables, the hope being that by pooling enough unreliable data something having statistical significance may emerge.

He never found a satisfactory solution, however.

Tryon (1934, p. 409) grasped the essentials of the problem and called attention to its modern solution early in his career:

The intensive study of the average behavior of a species . . . generally leads the . . . psychologist to ignore the more interesting and important differences between individuals from whom the "average individual" is abstracted. The "average individual" is, in fact, a man-made fiction, and the behavior of a species can properly be understood only by considering the variations in behavior of all (or of a random sample of) the individuals who are classed in it.

Furthermore, he contributed a series of experimental reports which contain some of the most valuable data so far collected by behavioral scientists (Tryon, 1940).

bright and maze-dull rats: "Although individual rates vary considerably . . . [in general] bright rats respond at a higher rate. . . ." Heron (1940, p. 30) then showed for the high- and low-activity populations selectively bred by Rundquist that "There is a clear-cut difference in the reaction of the two strains to a discrimination situation. The active rats show practically no learning in this situation while the inactive rats show slow but appreciable

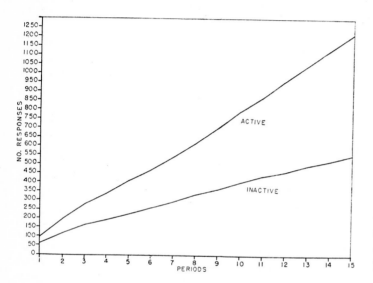

FIG. 1-1. Cumulative curves of discrimination for active and inactive strains of rats in Skinner box. (From Heron, 1940)

Skinner developed apparatus which affords probably the most reliable measure of IDs ever obtained in the laboratory. According to a principle of testing which is expressed by the Spearman-Brown formula and is well known to teachers and psychometricians, the reliability with which a test measures IDs increases with its length. Looked at in this way the Skinner box represents the longest test ever used and therefore should be one of the most reliable. As might be expected, it is very successful at measuring IDs. Heron and Skinner demonstrated that Skinner's apparatus can distinguish between genetically different populations of animals. They reported (1940, p. 13) of Heron's maze-

learning." The results of this experiment shown in Figure 1-1 raised important questions about the generality of the functions studied by experimental psychologists—"It hardly seems likely . . . that the lack of learning by the active rats of the discrimination is indicative of their inability to learn"—because in an earlier experiment Rundquist and Heron (1935) had found that " . . . the actives are better maze learners" (Heron, 1940, p. 30). Unfortunately for a science of behavior, careful empirical study of the question of generality has been bypassed in the race to announce general functions.

Clearly, Skinner (1950, p. 195) was disturbed enough by the problem of IDs to call attention to the limitations of descriptions of behavior based solely on group averages: "To show an orderly change in the behavior of the *average* rat or ape or child is not enough, since learning is a process in the behavior of the individual." Figure 1-2 (Herrnstein, 1955) presents the curves for individual subjects from a study from Skinner's laboratory in which the behavior of three pigeons was observed under identical conditions. Figures 1-3 through 1-8 (Weissman, 1958) show comparable results for an experiment from Schoenfeld's laboratory in which was studied the behavior of six groups of subjects each of which consisted of three rats. The performance of the three members of each group was observed under identical conditions. These and other unpublished dissertations testify to the sensitivity of the Skinner box to differences among individuals and to the limitations of an average.

Definitions with a rather wide currency at present are those of a reinforcing stimulus as one which supports and strengthens behavior and an aversive stimulus as one which depresses and weakens behavior. The data in Figures 1-5 and 1-6, however, show that the same stimulus conditions can be reinforcing for one animal and aversive for another within a single species!

Paradoxically, it has been asserted that the Skinner apparatus even fails to distinguish species differences:

Little more can be done than to suggest . . . the uniformity of results over a fairly wide range of species (Skinner, 1957, p. 368).

Surprisingly similar performances . . . have been demonstrated in organisms as diverse as the pigeon, mouse, rat, cat, and monkey (Ferster and Skinner, 1957, pp. 3, 4).

It is this state of affairs that was referred to above as an intellectual cul-de-sac. The unpublished data are apparently con-sidered unrepresentative. They remain so only so long as one eschews random sampling, insists on the sanctity of the uniformity postulate, and limits the scientifically acceptable to a representative curve from a representative organism where the criteria for determining representativeness remain esoteric. The study of behavior is fundamentally a problem in biology, and any methodology which obscures the

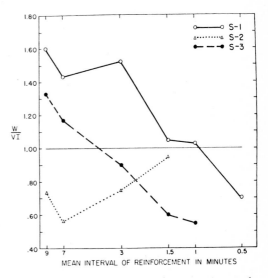

FIG. 1-2. Ratio of rate of responding (key-pecking) in warning period (W) to rate of responding in subsequent reinforcement period (VI) as a function of mean length of reinforcement period. (From Herrnstein, 1955)

differences between the food-getting behavior of predator and prey or carnivore and herbivore would appear to be self-defeating.

For many reasons the problem of biological standardization has received considerable attention in medical research. Extensive study in the fields of chemotherapy and pharmacology has revealed the ubiquity of variation:

The great progress . . . in biological methods . . . has come very largely from the

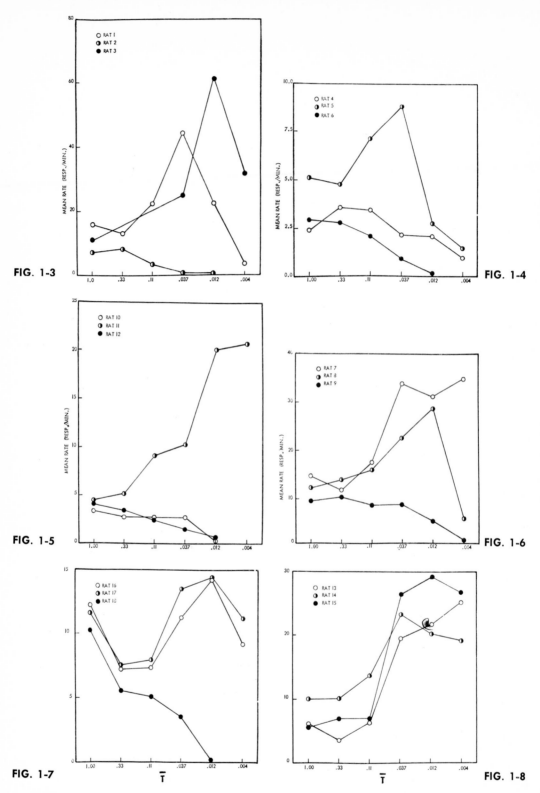

FIGS. 1-3, 1-4, 1-5, 1-6, 1-7, 1-8. Mean rate of responding as a function of $\bar{T}$ under six different stimulus conditions. $\bar{T}$ represents a ratio between the length of the reinforcement period and the length of the temporal cycle which includes both the reinforcement period and the nonreinforcement period. (From Weissman, 1958)

recognition of the fact of animal variation. . . . [occasionally] workers propose new methods which they claim are reliable because the animal response does not vary; these claims are like claims to have discovered perpetual motion (Burn, Finney, and Goodwin, 1952, p. 8).

The formal model builders, Bush and Mosteller, have incorporated the uniformity assumption explicitly into their models: "Organisms . . . can be considered 'identical' at the start of an experiment . . . " (1955, p. 3). To justify the assumption on the grounds that their models might fit some data is to commit the fallacy of affirming the consequent. Cohen and Nagel (1934) point out: "It is . . . a fallacy to affirm the consequent and infer the truth of the antecedent." If *p* implies *q*, finding that *q* is true can never establish *p*. They give as an example of the type of reasoning involved:

Suppose we know that *If there is a total eclipse of the sun, the streets are dark* is true. May we then offer as . . . evidence for *There is a total eclipse of the sun* the proposition *The streets are dark?* If we did the inference would be fallacious (Cohen and Nagel, 1934, p. 98).

It is the burden of this chapter to show that the uniformity assumption can no longer be justified on the grounds of plausibility, parsimony, or any other a priori considerations. Since it is well known that false premises can generate *any* conclusions, retaining counterfactual premises in spite of the knowledge we now possess about the nature of the populations we study can only hinder the development of a science of behavior by closing off whole areas of research of proved importance for its growth.

That the differences among individuals can cut a path directly across theoretical issues is well illustrated by a problem once believed to epitomize the difference be-

tween the two theories of learning dominant in the 1940's. The question at issue was how the rat learns the maze. For Hull, the rat knows where the food is at the end of the maze because he has learned what turn to make; i.e., specific turning responses get conditioned to the stimuli at the choice point. For Tolman, the rat knows what turn to make because he has learned where the food is; i.e., the spatial relations among the cues in the maze get integrated into a cognitive map. Many crucial experiments were devised to discriminate between the two theories.

The author knows of no experiments in which *all* of the animals behaved in a way consistent with only one of the theories (Woodworth and Schlossberg, 1954, pp. 630, 643). The experimenters were content to resolve the issue like a political contest. The majority won. The uniformity assumption had provided complete immunity against disconcerting thoughts about polymorphism.

Koch has aptly characterized the previous two decades as

. . . a period of heroic optimism in recent theoretical psychology. The keynote of this era is the belief in the imminent feasibility of comprehensive theory, having unrestricted range of application to the major phenomena of organismic behavior (Estes *et al.*, 1954, p. 3).

Quite appropriately he strongly criticized

. . . the tendency to base fundamental behavior laws of unspecified generality on single experiments, independently of any analysis of the generalization ranges within which the findings can rationally be expected to hold (Estes *et al.*, 1954, p. 24).

The argument in this chapter is not intended to imply that the variability observed in behavioral experiments is to be attributed solely to the underlying genotypic differences among all individuals. The problem of accounting for the observed variations is one that will require painstaking analysis, a kind of analysis from which the counterfactual assumptions just reviewed have been diverting attention. Ernst Mayr's recent examination of the behavior problem in the broader context of evolutionary biology provides an appropriate conclusion to the foregoing discussion:

The philosophical basis in much of early science was typological, going back to the *eidos* of Plato. This implies that the "typical" aspects of the phenomenon can be described, and that all variation is due to imperfect replicas of the type, all variants being, in the terms of Plato's allegory, "shadows on a cave wall." Such typological thinking is still prevalent in most branches of physics and chemistry and to a considerable extent in functional biology, where the emphasis is on the performance of a single individual. The typological concept has been completely displaced in evolutionary biology by the population concept. The basis of this concept is the fact that in sexually reproducing species no two individuals are genetically alike, and that every population is therefore to be characterized only by statistical parameters such as means, variances, and frequencies. . . . Genetic variability is universal, a fact which is significant not only for the student of morphology but also for the student of behavior. It is not only wrong to speak of *the* monkey but even of *the* rhesus monkey. The variability of behavior is evident in the study not only of such a genetically plastic species as man but even of forms with very rigid, stereotyped behaviors such as the hunting wasps. . . . The time has come to stress the existence of genetic differences in behavior, in view of the enormous amount of material the students of various forms of learning have accumulated on nongenetic variation in behavior. Striking individual differences have been described for predator-prey relations, for the reactions of birds to mimicking or to warning colorations, for child care among primates, and for maternal behavior in rats. It is generally agreed by observers that much

of this individual difference is not affected by experience but remains essentially constant throughout the entire lifetime of the individual. Such variability is of the greatest interest to the student of evolution, and it is to be hoped that it will receive more attention from the experimental psychologist than it has in the past (Mayr, 1958, pp. 351 ff.).

Results have been obtained, however, when the focus of research has been turned on the data unhampered by restrictive uniformity assumptions.

Pavlov, a functional physiologist of the first rank, reported that his animals showed enormous variability in their responsiveness to conditioning procedures:

One and the same injurious influence causes severe and prolonged disorders in some dogs; in others the disorders are only slight and fleeting; while yet other dogs remain practically unaffected. In many cases the deviation from normal produced by the same causative agent assumes in different dogs quite different aspects. The type and degree of pathological disturbance that develops from some definite cause was found in all cases to be determined primarily by the character of the individual nervous system of the animals (Pavlov, 1927, p. 284).

He was apparently aware of the distinction between using a well-chosen subject to illustrate some of the possibilities of his conditioning procedures and using the conditioning procedures to analyze the properties of nervous systems.

At a time when we were still quite unfamiliar with the subject of conditioned reflexes, we met with considerable difficulty on account of a drowsiness, which developed from the use of certain conditioned stimuli under certain conditions of experimentation. . . . We thought to get rid of this drowsiness by choosing for our experiments dogs which . . . were very lively . . . vivacious . . . always sniffing . . . gazing . . . intently . . . reacting quickly. . . . It was soon found that these very animals . . . were the quickest to become drowsy, so that their conditioned reflexes quickly diminished or even disappeared altogether, in spite of frequent reinforcement. . . . Our second type of dog . . . [may be described] "as a living instrument." . . . Such animals do not sleep . . . when the experimental conditions remain more or less constant; on the contrary their conditioned reflexes . . . remain extremely stable and regular (Pavlov, 1927, pp. 285, 286).

For lack of a better descriptive framework he resorted to "the ancient classification of the so-called temperaments . . . " and attempted to describe the "types of nervous systems" he believed his dogs possessed as choleric, phlegmatic, sanguine, melancholic, and intermediate types. These classifications were based on the differences in their behavioral reactions, not on either genetic considerations or direct study of the nervous system. They are of interest here because they call attention to the variation that Pavlov found in his data.

Many investigators have measured IDs in various behaviors and then attempted to analyze their genetic basis. Tolman (1924), Tryon (1940), and Heron (1935) measured IDs in the ability of rats to learn certain mazes, and Tryon began the analysis of the genetic variance for this behavior. He carried the analysis as far as the methods then available to mammalian genetics would permit. By selective breeding he produced populations of maze-bright and maze-dull animals. Attempts at further genetic analysis seemed to be unsuccessful. Similar experiments were done at McGill University where a set of extreme scoring populations was developed on the basis of an animal "intelligence test" (Hebb and Williams, 1946; Thompson and Bindra, 1952).

Analogous experiments on emotionality and activity were performed by Hall and

Rundquist respectively (1938, 1933). Das and Broadhurst (1959) report that recently a set of populations differing in emotionality has also been developed at Maudsley Hospital in England.

For use in medical and other research, many long-inbred populations of small mammals like mice, rats, guinea pigs, rabbits, etc. have been developed and are now maintained in various laboratories. By comparing the performance of two or more populations from a species it has been a relatively simple matter to measure IDs in behavior. When these measurements have been followed by the appropriate genetic crosses, which will be described in the next section, the underlying genetic diversity has usually been shown to be at least partially responsible for the observed differences. Experiments of this kind have been performed for a large variety of behaviors: hoarding (Stamm, 1954); alcohol consumption (Williams, 1956, p. 160; Rodgers and McClearn, 1959); audiogenic seizures (Ginsburg, 1954); mating competition (Levine, 1958); mating patterns (Valenstein *et al.*, 1955); exploratory behavior (McClearn, 1959); etc. However, it has not yet been possible to specify and analyze the nature of the genetic mechanisms involved.

In the study of human sensory mechanisms an unprejudiced approach to the data has revealed a similar picture. Probably the earliest findings on stable IDs with an undisputable genetic basis come from human sensory psychophysiology. Dalton reported on his own color blindness to the Royal Society in England at the beginning of the nineteenth century. Certain forms of color blindness have subsequently been followed in pedigrees, and the determining factors have been demonstrated to be inherited on the sex chromosomes. In 1931 the DuPont chemist, A. L. Fox, accidentally discovered that his laboratory associate was sensitive to the taste of phenylthio-carbamide (PTC) while he was not. Blakeslee and Fox subsequently related PTC insensitivity to a single autosomal recessive allele, and its frequency has been estimated in many populations by Snyder. Recently IDs have been reported in the reaction of human subjects to the taste of water; both distilled water and ordinary tap water were used, and both were found not to be tasteless to all subjects (Anderson, 1959). Several studies found that for some subjects water has a bitter taste. The implications of these findings for psychological theory and for psychophysical experimentation are clear: different "laws" may be found for different subjects, and all subjects must be screened and classified prior to experimentation just as is now done in the study of color vision.

By now IDs have been measured in enough behaviors and we have sufficient knowledge of the genetic structure of cross-fertilizing populations for it to be apparent how the problem of behavior study has to be approached. Variation, wherever it occurs, must be described, and the mechanisms producing it must be analyzed. Behavior traits, however, are not disembodied abstractions. They are properties of organisms, and organisms can exist only as members of populations. Hence, behavior should be studied in populations, and the applicability of any "laws" derived from the study of (1) the behavior of one member of a population to the behavior of other members of the population, or (2) the average behavior of many individuals to the behavior of a single individual, or (3) the behavior of the members of one population to the behavior of the members of another population will require experimental analysis for each behavior we wish to study for all populations in which we wish to study it.

Genetic Analysis[*]

Next I shall review a series of *Drosophila* studies which have recapitulated in a relatively short time the essential properties of the major attempts to analyze the genetics of behavior. The final part of this section illustrates how behavior genetic analysis has been carried to the chromosome level.

• MASS SCREENING

In order for behavior genetics to capitalize on the many advantages which make *Drosophila melanogaster* ideally suited for genetic analysis—a short-generation cycle, an extreme prolificacy, a low number of relatively well-mapped chromosomes, etc. —techniques were required for obtaining reliable measures of the behavior of large numbers of individuals with maximum efficiency. To this end the method of mass screening was developed (Hirsch and Tryon, 1956). It consists of presenting a stimulus on a trial to all the organisms in a group at one time and then dividing the group into two subgroups on the basis of whether or not the individuals responded to the stimulus on that trial. The procedure is the analogue of a mental test in which the individuals passing an item are assigned to one subgroup and those failing the item are assigned to another subgroup. The method calls for a series of repeated presentations of the same stimulus. The subgroups formed on one trial are retested separately on the next trial and on every subsequent trial. On each trial a subdivision is made on the basis of pass-fail performance. Passes are scored one, and fails are scored zero. Individual scores are

[*] Much of the material in this section represents a summary of the work of my students and myself both at the University of California and at Columbia University. Some of the data are presented in more detail elsewhere (Hirsch and Boudreau, 1958; Hirsch, 1959; Weiss, 1959).

cumulated over trials, and the individuals receiving identical cumulative scores are assigned to the same group (i.e., the order in which the zeros and ones are received is ignored as scores are cumulated). Hence, a series of n trials classifies the members of any size population into $n + 1$ categories so that every individual's performance on all trials is summarized in his ultimate category assignment.

> SELECTION TESTS FOR HERITABILITY

The response to selection provides a test for the heritability of a trait in a population. Using test-tube apparatus described in the original mass-screening report (Hirsch and Tryon, 1956, pp. 404–405) the screening technique was first employed in a selection study of the heritability of geotaxis. We attempted to breed strains of *Drosophila* differentiated with respect to the strength of their negative geotaxis. Ten mass screening trials were employed to classify an unselected foundation population into 11 groups. As can be seen in Figure 1-9 the response to selection for high scoring on the scale of negative geotaxis was rapid and clear-cut. The response to selection for low scoring failed to materialize in the expected way, and naïvely the experiment was discontinued as a failure. We did not realize at that time that no two samples from a cross-fertilizing population are ever likely to be genetically identical and that failure to obtain a desired response to selection in a single experiment does not prove lack of heritability for a degree of expression of a trait in a population. It has subsequently been shown in Dobzhansky's laboratory that replicate selection experiments will not always produce comparable results (Marien, 1958).

Students of behavior must learn to understand the populations with which they work. We have seen that a consequence of

the genetic structure of cross-fertilizing populations is that all zygotes produced are genotypically unique. For the student of behavior this means that except in the rare case of identical siblings there are no a priori grounds for assuming that the performance of any two individuals will be

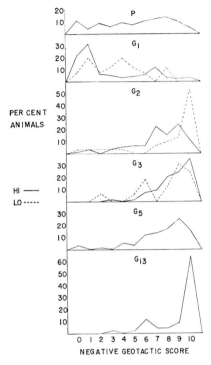

FIG. 1-9. Distribution of climbing scores for Generations P, 1, 2, 3, 5, and 13. Selection for low scoring was discontinued at Generation 3.

the same. Measures of variability are therefore as important in the description of behavior as measures of central tendency.

After the "failure" of the geotaxis study an analysis of phototaxis was undertaken. Following up the work of Brown and Hall (1936) the method of mass screening was used to measure IDs in, and to estimate the heritability of, phototaxis (Hirsch and Boudreau, 1958). Figure 1-10 shows that there was a rapid and clear-cut response to selection for both strong and weak phototaxis.

An apparently conservative estimate of heritability revealed that over half the phenotypic variance was genetic. The importance of this experiment lay in its demonstration (1) of the feasibility of studying *Drosophila* behavior, (2) of the feasibility of measuring IDs in their performance in large groups both reliably and efficiently, and (3) that the ID's variance contains a sizeable genetic component to

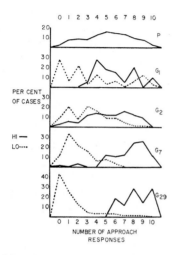

FIG. 1-10. Distribution of light-approach scores for Generations P, 1, 2, 7, and 29. (From Hirsch and Boudreau, 1958)

which the techniques of experimental genetics should be applicable.

• CLASSICAL GENETIC ANALYSIS

After over 30 generations of selective breeding had produced two strains well differentiated in their phototaxis, genetic analysis was attempted. A standard form of genetic analysis involves crossing two relatively pure-breeding strains and allowing their first filial generation hybrids, the F_1, to mate with one another to produce the second filial generation, the F_2.

According to genetic theory, if selection has succeeded in collecting together a group of "plus" alleles in one strain and

a group of "minus" alleles in another, then because of their greater genetic homogeneity the two strains should show less variation than the foundation population from which they were derived. The F_1 hybrid resulting from their cross should be uniformly heterozygous for the "plus" and "minus" alleles, and it therefore should also show considerably less variability than the foundation stock. By contrast, the F_2 progeny of the hybrid F_1 will contain individuals with all combinations of the segregating "plus" and "minus" alleles, and it therefore should show much greater variability than the F_1 and the selected pure lines.

Our first attempt at analysis for phototaxis seemed successful. The F_1 hybrid was no more variable than the selected strains, which were themselves less variable than the foundation population. Furthermore, the F_2 was more variable than the F_1. Behavior genetics was off the shoals. Or, so it appeared. (The attempts at genetic analysis of mammalian behavior have usually broken down at the F_1-F_2 variance comparison—Caspari, 1958, p. 118.) Since one of the advantages of *Drosophila* is the relatively short time period required to complete the various crossings essential to fundamental genetic studies, we immediately attempted to replicate this important result. Our replication foundered on the same shoals as much of the previous mammalian work. The F_1 hybrid was as variable as the F_2.

While James Boudreau was performing the analysis of phototaxis, I began to work on the problem of making the measurement of IDs in *Drosophila* behavior completely objective and automatic—the apparatuses used in both the geotaxis and the phototaxis experiments reported above involved the experimenter's reaction time at critical moments on every trial.

Figure 1-11 (Hirsch, 1959) shows the multiple-unit classification maze, a development which resolved the problem of objective and automatic measurement by providing a physical realization of the scoring procedure used in the method of mass screening (Hirsch and Tryon, 1956, Fig. 1). Furthermore, the maze eliminated a second disadvantage of the test-tube apparatuses previously employed. In both

words, the maze measures negative geotaxis, positive geotaxis, and varying degrees of both.

Using the multiple-unit classification maze, Jane Weiss (1959) performed a selection study in which she produced two populations which react in opposite fashion

FIG. 1-11. Photograph of 10-unit maze in vertical position facing fluorescent tube. (From Hirsch, 1959)

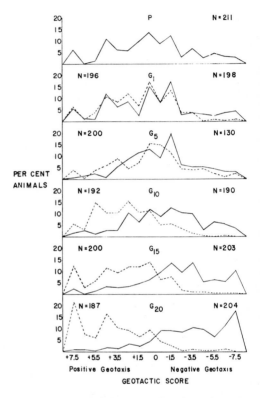

FIG. 1-12. Distribution of maze performance scores for males in Generations P, 1, 5, 10, 15, 20. (From Weiss, 1959)

test-tube apparatuses the alternatives before the animals are those of responding or not responding—i.e., in one case the alternatives are going against the pull of gravity or not; in the other case the alternatives are going toward the light or not. In the classification maze the alternatives before the animals require two different responses: (1) going against the pull of gravity by climbing up and (2) going toward the pull of gravity by climbing down. In other

to the same stimulus conditions. Starting with a foundation population having an average score neutral with respect to gravity, she developed one population that shows negative geotaxis on about 80 per cent of its trials and another that shows positive geotaxis on about 77 per cent of its trials. Figure 1-12 (Weiss, 1959) presents the results of 20 generations of selection for positive and for negative geotaxis, two diametrically opposite response dispositions emitted under a single set of stimulus conditions.

Once more the classical genetic analysis was attempted. The selected populations were crossed at the eleventh generation of selection, and their F_1 hybrid was allowed to produce an F_2. Again the expected variance difference failed to materialize. At the fifteenth generation of selection the same analysis was repeated. Once again the variance measures failed to show the expected F_1 uniformity followed by the F_2 segregation.

There is evidence, nevertheless, for the presence of additive genetic variance. A

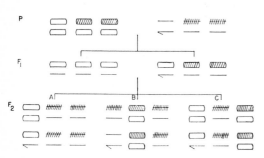

FIG. 1-13. Scheme of crosses used to obtain three experimental populations. (From Hirsch, 1959)

marked response to selection has been obtained. The central tendency of the F_1 and also of the F_2 is intermediate between that of the positively and negatively geotactic populations. Furthermore, a backcross between the F_1 and the twelfth generation as well as two successive backcrosses between the F_1 and the sixteenth and eighteenth generations showed central tendencies intermediate between F_1 and the selected population to which it had been backcrossed. Such data are consistent with the interpretation that additive genetic factors are assorting.

One criticism that has been made of the behavior-selection experiments emphasizes their failure to do close inbreeding along

with selection to achieve homozygous pure lines (Hall, 1951, p. 322). In order to study the effects of inbreeding we obtained two highly inbred lines of *Drosophila* which showed different geotactic response dispositions. Both lines had been brother-sister pair-mated, one for more than 300 generations, the other for over 150 generations. When they were crossed to produce F_1 and F_2 generations the expected variance difference again failed to appear.

Naturally, a single experiment like ours cannot resolve the question about the importance of inbreeding. Its results,

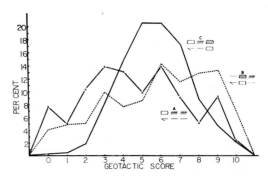

FIG. 1-14. Distribution of maze performance scores for males in three experimental populations. (From Hirsch, 1959)

however, are consistent with expectation according to the theory of genetic homeostasis, the "superiority of heterozygotes perpetuates the heterogeneity of the gene pool . . . " (Lerner, 1958, p. 95; also see Lerner, 1954). If, even with inbreeding, homozygosity is not attainable, then other methods are necessary for analyzing the genetic mechanisms underlying the differences we find.

• CHROMOSOME ANALYSIS

The *Drosophila* experiments we have reported parallel the mammalian behavior-genetic experiments, except for requiring only a fraction of the time to complete

(Hirsch and Boudreau, 1958, p. 648). Work with *Drosophila*, however, should permit a more direct approach to genetic analysis than is presently possible elsewhere. Through breeding procedures one can manipulate chromosome constitution and thus make genotype the independent variable. In order to examine the applicability of such an approach to the analysis of IDs in behavior, we made up populations which differed with respect to both the amount and the kind of free genetic variability they possessed (Hirsch, 1958, 1959). Figure 1-13 (Hirsch, 1959) illustrates the crosses which produced the three populations studied. A multiple-inversion stock (the three chromosome pairs on the left in the figure) was crossed with a wild-type stock (the three chromosome pairs on the right) to produce the F_1 types shown in the second row of the diagram. Next, the F_1 were mated together to produce Populations A, B, and C shown in the third row labeled F_2. In Population A, the X chromosome has been made isogenic, and homozygous in the female, and the autosomes left to random assortment. In Population B, Chromosome II has been made isogenic heterozygous and Chromosomes I and III left to random assortment. Population C was made isogenic for a homozygous X-chromosome pair and a heterozygous third chromosome pair with Chromosome II left to random assortment. In each experimental population, the randomly assorting major chromosomes come from wild-type stock and the controlled chromosomes come from a multiple-inversion stock.

Figure 1-14 shows how both the central tendency and the dispersion of the geotactic scores in the classification maze vary as a function of variations in chromosome constitution. These results demonstrated the feasibility of studying behavior in populations and also the possibility of analyzing the chromosomal mechanisms underlying IDs.

In her doctoral dissertation Loise Erlenmeyer-Kimling assays the role in geotaxis of the three major *melanogaster* chromosomes. The two populations developed in the Weiss experiment each contain genotypes which produce extreme geotactic behavior; one is positively geotactic, and the

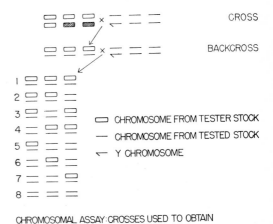

CHROMOSOMAL ASSAY: CROSSES USED TO OBTAIN COMBINATIONS OF TESTED CHROMOSOMES

FIG. 1-15. Scheme of crosses used to produce eight chromosome combinations. (From Erlenmeyer-Kimling, 1961)

other is negatively geotactic. The wild-type foundation population from which they were derived has an average geotactic response which is neutral. The chromosomes from these three populations are analyzed by a method employed by Mather and Harrison (1949) which is described in detail elsewhere (Erlenmeyer-Kimling, 1961). The crosses used in her experiment are shown in Figure 1-15. The chromosomes from each of the three populations to be tested are assayed in the genetic background provided by special tester chromosomes from a multiple-inversion stock. The eight combinations of tester and tested chromosomes used in the assay are ob-

TABLE 1-1 CONTRIBUTIONS OF CHROMOSOMES TO GEOTAXIS*

POPULATIONS	X	II	III
Selected for negative geotaxis	+	+0.86	−1.20
	+	+1.04	−0.34
	+	+1.09	−1.18
	−	+1.27	−1.07
	+	+0.01	−0.35
Unselected wild-type	+	+0.84	−
	+	+1.69	−
	+	+1.12	+
	−	+1.04	+
	+	+1.75	−
Selected for positive geotaxis	+1.66	+2.52	+
	+2.34	+2.04	+
	+0.54	+1.83	−
	+1.92	+2.93	+
	+1.25	+2.06	−

* Positive and negative signs refer to the direction of the taxis. (From Erlenmeyer-Kimling, 1961)

tained by crossing the stock to be tested with the tester stock and then backcrossing the results of the first cross to the tested stock.

The results of the first three replications of the analysis are shown in Table 1-1. A column with all negative signs indicates that a chromosome produces upgoing or negatively geotactic behavior. A column with all positive signs indicates that a chromosome produces downgoing or positively geotactic behavior. Columns with both positive and negative signs indicate chromosomes which show no measurable effects in a given population. It can be seen in the table that each of the three chromosomes produces an effect in at least one of the populations.

Erlenmeyer-Kimling's analysis demonstrates that the three chromosomes possess different properties with respect to their effects on the behavior geotaxis. The X chromosome contains factors which selec-

tion for positive geotaxis has shown can produce positive geotaxis but which have not responded to selection for negative geotaxis. The second chromosome contains factors which produce positive geotaxis in wild-type. The strength of the effect of the factors on this chromosome can be both increased by selection for positive geotaxis and weakened by selection for negative geotaxis. The third chromosome contains factors which have not responded to selection for positive geotaxis but which selection for negative geotaxis has shown can produce negative geotaxis.

In other words, there are genes distributed over almost the entire genome which influence the response to gravity. Genes on one chromosome respond to selection for both positive and negative geotaxis; genes on others respond to selection in one direction but not another. It should come as no surprise then if it turns out that the F_1 of a cross between two selected populations is quite variable and no less variable than the F_2. When a cross is made to produce an F_1 there are a large number of factors, probably of unequal strength, which are being combined in a multitude of ways in different individuals. Some of the combinations will push the response in one direction and others in the other direction.

CONCLUSIONS

There are several conclusions which follow from the foregoing survey of IDs in behavior and their genetic basis.

1. Pretending that IDs do not exist does not make them disappear. Populations are intrinsically polymorphic, and this property seems to be reflected in all behavior.

2. Interactions between genotype and stimulus conditions necessitate a far more precise specification of the "laws" of be-

havior and the conditions under which they hold than has heretofore been attempted.

3. Assessing the contribution to the phenotypic variance of the genotypic diversity existing among all individuals should prove to be a more fruitful approach to behavior genetic analysis than asking is this or that behavior inherited. Gene differences are inherited, and the task of behavior genetics is to learn what role they play in the observed behavioral differences.

4. The available evidence makes it appear unlikely that variations in many behaviors can be explained by simple Mendelian relations like the differences between the alleles of one or two genes. Hence, polygenic models and the application of the techniques of statistical genetics may be expected to play an important role in behavior genetics.

5. Analysis of the role of the chromosomes in behavioral variations suggests that it may now be possible to specify with greater precision the structural basis of behavior. In organisms whose chromosomes have been well mapped against their morphology the chromosome map will suggest what structures intervene between a given chromosome and the behavioral events with which it correlates. Furthermore, the chromosome-behavior correlations should help us to complete the chromosome map, since each behavior will, in turn, suggest the structures that are involved in its execution.

REFERENCES

ANDERSON, R. J. 1959. The taste of water. *Am. J. Psychol.* 72: 462–463.

BROWN, F. A., and HALL, B. V. 1936. The directive influence of light upon *Drosophila melanogaster* Meig and some of its eye mutants. *J. Exper. Zool.* 74: 205–220.

BURN, J. H., FINNEY, D. J., and GOODWIN, L. G. 1952. *Biological Standardization*. London, Oxford.

BUSH, R. R., and MOSTELLER, F. 1955. *Stochastic Models for Learning*. New York, Wiley.

CASPARI, E. 1958. "Genetic Basis of Behavior," in Behavior and Evolution, ed. by ROE, A., and SIMPSON, G. G. New Haven, Yale University Press.

COHEN, M., and NAGEL, E. 1934. *Introduction to Logic and Scientific Method*. New York, Harcourt, Brace.

DAS, G., and BROADHURST, P. L. 1959. The effect of inherited differences in emotional reactivity on a measure of intelligence in the rat. *J. Comp. & Physiol. Psychol.* 52:300–303.

ERLENMEYER-KIMLING, L. 1961. A genetic analysis of geotaxis in *Drosophila melanogaster*. Unpublished doctoral dissertation, Columbia University.

ESTES, W. K., KOCH, S., MacCORQUODALE, K., MEEHL, P. E., MUELLER, C. G., SCHOENFELD, W. N., and VERPLANCK, W. S. 1954. *Modern Learning Theory*. New York, Appleton-Century-Crofts.

FERSTER, C. B., and SKINNER, B. F. 1957. *Schedules of Reinforcement*. New York, Appleton-Century-Crofts.

GINSBURG, B. E. 1954. Genetics and the physiology of the nervous system. *Proc. A. Res. Nerv. & Ment. Dis.* Baltimore, Williams & Wilkins. 33: 39–56.

HALL, C. S. 1938. The inheritance of emotionality. *Sigma Xi Quart.* 26:17–27.

HALL, C. S. 1951. "The Genetics of Behavior," in *Handbook of Experimental Psychology*, ed. by STEVENS, S. S. New York, Wiley, pp. 304–329.

HEBB, D. O., and WILLIAMS, K. 1946. A method of rating animal intelligence. *J. Gen. Psychol.* 34: 59–65.

HERON, W. T. 1935. The inheritance of maze-learning ability in rats. *J. Comp. Psychol.* 19: 77–89.

HERON, W. T. 1940. The behavior of active and inactive rats in experimental extinction and discrimination problems. *Psychol. Rec.* 4: 23–31.

HERON, W. T. and SKINNER, B. F. 1940. The rate of extinction in maze-bright and maze-dull rats. *Psychol. Rec.* 4: 11–18.

HERRNSTEIN, R. J. 1955. The behavioral consequences of the removal of a discriminative stimulus associated with variable interval reinforcement. Unpublished doctoral dissertation, Harvard University.

HIRSCH, J. 1958. Recent developments in behavior genetics and differential psychology. *Dis. Nerv. System (Monogr. Suppl.)*. 19: 17–24.

HIRSCH, J. 1959. Studies in experimental behavior genetics: II. Individual differences in geotaxis as a function of chromosome variations in synthesized Drosophila populations. *J. Comp. & Physiol. Psychol.* 52: 304–308.

HIRSCH, J. 1961. The role of assumptions in the analysis and interpretation of data. *Am. J. Orthopsychiatry* 31: 475–478.

HIRSCH, J., and BOUDREAU, J. C. 1958. Studies in experimental behavior genetics: I. The heritability of phototaxis in a population of *Drosophila melanogaster. J. Comp. & Physiol. Psychol.* 51: 647–651.

HIRSCH, J., and TYRON, R. C. 1956. Mass screening and reliable individual measurement in the experimental behavior genetics of lower organisms. *Psychol. Bull.* 53: 402–410.

HULL, C. L. 1945. The place of innate individual and species differences in a natural science theory of behavior. *Psychol. Rev.* 52: 55–60.

HUNTER, W. S. 1952. "Walter S. Hunter," in *A History of Psychology in Autobiography*, ed. by BORING, E. G., *et al.* Worcester, Mass., Clark University Press.

LERNER, I. M. 1954. *Genetic Homeostasis*. New York, Wiley.

LERNER, I. M. 1958. *The Genetic Basis of Selection*. New York, Wiley.

LEVINE, L. 1958. Studies on sexual selection in mice: I. Reproductive competition between albino and black-agouti males. *Am. Naturalist.* 92: 21–26.

McCLEARN, G. E. 1959. The genetics of mouse behavior in novel situations. *J. Comp. & Physiol. Psychol.* 52: 62–67.

McGILL, W. J. 1957. Back to personal equations. *Am. Psychologist.* 12: 453.

MARIEN, D. 1958. Selection for developmental rate in *Drosophila pseudoobscura. Genetics.* 43: 3–15.

MATHER, K. 1949. *Biometrical Genetics*. London, Methuen.

MATHER, K., and HARRISON, B. J. 1949. The manifold effects of selection. *Heredity.* 3: (Part 1) 1–52, (Part 2) 131–162.

MAYR, E. 1958. "Behavior and Systematics," In *Behavior and Evolution*, ed. by ROE, A., and SIMPSON, G. G. New Haven, Yale University Press.

MUELLER, C. G. 1949. Numerical transformations in the analysis of experimental data. *Psychol. Bull.* 46: 198–223.

PAVLOV, I. P. 1927. *Conditioned Reflexes: An Investigation of the Physiological Activity of the Cerebral Cortex.* London, Oxford University Press.

POWERS, L. 1941. Inheritance of quantitative characters in crosses involving two species of *Lycopersicon. J. Agric. Res.* 63: 149–174.

RODGERS, D. A., and McCLEARN, G. E. 1959. Genetic factors in alcohol preference in laboratory mice. *Am. Psychologist.* 14: 396.

RUNDQUIST, E. A. 1933. Inheritance of spontaneous activity in rats. *J. Comp. Psychol.* 16: 415–438.

RUNDQUIST, E. A., and HERON, W. T. 1935. Spontaneous activity and maze learning. *J. Comp. Psychol.* 19: 297–311.

SKINNER, B. F. 1950. Are theories of learning necessary? *Psychol. Rev.* 57: 193–216.

SKINNER, B. F. 1957. The experimental analysis of behavior. *Am. Scientist.* 45: 343–371.

STAMM, J. S. 1954. Genetics of hoarding: I. Hoarding differences between homozygous strains of rats. *J. Comp. & Physiol. Psychol.* 47: 157–161.

THOMPSON, W. R., and BINDRA, D. 1952. Motivational and emotional characteristics of "bright" and "dull" rats. *Canad. J. Psychol.* 6: 116–122.

TOLMAN, E. C. 1924. The inheritance of maze-learning ability in rats. *J. Comp. Psychol.* 4: 1–18.

TOLMAN, E. C. 1932. *Purposive Behavior in Animals and Men.* New York, Appleton-Century-Crofts.

TRYON, R. C. 1934. "Individual Differences," in *Comparative Psychology*, ed. by Moss, F. A. Englewood Cliffs, N.J., Prentice-Hall.

TRYON, R. C. 1940. "Genetic Differences in Maze-learning Ability in Rats," in *Thirty-ninth Yearbook of the National Society for the Study of Education.* Bloomington, Ill., Public School Publishing.

VALENSTEIN, E. S., RISS, W., and YOUNG, W. C. 1955. Experiential and genetic factors in the organization of sexual behavior in male guinea pigs. *J. Comp. & Physiol. Psychol.* 48: 397–403.

WATSON, J. B. 1924. *Behaviorism.* New York, Norton.

WEISS, J. M. 1959. The hereditary determination of individual differences in geotaxis in a population of *Drosophila melonogaster.* Unpublished doctoral dissertation, Columbia University.

WEISSMAN, A. 1958. Behavior under some discriminative paradigms within a temporally defined framework of reinforcement schedules. Unpublished doctoral dissertation, Columbia University.

WILLIAMS, R. J. 1956. *Biochemical Individuality.* New York, Wiley.

WRIGHT, S. 1952. "The genetics of quantitative variability." in *Quantitative Inheritance*, ed. by REEVE, E. C. R., and WADDINGTON, C. H. London, Her Majesty's Stationery Office.

WOODWORTH, R. S., and SCHLOSBERG, H. 1954. *Experimental Psychology.* New York, Holt.

2

NEUROLOGICAL ASPECTS OF INSECT BEHAVIOR

V. G. Dethier

In looking about the animal world one is struck by the fact that behavior expresses itself most complexly in vertebrates, especially birds and mammals, and in insects. Not only is behavior most complex here, but the frequency of occurrence of intricate patterns is greater in these groups than in all others. Furthermore, there appear at first glance to be many similarities between the behavior of insects and that of vertebrates. One becomes so impressed with these similarities that he begins to make comparisons which sometimes lead to tenuous extrapolations. The twofold danger in extrapolating from superficial comparisons lies in the tendency to homologize uncritically and to subscribe to the belief that it is possible to construct some sort of behavior archetype or some abstraction called hunger drive, sex drive, maternal drive, or learning. To succumb to this temptation is to ignore the fact that arthropods and vertebrates went their separate evolutionary ways a very long time ago indeed. And, while the specialization and exquisite development of the properties of irritability and conduction in cells necessary to the formation of a neuron undoubtedly shared a common origin for the two groups, the subsequent development of the respective nervous systems has proceeded independently.

What we may hope to discover by a comparison of insects and vertebrates is insight into what kinds of behavior are possible with what kinds of neuronal substrata. Insofar as we can do this we may be able to learn about behavior in the abstract. What we may hope to learn is something about the "rules," prerequisites, or restraints which limit behavior. From this point of view insects lend themselves admirably to analysis at the neurological level.

THE CHALLENGE OF TERRESTRIAL EXISTENCE

If we consider behavior as function organized for living, we may conclude that its biggest challenge came when animals emerged upon land. By all counts the sea is a more permissive environment than land. It is above all a more stable and uniform environment. It exhibits no great temperature changes; humidity is no problem; osmotic relations are constant. Consequently, there is no need for the development of sense organs and complex behavior patterns to detect changes in these realms. The physical properties of water obviate the necessity of differentiating between olfaction and taste in the sense that terrestrial organisms do. Density precludes distant vision as well as limiting wave-length discrimination. Since water is a medium of transport, food procurement does not present all the problems which confront the terrestrial animal. By the same token, water serves as a medium of dispersal of eggs and sperm and as a cradle for the young so that the complex behavior patterns which have evolved among land animals for reproduction and parental care are largely absent in the sea. Those few animals in the sea which do exhibit very complex behavior are generally those which have become secondarily adapted for marine life after a sojourn on land (whales, seals, porpoises) or in fresh water (bony fishes).

One of the more fundamental problems which confronted animals on emergence to land was that of support, since air does not lend the helping hand that water does. Before emerging on land, animals had already set out on two paths of skeletal development. The arthropods cast the die for an exoskeleton; the chordates, for an internal skeleton. The choice of skeleton had profound effects upon the direction which the development of the nervous system followed. The skeleton is a major limiting factor; all other organs accommodate to it (as seen, for example, in an achondroplastic dwarf whose muscles, nerves, etc. are fitted to the reduced length of his bones). The arthropod exoskeleton determined the method of growth; the only way to increase size is by molting. It also limited the over-all size of the animal. Once free of the support of the sea, the animal was limited in size by the engineering principles of a frame dwelling (cf. Thompson, 1943). This may be one of the reasons why insects in general are small animals (although during the Carboniferous one dragonfly attained a wingspread of more than two feet). The largest living species of insects are somewhat larger than the smallest mammals while the smallest are smaller than many protozoa (Folsom and Wardle, 1934). The range extends from about 166 mm. (the Venezuelan grasshopper *Tropidacris latreillei* and some East Indian walking sticks which are even larger) down to a fraction of a millimeter (some springtails, ceratopogonine midges, and beetles of the family Trichopterygidae).

LIMITATIONS IMPOSED BY SMALL SIZE

Small size, therefore, is the outstanding characteristic of insects. Clearly it must impose certain restrictions upon the nervous system which will be reflected in behavior. For example, it reduces the distance over which conduction of impulses is required. This would imply, other things being equal, more rapid response and movement. At the same time, however, size limitations compel a reduction in the number of neurons possible in the system. A reduction in number of units implies a reduction in the informational capacity of the system. Reduction is carried further by the development of so-called giant fibers. Thus, in the abdominal nerve cord of the cockroach *Periplaneta americana* the giant fibers occupy about 12 per cent of its cross-sectional area (Roeder, 1948). The largest of these fibers measure 30 microns in diameter, exceeding in this respect the largest (alpha) fibers in the mammalian system.

Roeder (1959) argues persuasively that the relative merits of a nervous system composed of a few large units versus one consisting of many small units can be appreciated if one concludes that detail of information has been sacrificed for speed. It is noteworthy that large insects tend to react more slowly than smaller ones and that one at least, the giant Australian cockroach (*Macropanesthia rhinocerus* Sauss.), lacks giant fibers (Day, 1950). A large fiber cannot carry as much information from one point to another as can a number of smaller fibers because of the on-off or all-or-none nature of the nerve impulse, but it can transmit its information more rapidly. The giant fibers are the internuncial units in an alarm reaction. In the detection of, and escape from, predators, speed has greater survival value than detailed information. From the point of view of a predator also, speed is important since attack must be as rapid as the startle response of a prey. Here, however, the information required is of a much more complex nature, but it too must be handled by a small nervous system with relatively (as compared with vertebrates) few units.

Another example of the parsimony of a neuronal element is seen in the motor system of insects. As Hoyle (1957) has pointed out, there are functionally important muscles which are microscopically small and yet move joints with precision and delicacy. In contrast with vertebrate muscles, which are innervated by hundreds of nerve fibers under a complex central control, the insect muscle is supplied with a very small number of motor fibers. Some muscles are supplied by four or more axons; some are mono-axonic. More commonly a muscle is supplied by two axons. Thus, the entire system of nervous control differs from that in the vertebrates (Hoyle, 1957).

In the sensory systems too there is a reduction in the number of sensing elements. As Roeder and Treat (1957) showed, for example, the acoustic response in phalaenid moths is mediated by only two receptor units. These differ in relative acoustic sensitivity and can discriminate intensity but not pitch. They are particularly adapted to receive pulsed sounds of the sort made by hunting bats which are echo-locating. The moths respond by stopping flight and falling to the ground. In short, stimulation of only two bipolar neurons is sufficient to mediate a complete behavioral response. Another example—that in which stimulation of a single bipolar neuron in the mouthparts of the blowfly elicits an integrated feeding response—will be discussed in detail below.

Thus, in the central nervous system, in the effector system, and in the sensory system, there is a paucity of neuronal units. It is within these limitations that all insect behavior must operate.

SEGMENTAL ORGANIZATION

Although the exoskeleton shaped the future of the nervous system indirectly by limiting the size of the animal, it may also have had other more direct effects. To permit mobility, an exoskeleton must be an articulated one. Coincidental with the development of an articulated skeleton there developed pronounced segmentation of the soft tissues. In the case of the nervous system there tended to be a concentration of neurons and cell bodies within each segment. Thus, another striking characteristic of the insect nervous system by which it differs from that of the mammal is its extreme segmental organization.

The segmental nervous system is seen at its best in the more primitive insects. In the course of evolution there has been a tendency to fuse segments and consolidate ganglia; however, centralization has not proceeded so far as in the vertebrates. Retention of a segmental system of ganglia has reduced the primacy of the head and resulted in a marked degree of segmental autonomy. If, for example, a fly is decapitated, the headless body not only lives as long as its stored food reserves last and it is protected against desiccation, but is still capable of performing complicated behavior patterns. All grooming behavior is retained intact. If a bit of dust is placed on the right wing, it is removed by the right hind leg; if a particle is placed on the left middle leg, that leg is cleaned by the other two on the same side. Even the isolated head is able for a short time to feed. Similarly, an isolated abdomen of some insects is capable of laying eggs efficiently (McCracken, 1907).

A still more striking example of autonomy is seen in the copulatory behavior of praying mantids as described by Roeder (1937). Here the female in the process of courtship by the male chews off his head. Severance of the head removes central inhibition of copulatory behavior, and the male trunk cooperates actively in copulation.

These observations suggest not only that there is marked segmental autonomy but also that a great deal of behavior must be programed into the animal. Although the idea (Lorenz, 1935, 1937, 1950; Tinbergen, 1951) that behavior patterns have at their core an automatism or movement pattern that is *entirely* centrally formed and centrally coordinated has been sharply criticized by Lehrman (1956) and Schneirla (1956), a mounting body of evidence suggests that, at least in insects, the possibility of endogenous activity in the central nervous system playing a prominent role in behavior cannot be dismissed lightly (see Roeder, 1955). Spontaneous activity in deafferentated insect ganglia has been demonstrated repeatedly. In the intact insect much of this activity is under control of inhibitory influences from the head (Roeder, 1955; Weiant, 1958). The relations of this activity to sexual behavior in the mantis have already been noted.

The foregoing considerations—short conduction distances, parsimony of neuronal units, giant fibers, segmental autonomy, endogenous activity in ganglia—suggest that the nervous system of insects is best equipped to mediate behavior patterns which exhibit a high degree of stereotypy. Indeed it is stereotypy which characterizes the behavior of insects. That is not to say that the behavior of an individual lacks modifiability. To maintain such a position as rigidly as did Fabre would be to present a false picture; however, aside from some exceptions among the Hymenoptera, learning is conspicuous by its absence. Here again it is possible that size has been a contributing factor. As Roeder (1959) has pointed out, if the number of neurons in a system is strictly limited, one might expect behavior to be dominated by instinctive patterns. Such systems would tend to be under rather rigorous control of stimuli, and one would expect insects to be more "stimulus-bound" than vertebrates. The analysis of the cocoon-building behavior of the cecropia caterpillar by Van der Kloot and Williams (1953a, 1953b, 1954) is a beautiful illustration of the degree to which a complex behavior pattern is slave to the stimuli from a changing internal environment (glandular changes) and tactile and gravitational stimuli in the external environment.

PREY-PREDATOR RELATIONS IN THE MANTIS

Two of the more thoroughly analyzed behavior patterns which illustrate the stereotypy of insects and the degree to which they are "stimulus-bound" are the prey-predator relations in the praying mantis and feeding in the blowfly. The first has been studied by Mittelstaedt (1957), Rilling, Mittelstaedt, and Roeder (1959), and Roeder (1937, 1959); the second by Dethier (1955, 1959), Dethier and Bodenstein (1958), Dethier, Evans, and Rhoades (1956), Dethier and Rhoades (1954), Evans and Dethier (1957), Wolbarsht (1958), and Wolbarsht and Dethier (1958).

The praying mantis normally hangs upside down in ambush. In this position it remains motionless except for antennal vibration. The large, spined prothoracic legs are held flexed in the "praying" position. Prey moving into the visual field, but beyond reach, elicits one of the following: no reaction, saccadic head movements which follow the prey, or saccadic head movements accompanied by a slow or rapid approach to the prey. When the distance is reduced to about twice the reach of the strike, the saccadic head movements are replaced by smoother, continuous head-following movements. When the prey is within 1–2 cm., strike may occur.

Prey capture is an example of the problem of absolute optic localization. The message steering the prothoracic legs must contain information about the direction of the prey relative to the body. Since the stroke has a time duration of about 10–30 milliseconds, it is hardly possible that the stroke is controlled by watching the difference between its direction and that of the prey. Furthermore, although the mantis tends to bring its head and its prothorax into line with the prey, it is able to hit a prey which has a considerable lateral deviation from the median plane of the prothorax (it should be noted that the eyes are not movable in the head). Consequently, the direction of stroke must be determined by a message representing not only the direction of the prey relative to the head but also the position of the head relative to the body.

Mittelstaedt (1957) has analyzed the functional organization of this system in detail by a series of ingenious experiments in which the hitting performance was observed after various operations. Normal mantids hit about 85 per cent of the flies they intend to capture. If the proprioceptors in the neck which give information of

the position of the head relative to the prothorax are eliminated by nerve section, the hitting performance is irreversibly reduced to 20–30 per cent. If the head is given a fixed position relative to the prothorax by a little bridge of balsa wood, performance is normal. If the head is fixed at an angle of 10–30 degrees to the axis of the body, hits decrease to 25 per cent. If the head is turned to the right, the prey is missed to the left and vice versa. If fastening and unilateral elimination of the proprioceptors are combined, the effects of both are superposed.

By these and comparable experiments Mittelstaedt concluded that the direction of stroke depends upon feedback processes controlling the position of the head in the following manner. Fixation movements of the head, which precede release of the stroke, are steered by the difference between the optic-center message (which is a function of the angle between the prey and the fixation line) and the proprioceptive-center message (which is a function of the angle between the head and the body axis). If the fixation movements have come to rest, the direction of the stroke is determined by the optic and (to a smaller extent) the proprioceptive-center messages, which then both contain the required information.

The entire feeding pattern may be divided into a sequence of separate actions: mantis in ambush, visual following, strike, catch, raising to mouth, eating (Rilling, Mittelstaedt, and Roeder, 1959). The question of which characteristics of the prey released strike was studied by presenting hungry mantids with dummies designed so as to vary single characteristics of the prey (flies)—namely, odor, size, shape, color, distance, movement. It was concluded that an optimal prey must be moving with jerks, stops, and starts and that it should have moving legs and wings.

With great patience Rilling hand-fed isolated mantids every day (six days a week) from within a few minutes of hatching until they reached adulthood 30+ days later. The food was dismembered flies; the initial stimulus was the chemical and tactile contact with the mouthparts. Accordingly, these mantids never experienced whole, live flies and never had to strike for food. When these hand-fed mantids were finally confronted with flies, they behaved like the controls. They reacted to dummies in the same way as did their normally fed siblings. It seems clear that strike-releasing qualities of prey are not learned through experience.

Normal mantids catch 85–90 per cent of the flies they aim at. The failures are due presumably to aiming errors. When dummies are used, the number of catches decrease—i.e., catch is reduced. Hand-fed mantids catch even fewer. Thus, catch is presumably perfected by experience, but strike is not learned. The hand-fed mantids struck from the first opportunity.

For survival, the mantis from its time of hatching must be able to capture its food. This involves recognizing it, striking with sufficient accuracy to catch it most of the time, and striking rapidly enough to prevent it from escaping. Since the young mantis is on its own from hatching, at least the rudiments of the entire mechanism must be built in. A high degree of automicity and innateness is required. As Roeder (1959) remarks, where speed is a prime requisite, it seems reasonable that simplicity of mechanism is indicated.

FEEDING BY THE BLOWFLY

The blowfly (*Phormia regina* Meigen) generally feeds upon sugary substances and the liquids associated with organic material in various stages of fermentation and putrefaction. A fly which has been deprived of food for many hours is very active, indulging in much flying and walking. It may locate food by orienting to odors emanating from the food or by chance encounters with it while walking. The events which follow when food is encountered are under the rigid control of chemoreceptors located principally on the legs and mouthparts. The receptor organs are hollow hairs innervated with three bipolar neurons. Behavioral (Dethier, 1955) and electrophysiological experiments (Wolbarsht and Dethier, 1958; Wolbarsht, 1958) have shown that one of these cells mediates response to mechanical bending of the hair; one, to acceptable substances such as sugars; and one, to unacceptable substances such as salts, acids, alcohols, etc. Stimulation of a single hair with sugar is sufficient to elicit a complete behavioral response in the form of proboscis extension. Dethier (1959) has shown that this involves distribution of excitation from one afferent fiber to six different sets of ipsilateral motor fibers and six sets of contralateral fibers. The intensity of the stimulus can control the speed and extent of the response.

When a walking fly normally encounters food with one of its legs, it immediately stops, turns toward the side of stimulation, extends its proboscis, and commences to feed. The normal pattern of feeding consists essentially of extension of the proboscis, spreading of the labellar lobes, sucking, and regurgitation (Dethier, Evans, and Rhoades, 1956). Apparently, any one of three factors may initiate proboscis extension: (1) olfactory stimuli operating primarily through the antennae; (2) taste and possibly tactile stimuli operating through the tarsal receptors; (3) internal factors causing extension spontaneously. In the presence of vapors of an attractive nature a fly will extend its proboscis (cf. Minnich, 1924). If the antennae are amputated, this faculty is impaired. Water (if a fly is thirsty) or specific carbohydrates can stimulate the tarsi with a resultant proboscis extension. In the absence of any specific external stimuli the fly will frequently repeatedly extend its proboscis in an exploratory manner.

The proboscis having been extended in response to any one or combination of these clues, the first parts which come into contact with the substrate are the long hairs of the aboral labellar surface. If the stimulus now received is favorable, the labellar lobes are opened, thus presenting the oral surface to the food. Sucking then commences. The labellar hairs, therefore, can regulate spreading of the lobes and sucking. They can also regulate extension, although under natural conditions it must be quite unusual for the hairs of the retracted proboscis to be stimulated. It could well be that in the event of the omission of an initial step in the normal sequence of stimulation—e.g., stimulation of the labellar hairs before the proboscis is extended— the hairs trigger the missing step—in this case, extension—before initiating the remaining steps. Control of the hairs over sucking is easily demonstrated. If, in a fastened fly, a drop of liquid just at the threshold of rejection is placed on the open labellum, it remains undisturbed, and the fly regurgitates into it. Surface tension prevents the fly from closing the labellum, and the feet cannot be employed to remove the drop because they are fastened. If now a single labellar hair is stimulated with a concentrated sugar solution (e.g., 1 M sucrose), the drop, diluted with regurgitated fluids, is immediately swallowed.

Having opened the labellar lobes and

commenced swallowing, the fly would no longer be in complete sensory control of the situation were it not for the interpseudotracheal papillae. Once the labellar lobes are opened, the majority of the aboral hairs are no longer in contact with the solution. Even if they had been, the speed with which they adapt would certainly prevent a continual input from sugar stimulation from reaching the central nervous system. There is ample evidence that the papillae supply this defect.

Feeding can be monitored at four levels. If an odorous component of food attains a repellent level of concentration, feeding may be inhibited, although ordinarily feeding will not have commenced under these conditions. Secondly, if the tarsal receptors are stimulated by unacceptable compounds, feeding is ordinarily stopped and the proboscis withdrawn. This reaction is, of course, the basis of all measurements of tarsal rejection thresholds. Thirdly, if the labellar hairs are affected by adverse stimuli, feeding stops. Fourthly, if the papillae are stimulated by unacceptable compounds, feeding is terminated.

As might be expected, these various levels of control are finely balanced. The coordination of sensory input from all of the receptor systems involved is extremely important for the proper accomplishment of feeding. Consider, for example, the relation between tarsal receptors and those on the mouthparts. Normally a fly will not commence feeding on a solution which has first been rejected by the tarsi. However, if arrangements are made to stimulate tarsi and mouthparts simultaneously with different solutions, the tightness of control of each system over feeding can be assessed. Application of sugar, however concentrated, on the tarsi will not cause feeding if a critical concentration of NaCl is placed on the labellum; but a low concentration of

NaCl can be found which will be imbibed when the tarsi are stimulated with sugar, even though this salt is refused in the absence of tarsal stimulation. Conversely, concentrated NaCl on the tarsi will not prevent imbition of sucrose applied to the labellum. The mouthparts, as might be expected, exert a tighter control.

On the mouthparts themselves, the actions of the labellar hairs and interpseudotracheal papillae are usually coordinated. Experimentally, either can be stimulated alone. The papillae alone are stimulated by inserting a micropipette between the closed labellar lobes or by rendering the hairs inoperative through waxing. The papillae are extremely sensitive to NaCl, and the application of salt by pipette causes an immediate cessation of feeding. However, it is sometimes possible to force salt imbibition by simultaneous stimulation of labellar hairs with concentrated sucrose. Swallowing is accomplished with great hesitation on the part of the fly if the salt solution is at all concentrated. Conversely, if the hairs are stimulated with NaCl while the papillae are stimulated with sucrose, feeding can be stopped, albeit somewhat slowly and temporarily. From the results of these two experiments it would appear that the papillae exercise tighter control over actual feeding than do the labellar hairs. The behavior of the fly toward L-arabinose confirms this. The hierarchy of command over sucking, in ascending order, is tarsi, labellar hairs, interpseudotracheal papillae. For proboscis extension and spreading of the labellar lobes, it is tarsi, labellar hairs. Stimulation of the papillae seldom causes proboscis extension or spreading of the lobes so that by means of a micropipette a fly can be induced to feed without extending its proboscis or expanding the labellum. In every case mentioned above the relative concentrations of the opposing stimuli are extremely critical insofar as the nature of the final response is concerned.

Although the various chemoreceptors generally work in harmony to regulate the economy of feeding response, the imbibition of liquids is only the beginning of a longer and more complex chain of events. Once the insect has begun to feed, it obviously does not continue indefinitely. Assuming that the substance being eaten or drunk is an acceptable one and that its stimulating effect (odor or taste) initiated feeding, what are the factors which ensure continuance of feeding and control of volume intake? It seems unlikely that the initial stimulation is alone sufficient to supply momentum for continued feeding without itself continuing, or, in other words, that feeding once started continues automatically until shut off. It is more probable that there is an additional factor which drives continuous feeding and another which terminates it.

Food not only can supply the initial stimulus but can also continue to stimulate for the duration of feeding. If the fly is standing in sugar, the tarsal receptors can supply a continuous sensory input to the central nervous system until they become adapted. The principal stimulation from the mouthparts during feeding originates at the interpseudotracheal papillae because most of the labellar hairs are no longer in contact with the solution once the lobes have been spread. Even if the labellar hairs are in contact with the sugar, they adapt very rapidly. An experiment can be designed to show that in the absence of any stimulation except that from the labellar hairs complete adaptation of these hairs brings an end to feeding. For example, a fly which is not thirsty can be made to drink water if one or more of the labellar hairs are stimulated with sugar. Adaptation of the hair or hairs being stimulated causes feeding to cease, whereupon stimulation of different hairs which are still sensitive results in resumption of swallowing. From this result it would appear that a continual sensory input is indeed essential to uninterrupted feeding. Even stimulation of the tarsal receptors can drive feeding, and one way to force flies to imbibe nonstimulating fluids (i.e., those which are neither acceptable nor repellent) is to apply sucrose to the legs. For many of the insects in which feeding reactions have been studied, the prerequisite of sensory input is the rule (cf. Dethier, 1953).

Under natural circumstances a fly does not feed to full capacity upon first contact with an acceptable food but rather takes repeated samples. This behavior is graphically demonstrated by automatic recording. In this way each new extension of the proboscis places the labellar hairs again in contact with the solution for fresh stimulation which imparts renewed impetus to feeding. At some point in the proceedings, however, feeding finally ceases; a definite quantity has been consumed. This volume is not constant but depends upon the hunger state of the fly, the nature of the food, and its concentration. Clearly, neither gut capacity nor carbohydrate requirements immediately controls volume intake (cf. also Dethier and Rhoades, 1954). It was shown furthermore by Evans and Dethier (1957) and Hudson (1958) that none of the following could be considered to be regulatory factors: blood-sugar levels, stored glycogen depletion, and crop contents. Dethier and Bodenstein (1958) by means of experiments which involved loading of the mid- and hind-gut, ligation of the hind-gut, and ligation of the crop showed that these areas of the alimentary canal were not involved in either satiation or hunger. They did demonstrate that cutting of the recurrent nerve (that nerve which connects the autonomic nervous system of the gut with the brain) interfered with feeding to the extent that cessation is impossible. The flies become hyperphagic.

It has been postulated that feeding is driven by input from the chemoreceptors of the mouth and legs and that the presence of food in the fore-gut region acts by way of the recurrent nerve to inhibit sensory input. Accordingly, in the fly, feeding appears to be under the rigid control of chemoreceptor organs consisting of a small number of cells plus a feedback mechanism operating by way of the recurrent nerve. There is no evidence that feeding (insofar as carbohydrates are concerned) is controlled by metabolic need.

CONCLUSION

Although one may become aware of the complexity and nuances of insect behavior simply by observation, analyses of the sort described begin to reveal the means whereby small nervous systems with relatively few cells operate to achieve these ends. We see that the number of neurons necessary to assess, even in some detail, changes in the environment and to translate these into complex response patterns need not be great. Different means have been adopted by vertebrates to achieve strikingly similar behavior but at a greater cost in cells. It is clear that much of the automatic behavior characteristic of insects has been subordinated in the vertebrates. The increase in number of cells in the vertebrate system, however, is given over to adding, if not a new, at least a more exquisitely refined characteristic, learning of a high order.

REFERENCES

DAY, M. F. 1950. The histology of a very large insect, *Macropanesthia rhinoceros Sauss* (Blattidae). *Australian J. Scient. Res., Series B, Biol. Sc.* 3(1): 61–75.

DETHIER, V. G. 1953. Host plant perception in phytophagous insects. *Tr. Ninth Internat. Cong. Entomol.*, Amsterdam. 2: 81–89.

DETHIER, V. G. 1955. The physiology and histology of the contact chemoreceptors of the blowfly. *Quart. Rev. Biol. 30:* 348–371.

DETHIER, V. G. 1959. The nerves and muscles of the proboscis of the blowfly *Phormia regina* Meigen in relation to feeding responses. *Smithsonian Misc. Coll. 137:* 157–174.

DETHIER, V. G., and BODENSTEIN, D. 1958. Hunger in the blowfly. *Ztschr. f. Tierpsychol. 15:(2):* 129–140.

DETHIER, V. G., EVANS, D. R., and RHOADES, M. V. 1956. Some factors controlling ingestion of carbohydrates by the blowfly. *Biol. Bull. 111(2):* 204–222.

DETHIER, V. G., and RHOADES, M. V. 1954. Sugar preference-aversion functions for the blowfly. *J. Exper. Zool. 126:* 177–204.

EVANS, D. R., and DETHIER, V. G. 1957. The regulation of taste thresholds for sugars in the blowfly. *J. Insect Physiol. 1:* 3–17.

FOLSOM, J. W., and WARDLE, R. A. 1934. *Entomology with Special Reference to Its Ecological Aspects*, 4th ed. Philadelphia, Blakiston, p. 30.

HOYLE, G. 1957. Nervous control of insect muscles. *Recent Advances in Invertebrate Physiology, Univ. Oregon Publications*, pp. 73–98.

HUDSON, A. 1958. The effect of flight on the taste threshold and carbohydrate utilization of *Phormia regina* Meigen. *J. Insect Physiol. 1(4):* 293–304.

LEHRMAN, D. 1956. "On the Organization of Maternal Behavior and the Problem of Instinct," in *L'Instinct dans le Comportement des Animaux et de l'Homme*, ed. by GRASSÉ, P.-P. Paris, Masson & Cie, pp. 475–520.

LORENZ, K. 1935. Der Kumpan in der Umwelt des Vogels. *J. Ornithol. 80:* 50–98.

LORENZ, K. 1937. Ueber den Begriff der Instinkhandlung. *Folia Biotheoret. 2:* 17–50.

LORENZ, K. 1950. The comparative method in studying innate behavior patterns. *Symposia Soc. Exper. Biol. 4:* 221–268.

McCRACKEN, I. 1907. The egg laying apparatus in the silkworm (*Bombyx mori*) as a reflex apparatus. *J. Comp. Neurol. Psychol. 17:* 262–285.

MINNICH, D. E. 1924. The olfactory sense of the cabbage butterfly, *Pieris rapae* Linn., an experimental study. *J. Exper. Zool. 39:* 339–356.

MITTELSTAEDT, H. 1957. Prey capture in mantids. *Recent Advances in Invertebrate Physiology, Univ. Oregon Publications*, pp. 51–71.

RILLING, S., MITTELSTAEDT, H., and ROEDER, K. D. 1959. Prey recognition in the praying mantis. *Behaviour. 14(1–2):* 164–184.

ROEDER, K. D. 1937. The control of tonus and locomotor activity in the praying mantis (*Mantis religiosa* L.). *J. Exper. Zool. 76:* 353–374.

ROEDER, K. D. 1948. Organization of the ascending giant fiber system in the cockroach (*Periplaneta americana*). *J. Exper. Zool. 108:* 243–262.

ROEDER, K. D. 1955. Spontaneous activity and behavior. *Scient. Month. 80:(6):* 362–370.

ROEDER, K. D. 1958. The nervous system. *Ann. Rev. Entomol. 3:* 1–18.

ROEDER, K. D. 1959. A physiological approach to the relation between prey and predator. *Smithsonian Misc. Coll. 137:* 287–306.

ROEDER, K. D., and TREAT, A. E. 1957. Ultrasonic reception by the tympanic organ of noctuid moths. *J. Exper. Zool. 134:* 127–157.

SCHNEIRLA, T. C. 1956. "Interrelationships of the Innate and the Acquired in Instinctive Behavior," in *L'Instinct dans le Comportement des Animaux et de l'Homme*. ed. by GRASSÉ, P.-P. Paris, Masson & Cie, pp. 387–452.

THOMPSON, D. W. 1943. *On Growth and Form*. Cambridge, Cambridge University Press, p. 52.

TINBERGEN, N. 1951. *The Study of Instinct*. Oxford, Oxford University Press.

VAN DER KLOOT, W. G., and WILLIAMS, C. M. 1953a. Cocoon construction by the cecropia silkworm: I. The role of the external environment. *Behaviour. 5(2):* 141–156.

VAN DER KLOOT, W. G., and WILLIAMS, C. M. 1953b. Cocoon construction by the cecropia silkworm: II. The role of the internal environment. *Behaviour. 5(3):* 157–174.

VAN DER KLOOT, W. G., and WILLIAMS, C. M. 1954. Cocoon construction by the cecropia silkworm: III: The alteration of spinning behavior by chemical and surgical techniques. *Behaviour.* 6(4): 233–255.

WEIANT, E. A. 1958. Control of spontaneous activity in certain efferent nerve fibers from the metathoracic ganglion of the cockroach, *Periplaneta americana. Proc. Tenth Internat. Cong. Entomol.* 2: 81–82.

WOLBARSHT, M. L. 1958. Electrical activity in the chemoreceptors of the blowfly: II. Responses to electrical stimulation. *J. Gen. Physiol.* 42(2): 413–428.

WOLBARSHT, M. L., and DETHIER, V. G. 1958. Electrical activity in the chemoreceptors of the blowfly: I. Responses to chemical and mechanical stimulation. *J. Gen. Physiol.* 42 (2): 393–412.

3

BEHAVIOR AND GENETICS

William C. Dilger

Since the beginnings of animal life, genotypes have been subject to the continuing impingement of environmental selective pressures acting differentially on the genetic make-up of populations. The molding influence of these pressures is responsible for the great variety of animal life that now exists and has existed in the past. An animal may be looked upon as a beautifully integrated, complex set of genetically controlled adjustments to an equally complex array of problems presented by the environment. Since the environment, in one respect or another, is in an almost constant state of change, the gene pool must constantly undergo modifications. This is made possible, of course, through the variation that results from genetic recombinations and mutations. Variants which increase the probability of survival tend to be conserved in the population, and variants which decrease the probability of survival tend to be eliminated. This differential selection of genotypes through environmental effects applies both to the structures of animals (morphology) and to what they do with these structures (behavior). It is obvious that structure and behavior are intimately associated and evolve together.

In order to appreciate the importance of recombination as a source of essential variation, one has but to realize that the occurrence of two sexes linked to elaborate sexual behaviors has evolved with the function of providing such variability.

LEARNED AND NOT-LEARNED BEHAVIOR

Realizing that all behavior is essentially genetically based, we should evaluate such terms as "innate" and "learned." Psychologists have generally been concerned with learned behavior and have neglected the so-called "innate" elements. Ethologists on the other hand, have traditionally been primarily concerned with "innate" elements of behavior. The former's interests no doubt have been shaped largely by a primary concern for the behavior of humans, which is felt to be largely learned. On the other hand, ethologists, being zoologists, have been struck by the apparent relative simplicity and rigidity of many behaviors which in these respects resembled structure. It has taken time for some psychologists to realize that innate elements commonly underlie learned behavior and for ethologists to recognize that many of these simple, rigid behaviors are wholly or partly the result of learning. Now there is an ever increasing tendency for psychologists and ethologists to cooperate in their investigations.

Unfortunately, some have equated the term "genetically determined" with such terms as "innate" or "inborn." This indirectly implies that learned behavior is not genetically determined, something which is certainly not the case. It is essential at this point to reach some sort of understanding concerning the differences between learned and inborn behavior. Thorpe (1951) provides a definition of learning which is acceptable to most zoologists: "The process which produces adaptive change in individual behavior as a result of experience. It is regarded as distinct from fatigue, sensory adaptation, maturation, and the results of surgical or other injury." The difficulty, of course, largely centers on the word "experience." Ethologists have commonly taken experience to mean the influences of the environment, both animate and inanimate, after the animal is hatched or born. This may be a somewhat troublesome point of view since it is known that such influences may reach the unborn or unhatched animal if its sense organs have developed sufficiently to perceive them. Many are now aware of this difficulty and are making allowances for it in their experiments and observations.

There are many kinds of behavior where it is difficult to see how the animal could be influenced by experience—for instance, the drinking movements of birds of which there seem to be at least three major types: the common dipping of the bill in the water, raising the head, and letting the water flow down the esophagus by gravity; the "pumping" up of water as demonstrated by pigeons and doves (Columbidae) and by sandgrouse (Pteroclidae) and by some estrildine finches (Poulsen, 1953) in which the bill remains in the water during drinking; and the "lapping" of parrots (Psittacidae) in which the head remains in or near the water while drinking but the water is drawn in by action of the tongue which forces the water back into the throat. No amount of experience short of seriously damaging the animal structurally would interfere with these ways of drinking. The same could be said for the various grooming movements of birds and mammals. These are all highly stereotyped and specific for certain taxonomic groups and are not capable of being altered through experience. The zoological and ethological literature provides many examples of this type of *not*-learned activity and the reader is referred, for instance, to Tinbergen (1951) and to Thorpe (1956).

What is the nature of the genetic control of learned behavior? To my knowledge no one has experimentally demonstrated the exact genetics underlying an individual case of learned behavior. What seems apparent, however, is that learned behavior as such is not inherited but that a framework of possibilities permitting such behavior is. In other words, an animal can inherit limitations permitting certain definite expressions of behavior such as *what, how much, in what way*, and *when* learning can take place. The "what" and "how much" are self-explanatory. The "in what way" refers to the type of learning permitted, such as habituation, conditioning, trial and error, imprinting etc. The "when" refers to sensitive periods for learning, before and after which the possibilities are either much reduced or eliminated entirely. These inherited limitations may be very broad in some respects and narrow in others, depending upon the natures and severities of the environmental selective pressures exerted on the gene pool and on the nature and amount of the normal genetic variability and other limitations of the animals concerned. Much of man's learned behavior, for instance, is based on very broad limitations—limitations which in some cases are rarely, if ever, actually reached. On the other hand, the behavior of many animals, particularly those which are less highly evolved behaviorally, are endowed with very narrow limitations or possibly none at all in the case of protozoans which have been studied—although the evidence here is somewhat contradictory (e.g., Mast and Pusch, 1924; Reynolds, 1924; Mast, 1932).

Hinde (1959) points out that in practice ethologists often use the term "inborn" to mean not-learned. He also goes on to say that "not-learned" is a better term than "inborn" as the latter is etymologically inaccurate. As indicated above, the term "innate" is often used synonymously with "not-learned" or "inborn." Spurway (1953), however, rightly emphasizes that "innate" can only properly be used to describe *differences* between characters; not the characters themselves. This is because biologists of other disciplines have traditionally used the term in this way and behaviorists, to avoid confusion in this age of rapid integration of points of view as applied to evolutionary problems, should follow suit.

Presumably, if "not-learned" behavior is indeed not learned, this implies that it does not have an inherited framework within which learning can be expressed in some fashion. A not-learned unit of behavior is usually thought of in the same way as is a unit of morphology such as a feather, an eye, or a tooth which for each species, has only the normal amount of variability characteristic of genetic recombination or, more rarely, mutation. This suggests that such behavior is under some sort of more direct genetic control and not a potentiality within a characteristically limiting framework as is learned behavior. Actually, many such behavioral units seem to have what may be thought of as a "not-learned" core occurring within a set of limitations permitting subsequent plasticity of expression through learning.

An analogous situation exists in morphology. For example, the presence of a muscle is not learned, but if it is made to experience certain stimuli it can "learn" to become larger, harder, more heavily vascularized, smaller, softer, or less heavily vascularized. However, these changes as a result of experience are not unlimited. There is a maximum size beyond which no amount of experience will cause it to become larger. It must be remembered that a species-typical muscle, like a species-typical behavior, is the result of an integrated complex of not-learned and learned factors.

Often these experiences which impinge upon an animal's morphology and behavior are quite uniform for each individual of a population. This, of course, results in a high degree of uniformity throughout the population. It was thought at one time that one of the criteria for distinguishing not-learned behavior was its uniform appearance throughout a population. In the light of present knowledge this is obviously fallacious.

The normal species-typical development of an individual within the uterus or egg depends, of course, upon an intricate complex of interacting influences. Some of these influences are intrinsic to the developing organism itself—for example, the organism's genetic constitution is responsible for a definite kind of development and for the order in which it occurs. Moreover, these development features in turn influence what has developed and what is to develop. Other influences are extrinsic in the sense that they depend directly or indirectly on the genetic constitution of the parent caring for the developing young. In cases of development in the uterus it is, of course, the female parent who provides these extrinsic influences. In the case of egg-laying species it may be the female or both the male and the female. Extrinsic influences mediating the proper genetically controlled development of the embryo include such things as the physiochemical surroundings of the embryo, incubation behavior, nest-building behavior, and so forth.

It is obvious that if this species-typical development is interfered with in some way by accident, such as an unfortunate genetic recombination or mutation affecting either the responsible parent(s) or the embryo itself, the resultant individual will be abnormal in some respect and liable to extermination. The same will be true if such development is interfered with by some nongenetic accident such as a physical injury. We must assume that the existence of a normal, adequately functioning individual must depend upon a normal history of development within the egg or uterus. Also, since the development of behavioral and morphological features does not cease upon hatching or birth, it is equally important that the animal not be interfered with at this time either.

This normal developmental history is quite rigidly controlled, as has been pointed out, by the genetic constitution of the developing animal and of its parent(s). It is far too limited in permissible variability to be left to the possible vagaries of some of the more plastic types of learning; consequently the development of the young from zygote to birth or hatching depends upon not-learned features.

During the course of development the various sense organs, by means of which the animal will gain information for the rest of its life, become operational along with the attendant neurophysiological mechanisms. Some of these senses become operational before others, and some do not become operational until after the animal has been born or hatched. It would be perhaps more realistic to restrict the term *learning* to the adaptive modification of behavior as a result of sensory perception of stimuli impinging upon the individual whether or not such an individual is already born or hatched.

It is possible for the individual to provide its own sensory stimulation through which learning can take place. These "feedback" phenomena are instances where a species-typical behavior is acquired through individual practice in the absence of stimulation afforded by another experienced individual. The animal at first performs behavior that is allied to, but different from, that of the definitive product, and it gradually expands, restricts, or otherwise modifies these responses as a result of experiencing its own behavior. It is as if the animal has a not-learned specific sensitivity or "appreciation" for the proper behavior and gradually acquires the proper responses by retaining those elements of the variably performed behavior which have the most "satisfactory" feedback value. The propensity for responding selectively to definite portions of this stimulation is probably not learned. The kind and range of variability of the original spectrum of stimulation are also probably not learned. Beach and Jaynes (1954) give an excellent review and bibliography relating to the effects of experience on the development of behavior.

GENETIC STUDIES OF BEHAVIOR

Insects

Precise knowledge of the genetic basis of behavior is exceedingly limited. The genetic basis for the morphology of a few animals has been worked out in some detail, particularly, of course, for *Drosophila melanogaster*. The same desirable qualities possessed by *Drosophila* which render it such a useful animal for studying the genetics of morphology lend themselves well to the study of the genetics of behavior. It is not surprising, therefore, that much of our knowledge of this subject stems from studies of this insect. For instance, Reed and Reed (1950) found that the gene *w* decreases the frequency of matings (copulations) by about 25 per cent. Rendel (1951) found that the gene "ebony" reduces the mating activity of the homozygous males in the light, but in the dark these males are equal to or perhaps even superior to vestigial control males. Bastock (1956) found that the gene *y* (yellow body color) reduces the strength and duration of wing-vibration, a component of male sexual display. Males possessing this gene are therefore less successful in breeding.

Much of the remainder of our knowledge of the direct effects of genes on behavior also stems from work on insects. Some information is available for mammals and very little for birds. Other work on the genetics of behavior of insects indicates that genes may directly affect the frequency of matings (Merrell, 1953, for *Drosophila*), may control "preference" for sexual partner (Merrell, 1949; Rendel, 1951, for *Drosophila;* and Sheppard, 1953, for *Panaxia,* a moth), may change behavior through changes in morphology (Scott, 1943, relative to sense-organ changes in *Drosophila*), may cause changes in selection of environments (Waddington, Woolf, and Perry, 1954, for *Drosophila*), and that many such behavioral changes may be a result of pleiotropic effects (Caspari, 1951, for *Ephestia,* a moth). In addition, Haskins and Haskins (1958) found by studying the moths *Callosamia promethea, C. angulifera,* and their F_1 hybrids that food-plant selection was probably monogenic whereas the method of cocoon

spinning was probably multigenic. Hörman-Heck (1957), working with the crickets *Gryllus campestris, G. bimaculatus,* and their hybrids, concluded that the following behaviors are affected by genetic changes: (1) which leg males use in stridulation; (2) aggressivity in larvae; (3) frequencies of antennal tremblings in courtship; (4) presence or absence of head and prothorax oscillations during copulations; and (5) the number of times the elytra are raised prior to stridulation. Backcross observations suggest that larval aggressivity and elytra raising may be cases of monofactorial inheritance.

Fish

Direct evidence of the genetic control of behavior in vertebrates is, unfortunately, even scarcer, and the precise identification of responsible genes is almost nonexistent. Clark, Aronson, and Gordon (1954) studied the genetics of mating behavior patterns in certain xiphophorin fishes (the familiar swordtails and platies of aquarists). They found that the most striking differences among swordtails, platies, and their hybrids had to do with the duration, frequency, quickness, and effectiveness of copulations. Swordtails copulated sooner in bouts of sexual activity and also copulated longer. However, platies copulated more frequently than swordtails, and the percentage of resulting inseminations was higher. In the F_1 hybrids the frequency of copulations was slightly higher than in platies, thus more frequent then in either parental type. These F_1's, however, had percentages of resulting inseminations intermediate between the parental types. In the F_2's and backcrosses these values were much lower. They (Clark, Aronson, and Gordon, 1954) go on to say:

In general, copulatory behavior in F_1 hybrids was either intermediate or more like that of the swordtail. Some features of male sexual behavior in these xiphophorin fishes apparently are influenced by genetic factors, but we cannot offer any specific mode of inheritance to account for the data obtained. The inheritance is likely to be based on many genes, each of small effect.

As in many other animals (see below) aggression may be affected by the genetic constitution of the animal. The most familiar example in fish is probably that of the anabantid *Betta splendens*, the Siamese Fighting Fish. The Siamese have selectively bred these fish for hundreds of years in order to enhance the fighting ability. These animals are used by the Siamese as a sport in which considerable money changes hands. The fighting of these fish differs from that of their wild relatives principally in the fact that their fighting is more prolonged and more easily evoked. The motor patterns themselves seem to differ little, if at all.

Birds

I have not been able to find any references to studies on the genetics of behavior in reptiles and amphibians. The data on birds are almost as unsatisfactory, with a few notable exceptions. Hinde (1956) reports on behavior exhibited by interspecies hybrids among cardueline finches (*Carduelis carduelis, Chloris chloris,* and *Serinus canarius*). From his study of the parental species and the resultant hybrids he concluded: (1) The behavior patterns common to both parents were found unchanged in the hybrids; (2) Behavior patterns differing in form or frequency in the parents were intermediate in these respects in the hybrids; and (3) Behavior occurring in only one parent species was also intermediate in the hybrids. He also found that the relationships of the various behavior patterns to each other as well as their re-

sponsible tendencies were qualitatively unchanged in hybrids.

It has long been known that certain behavior patterns of domestic chickens, such as agonistic and parental-care behavior, have hereditary bases. Certain heritable traits have been differentially selected for in different breeds of chickens. For instance, fighting cocks have been selected for increased aggressiveness, and other breeds are noted for their "broodiness" or superior egg-laying qualities. Papers by Fennell (1945), Guhl and Eaton (1948), and Kaufman (1948) are useful in this regard.

Dr. Konrad Lorenz has long been interested in the behavior of anatine ducks and has made observations on many hybrid individuals. These investigations have been carried out under natural conditions. He has found (personal communication), for instance, that some sexual displays of hybrids are intermediate between the parental types and that others are indicative of an ancestral condition not found in either parent species. He has also found (personal communication) that an F_2 individual (offspring of *Anas bahamensis* X *A. spinicauda* mated to each other) starts the motor patterns for the display termed a "grunt-whistle" and finishes with the "bridling" display. Another such individual starts the "bridling" movement but then raises the tail as in the "head-up-tail-up" display. Here we have a case where the motor patterns of closely allied displays are disrupted and recombined in various ways. Certainly these displays must have a multifactorial basis.

A female F_1 hybrid between a male *Turdus merula* and a female *T. migratorius* performs tail-raising movements intermediate in amplitude between the parent species (Dilger, 1959c).

We now have data (unpublished) on the

behavior of F_1 hybrids between the African parrots *Agapornis roseicollis* and *A. fischeri*. All of the resultant hybrids, about 30 in number so far, are similar in appearance and behavior. We have investigated their behavior in a number of different situations, and our findings may be summarized as follows: (1) The males perform vigorous and prolonged precopulatory displays, but the females are more refractory than parental females in reaching sexual readiness as a result of these activities; (2) There seems to be a partial loss of the ability to recognize individuals of their own kind, and they also are much more prone to violate the territories of other pairs; (3) The forms of the various precopulatory displays given by the males are intermediate between the parental types, but the relative frequencies of these various activities are quite variable; some are intermediate, others seem to favor one parental type or the other; (4) Curiously enough, it makes a difference to what sort of female the male is paired—*fischeri*, *roseicollis*, or hybrid. For instance, "switch-sidling," a common precopulatory display, comprises about 32 per cent of the precopulatory activities of *roseicollis* males mated to *roseicollis* females. This same display comprises about 51 per cent of the precopulatory activities of *fischeri* males mated to *fischeri* females. Hybrid males mated to hybrid females utilize this display about 40 per cent of the time relative to the number of times other displays are given. It can thus be seen that hybrid males are almost exactly intermediate in this regard when mated to hybrid females. However, if hybrid males are mated to parental-type females, the situation is quite different, and the following figures are obtained: hybrid males with *roseicollis* females, 33 per cent; with *fischeri* females, 50 per cent. It seems that this is a case

where the female's response is all-important in determining what sort of behavior is elicited in males. The rest of the precopulatory displays of hybrid males shows, in general, the same sort of pattern, but not as perfectly.

Perhaps the most interesting behavior demonstrated by these hybrids concerns the nest material carrying of the females (Dilger, 1959*b*). Females of *roseicollis* carry strips of nesting material (paper, bark, or leaves) tucked amidst the feathers of the lower back or rump. Several such strips are carried at a time, and if a strip is dropped for some reason before the bird reaches the nest cavity it is not picked up and retucked. On the other hand, *fischeri* females carry nesting material (strips of bark, paper, or leaves and more substantial items such as twigs) one piece at a time in the bill. Hybrid females almost always attempt, at least, to tuck nesting material in the feathers but are never successful in carrying in this way for several reasons: (1) Proper movements for tucking are made, but the bird seems unable to let go of the strip even after repeated attempts at tucking; (2) The strip is tucked but soon falls out—usually while the bird is busy cutting the next one; (3) Tucking is attempted at locations other than the lower back and rump—a more "primitive" or ancestral pattern; (4) The strip is grasped somewhere other than at one end, making proper tucking impossible; (5) Tucking movements are begun; but the behavior gradually merges into preening movements, and the strip falls unnoticed to the ground; (6) Tucking-intention movements are made but not completed; (7) Inappropriate objects such as twigs are tucked; and (8) Sometimes the bird attempts to get its bill near its rump by running backward. These hybrids are only successful in carrying material in the mouth. After two years of this behavior, in the presence of both normal *fischeri* and *roseicollis* females, these hybrids have not learned to carry nesting material more efficiently and still spend as much time in attempting to tuck before flying off with a single piece. This is interesting as these birds are amazingly quick to learn new behaviors in other contexts such as opening cage doors, evading capture, and so on. They are also favorite birds for use in trained-bird acts where they are easily taught all manner of tricks such as riding miniature railroad trains, washing clothes, posting letters, and pushing little wagons. The hybrids give every indication of being as quick to learn such behaviors. This merely emphasizes the fact that abilities to learn various behaviors do not extend equally throughout the entire spectrum of an animal's activities.

Some of the inability to carry nesting material by tucking is a result of the employment of behavior intermediate between that of *fischeri* and *roseicollis;* Items 1, 2, 4, and 7 as listed above seem to be examples of this. Item 3 is indicative of a more ancestral condition; Item 6 probably is merely indicative of a low tendency to tuck but, oddly enough, is rarely seen in *roseicollis.* The proximity of the bill to the ruffled feathers may stimulate preening movements if the tendency to tuck is rather weak. Running backward as if trying to place the bill near the rump is rather rare and difficult to interpret. All birds find no difficulty in placing the bill in this position during preening of this area, and it seems strange that these hybrids should have difficulty, however rare, in placing the bill there in the tucking context.

We have not yet obtained F_2's and backcrosses enabling us to probe the genetic control of these and other patterns more thoroughly. The data so far do suggest

that this behavior is determined by multigenic factors. All of the female F_1 hybrids behave identically to each other with regard to their attempts at carrying nesting material.

Mammals

There is some evidence on the genetic control of mammal behavior, and Caspari (1958) provides an excellent review. He points out that our knowledge of this subject is based on three types of observations: (1) Spontaneous mutations at well-known loci show pleiotropic effects on behavior (Keeler and King, 1942, aggression and tameness in mice); (2) Different inbred strains of mammals are distinguished not only by certain morphological traits but by behavioral ones as well (Scott, 1942; Fredericson, 1953; and Thompson, 1953 and 1956, aggressivity in mice; Scott and Charles, 1953; Fuller and Scott, 1954; Scott, 1954; Fuller, 1955, timidity, aggressivity, friendliness, response to food rewards, and proficiency tests in dogs; Sawin and Crary, 1953, nest building and care of young in different strains of rabbits); and (3) Given genetically nonuniform material, it is possible to select for certain desired traits (Tryon, 1940, 1942; Hall, 1951, maze-learning ability and "emotionality" respectively in the rat). Rundquist (1933), working with the amount of motor activity of rats as recorded in a revolving cage, could select for or against such activity.

Goy and Jakway (1959) and Jakway (1959) investigated the inheritance of mating behavior patterns in male and female guinea pigs, *Cavia* sp., of different strains. The mating behavior was separated into various components and each investigated separately. They found, for instance, that certain types of activities in the males were dominant over others. For example, the rates of lower measures of activities in the lethargic Strain-13 type were dominant (circling-nuzzling and mounting). The higher measures of activity (intromission rate and number of ejaculations) had a separate type of inheritance from the lower measures. This certainly suggests that separate underlying mechanisms are responsible. The coefficients of variation for the F_1 hybrids were less than those for animals in either pure strain. For females, the results indicated that three independent genetic factors determine the character of estrus as they measured it. Latency of heat, duration of heat, and the per cent of response all showed correlated inheritance and may have been multiple manifestations of a single set of factors which determined the responsiveness of the individual to estradiol benzoate. A completely independent genetic mechanism determined the duration of the maximum lordosis. Male-like mounting behavior seemed to be completely independent of the genetic mechanisms for maximum lordosis. It was also concluded that sensitivity to a hormone is genetically independent of the factors determining the quantitative character of the behavioral response.

Attempts at determining the number of genes involved in behavioral changes in mammals have not been completely successful, but several approximations have been made. In each case the number was found to be low. The wildness or tameness of both wild and inbred strains of mice was found to be determined by about three genes (Dawson, 1932). Certain different behavioral traits demonstrated by various breeds of dogs were found to be determined by a minimum of one or two segregating pairs of genes (Scott, 1954).

GENERAL CONSIDERATIONS

Caspari's (1958) useful summary of present knowledge concerning the genetic bases of behavior provides several general conclusions which may be summarized as follows:

1. Genes have highly specific actions which, however, may be at least partially obscured through pleiotropic effects. This is, of course, because animals are highly integrated organisms in which any gene substitution is almost bound to have secondary effects, sometimes far-reaching ones.

2. Different characters demonstrate different degrees of stability against genetic and environmental influence. Characters of great selective importance will tend to incorporate a more variable base, presumably as added insurance permitting them to adapt more readily to a changing environment.

3. Genes at different loci interact in the production of phenotypic characters. Such gene combinations are called "coadapted gene systems."

4. The frequency of a given gene in a gene pool is determined by selective pressures, mutation pressure, breeding structure of the population, and other factors.

5. Heterozygotes frequently have adaptive values superior to either homozygote. This phenomenon of "heterosis" permits two alleles to remain in a gene pool and thus may contribute to beneficial amounts of variability. Of course such hybrids may be superior in some respects but may also be definitely at a disadvantage in others as is mentioned and discussed by Dilger (1956), Dilger and Johnsgard (1959), and Sibley (1957).

6. In insects, numerous cases are known in which behavior is influenced by pleiotropic effects of gene substitutions affecting primarily morphological characters.

7. It is possible for a gene with a certain morphological effect to become established in a population because of a favorable

adaptive value of another character produced by the same gene. In either case, selection pressure will adjust the remaining genotype so that a coadapted gene system is established.

A rather curious effect of hybridization on behavior not mentioned by Caspari is the fact that hybrids sometimes demonstrate behavior patterns which are not found in either parental species but which are characteristic of some ancestral condition. Lorenz's hybrid ducks and our hybrid parrots, mentioned above, provide examples of this.

Caspari goes on to say that evidence in mammals indicates that behavior traits seem to have multigenic bases and that differences in behavior seem to be caused by pleiotropic effects of well-known morphological genes. He also suggests that evolution has favored higher degrees of variability in mammals in general. In this respect it might be suggested that the evolution of sex with the consequent morphological and some behavioral variability through genetic recombination was a highly successful "experiment" since it afforded a greater assurance of survival through greater ease of adaptation to a changing environment. The next logical evolutionary step, in view of this great success of sex and its consequences, would perhaps be to establish greater plasticity of behavior. Selection does seem to be working in this way, and the mammals, the most recently evolved vertebrate group, do seem to incorporate the greatest amount of behavioral plasticity through the operation of learning. Among mammals, man has evolved with the greatest amount of behavioral possibilities. Judging from recent events, the biological advantage of this type of almost unlimited behavioral capability is certainly not above reproach! Humans are unique among animals in that

they are the only species which has evolved a capacity to consciously control its own survival.

Behavioral studies of closely related species which will hybridize are a great potential source of information concerning the mode of inheritance of behavior patterns. The work that has been done testifies to this. However, there are certain difficulties with this method of attack. Species which are closely enough related to hybridize freely are usually so similar in their behavior that it is difficult or even impossible to obtain useful information from hybrids and other crosses. Species pairs are needed which are sufficiently closely related to produce completely fertile hybrids, yet sufficiently different in regard to some clearly definable pattern of not-learned behavior. Such species pairs are difficult to find. Lorenz (1956) has found such a pair in the ducks *Anas bahamensis* and *A. spinicauda.* We have found such species pairs in our *Agapornis* parrots. Work is now under way with both these groups. Useful information can also be obtained by studying crosses between different breeds or strains of domesticated animals, some of which perhaps best approximate the zoologist's subspecies and their intergrades. Scott (1954), for instance, is acquiring some very useful data by working with different breeds of dogs. The most serious disadvantage to this type of approach is that the findings are difficult to apply to an understanding of the natural evolution and causation of the behavior as expressed in the species ancestral to the domesticated forms.

Scott and Charles (1953) and Scott (1954), working with dogs, have had to conclude that there is no evidence for the genetic transmission of what might be called "mental ability" or "general intellectual organization." Differences among their dogs in this regard seem to be related to one or more of the simple components of behavior such as aggressiveness, timidity, agility, reactivity to awards, and peripheral characters such as sensory and motor abilities and preferences. It seems obvious that animals can be encouraged to increase their performances closer to the limits of their inherent capacities to respond, as well as selectively bred to increase the limits of these capacities. In connection with this it seems probable that one of the most important aspects of applied behavioral knowledge is to explore ways in which humans can be taught to approach a greater realization of latent mental abilities. Selective breeding for greater mental capacity is impossible at the moment because of inadequate information on the factors involved and, of course, for other obvious reasons.

Rensch (1954) has found that among related animals the larger species possess brains which are not only actually larger but also relatively larger than in their smaller relatives. He has also found that, in general, the smaller species are more "lively" and more "nervous" in their behavior. The larger animals are quieter and more "thoughtful." The smaller animals either tend to learn more quickly if the tasks are relatively easy, or these animals are worse at learning at the start of the experiment, apparently because of "nervousness" and timidity. They then, however, outstrip their larger relatives later in the experiments. He has found that only the smaller animals are subject to "experimental neuroses." The larger animals are able to learn more, retain it longer, and learn more complicated tasks than the smaller ones.

It is of interest that all these differences depend more on the *relative* size differences than on absolute differences. For instance, large cyprinodontid fishes (5–6 cm.) behave similarly to their smaller relatives, as do the large breeds of chickens compared to smaller breeds. Rensch concludes that the data already available allows the statement that the evolutionary increase in absolute brain size and in the proportion of the parts of the brain and of its cytoarchitectonic organization causes essential changes in central nervous functions and "psychic" performance.

Rensch postulates that the performance of the larger animals may be due to their greater potential for a more complex switch-mechanism (more dendritic connections). This suggests that one of the ways animals can be selected for more learning ability is to evolve relatively and absolutely larger brains.

REFERENCES

BASTOCK, M. 1956. A gene mutation which changes a behavior pattern. *Evolution. 10:* 421–439.

BEACH, F., and JAYNES, J. 1954. Effects of early experience upon the behavior of animals. *Psychol. Rev. 51:*239–263.

CASPARI, E. 1951. On the biological basis of adaptedness. *Am. Scientist. 39:* 441–451.

CASPARI, E. 1958. "Genetic basis of behavior," in *Behavior and Evolution,* ed. by ROE, A., and SIMPSON, G. G. New Haven, Yale University Press, pp. 103–127.

CLARK, E., ARONSON, L., and GORDON, M. 1954. Mating behavior patterns in two sympatric species of xiphophorin fishes: their inheritance and significance in sexual isolation. *Bull. Am. Mus. Natural Hist. 103:* 141–225.

DAWSON, W. 1932. Inheritance of wildness and tameness in mice. *Genetics, 17:* 296–326.

DILGER, W. 1956a. Hostile behavior and reproductive isolating mechanisms in the avian genera *Catharus* and *Hylocichla. Auk. 73:* 313–353.

DILGER, W. 1959b. Nest material carrying behavior of F$_1$ hybrids between *Agapornis fischeri* and *A. roseicollis*. *Anat. Rec. 134:* 554.

DILGER, W. 1959c. Notes on a hybrid thrush (male blackbird X female American robin) and notes on a male American robin paired with a female song thrush. *Avic. Mag. 65:* 125–131.

DILGER, W., and JOHNSGARD, P. 1959. Comments on "species recognition" with special reference to the wood duck and mandarin duck. *Wilson Bull. 71:* 46–53.

FENNELL, R. 1945. The relation between heredity, sexual activity, and training to dominance subordination in game cocks. *Am. Naturalist. 79:* 142–151.

FREDERICSON, E. 1953. The wall-seeking tendency in three inbred mouse strains (*Mus musculus*). *J. Genet. Psychol. 82:* 143–146.

FULLER, J. 1955. Hereditary differences in trainability of purebred dogs. *J. Genet. Psychol. 87:* 229–238.

FULLER, J., and SCOTT, J. 1954. Heredity and learning ability in infra-human mammals, in Genetic factors effecting intelligence. *Eugenics Quart. 1:* 28–43.

GOY, R. W., and JAKWAY, J. S. 1959. The inheritance of patterns in sexual behaviour in female guinea pigs. *Animal Behaviour 7:* 142–149.

GUHL, A., and EATON, R. 1948. Inheritance of aggressiveness in the fowl. *Poultry Sc. 27:* 665.

HALL, C. 1951. "The Genetics of Behavior," in *Handbook of Experimental Psychology*, ed. by STEVENS, S. S. New York, Wiley, pp. 304–329.

HASKINS, C., and HASKINS, E. 1958. Note on the inheritance of behaviour patterns for food selection and cocoon spinning in F_1 hybrids of *Callosamia promethea* X *C. angulifera*. *Behaviour. 13:* 89–95.

HINDE, R. 1956. The behaviour of certain cardueline F_1 inter-species hybrids. *Behaviour. 9:* 202–213.

HINDE, R. 1959. "Some Recent Trends in Ethology," in *Psychology, a Study of a Science*, ed. by KOCH, S. New York, McGraw Hill, Study I, Vol. II, pp. 561–610.

HÖRMANN-HECK, S. VON 1957. Untersuchungen über den Erbgang einiger Verhaltenweisen bei Grillenbastarden (*Gryllus campestris* L.– *Gryllus bimaculatus* De Greer). *Ztschr. f. Tierpsychol. 14:* 137–183.

JAKWAY, J. S. 1959. The inheritance of patterns of mating behavior in the male Guinea Pig. *Animal Behaviour 7:* 150–162.

KAUFMAN, L. 1948. On the mode of inheritance of broodiness. *Proc. Eighth Poultry Cong.*, Copenhagen. Pp. 301–304.

KEELER, C., and KING, H. 1942. Multiple effects of coat color genes in the rat, with special reference to temperament and domestication. *J. Comp. Psychol. 34:* 241–250.

LORENZ, K. 1956. "The Objectivistic Theory of Instinct," in *L'Instinct dans le Comportement des Animaux et de l'Homme*. Paris, Masson & Cie, pp. 51–76.

MAST, S. 1932. Localized stimulation, transmission of impulses, and the nature of response in *Amoeba*. *Physiol. Zool. 5:* 1–15.

MAST, S., and PUSCH, L. 1924. Modifications of response in *Amoeba*. *Biol. Bull. 46:* 55–60.

MERRELL, D. 1949. Selective mating in *Drosophila melanogaster*. *Genetics. 34:* 370–389.

MERRELL, D. 1953. Selective mating as a cause of gene frequency changes in laboratory populations of *Drosophila melanogaster*. *Evolution. 7:* 287–296.

POULSEN, H. 1953. A study of incubation responses and some other behaviour patterns in birds. *Vidensk. Medd. fra Dansk naturh. Foren. 115:* 1–131.

REED, S., and REED, E. 1950. Natural selection in laboratory populations of *Drosophila*: II. Competition between a white-eye gene and its wild-type allele. *Evolution. 4:* 34–42.

RENDEL, J. 1951. Mating of ebony, vestigial and wild type *Drosophila melanogaster* in light and dark. *Evolution. 5:* 226–230.

RENSCH, B. 1954. "The Relation Between the Evolution of Central Nervous Functions and the Body Size of Animals," in *Evolution as a Process*. ed. HUXLEY, J., HARDY, A. C., and FORD, E. B. Allen & Unwin. London, pp. 181–200.

REYNOLDS, B. 1924. Interpretation of protoplasmic masses in relation to the study of heredity and environment in *Arcella polypera*. *Biol. Bull. 46:* 106–142.

RUNDQUIST, E. 1933. Inheritance of spontaneous activity in rats. *J. Comp. Psychol. 16:* 415–438.

SAWIN, P., and CRARY, D. 1953. Genetic and physiological background of reproduction in the rabbit: II. Some racial differences in the pattern of maternal behavior. *Behaviour.* 6: 128–146.

Scott, J. 1942. Genetic differences in the social behavior of inbred strains of mice. *J. Hered. 33:* 11–15.

Scott, J. 1943. Effects of single genes on the behavior of *Drosophila. Am. Naturalist. 77:* 184–190.

Scott, J. 1954. The Effects of selection and domestication upon the behavior of the dog, in symposium on 25 years of progress in mammalian genetics and cancer, ed. by Russell, E. S. *J. Nat. Cancer Inst. 15:* 739–758.

Scott, J., and Charles, M. 1953. Some problems of heredity and social behavior. *J. Genet. Psychol. 48:* 209–230.

Sheppard, P. 1953. "Polymorphism and Population Studies," in *Evolution Symposium on Experimental Biology,* New York, Academic Press, No. 7. pp. 274–289.

Sibley, C. 1957. The evolutionary and taxonomic significance of sexual dimorphism and hybridization in birds. *Condor. 59:* 166–191.

Spurway, H. 1953. Territory and evolution in sticklebacks. *Penguin New Biol. 14:* 33–43.

Thompson, W. 1953. The inheritance of behavior; behavioral differences in fifteen mouse strains. *Canad. J. Psychol. 7:* 145–153.

Thompson, W. 1956. The inheritance of behavior; activity differences in five inbred mouse strains. *J. Hered. 47:* 147–148.

Thorpe, W. 1951. The definition of some terms used in animal behaviour studies. *Bull. Animal Behaviour 9:* 34–40.

Thorpe, W. 1956. *Learning and Instinct in Animals.* London, Methuen, vi+ 493 pp.

Tinbergen, N. 1951. *The Study of Instinct.* London, Oxford University Press, xii + 228 pp.

Tryon, R. 1940. "Genetic Differences in Maze-learning Ability in Rats," in *Thirty-ninth Yearbook of the National Society for the Study of Education.* Bloomington, Ill., Public School Publishing, Part I: 111–119.

Tryon, R. 1942. "Individual Differences," in *Comparative Psychology,* ed. by Moss, F. A. Englewood Cliffs, N.J., Prentice-Hall, pp. 330–365.

Waddington, C., Woolf, B., and Perry, M. 1954. Environment selection by *Drosophila* mutants. *Evolution. 8:* 89–96.

4

DOMINANCE AND SEGREGATION IN THE
INHERITANCE OF QUANTITATIVE BEHAVIOR IN MICE

Jan H. Bruell

Anyone who examines the literature dealing with the inheritance of behavior is struck by the fact that Mendel had but little influence on it. Most studies in this field used either of two methods: the method of selective breeding for a given behavior trait, or the method of comparing the behavior of pure strains which had been developed by selective breeding for other than behavioral traits (Hall, 1951, Caspari, 1958, Fuller and Thompson, 1960). These methods of genetic research were developed long before Mendel, and one is tempted to say that they are of pre-historic origin. Before the dawn of history, man had captured wild animals and had bred them selectively for tameness. And the knowledge that breeds of animals (for example, breeds of horses or dogs) differ in their behavior is ancient indeed (Zirkle, 1951).

Mendel's name is associated with neither of these approaches. When his name is mentioned, concepts such as dominance and recessiveness, segregation and recombination, come to mind. One also tends to think of linkage, although linkage was not described by Mendel himself. Very few of

these phenomena have been studied by psychologists because it was long thought, even by geneticists, that Mendel's concepts and methods applied only to qualitative characters. But most behavior traits, are quantitative rather than qualitative, and thus it seemed that Mendelian methodology was of limited usefulness to psychologists. This disregard is no longer warranted. In recent decades a brilliant synthesis has been achieved between Mendelian genetics and "biometrical genetics" (Mather, 1949; Falconer, 1960), the study of the inheritance of continuous variation. These newer developments in genetics offer the key to the study of behavior genetics and cannot fail to have a profound influence on psychology once they become more generally known. The purpose of this paper, therefore, is to present some of the concepts of biometrical genetics and to show that they can be applied to the study of inheritance of behavior.

THEORETICAL FOUNDATIONS

Dominance and Segregation in Qualitative Inheritance

In discussing the results of his breeding experiments, Mendel used what became known as Mendelian algebra. In his sys-

Experimental work supported by Grant No. M2625A from the U.S. Public Health Service, and Grant No. G7020 from the National Science Foundation.

TABLE 4-1   MENDELIAN NOTATION OF POPULATIONS AND GENOTYPES

NAME OF POPULATION	MATING TYPE	GENOTYPE	PHENOTYPE	PER CENT
P_1—Parent 1	$P_1 \times P_1$	A_1A_1	white	100
F_1—Filial 1	$P_1 \times P_2$	A_1A_2	pink	100
P_2—Parent 2	$P_2 \times P_2$	A_2A_2	red	100
B_1—Backcross to P_1	$P_1 \times F_1$	A_1A_1	white	50
		A_1A_2	pink	50
F_2—Filial 2	$F_1 \times F_1$	A_1A_1	white	25
		A_1A_2	pink	50
		A_2A_2	red	25
B_2—Backcross to P_2	$F_1 \times P_2$	A_1A_2	pink	50
		A_2A_2	red	50

tem, letter symbols represented the hereditary "elements" which determine qualitative attributes of organisms such as color or shape. Table 4-1 presents various populations in Mendelian notation. It is placed at the beginning of this paper because it permits us to recapitulate briefly some of the symbols (P_1, F_2, etc.) and terms (*allele, segregation*, etc.) commonly used by geneticists. P_1 and P_2 are true-breeding strains which differ, for example, in color. P_1 is white, and its color is assumed to be determined by gene pair A_1A_1. P_2 is red, and its color is determined by gene pair A_2A_2. F_1 is pink, and this color is assumed to result from the interaction of genes A_1 and A_2.

Gene pairs of the type A_1A_1 or A_2A_2 are said to be homozygous, while gene pairs of the type A_1A_2 are referred to as heterozygous. Genes which can form pairs of the type A_1A_2 because they occupy the same locus on homologous chromosomes are called alleles. In the example of Table 4-1 the allelic pair A_1A_2 results in a phenotype intermediate between the white phenotype of P_1 and the red phenotype of P_2. Frequently, however, heterozygous organisms of the type A_1A_2 are phenotypically indistinguishable from one of the parents. For example, the heterozygote A_1A_2 may be red and indistinguishable from P_2. In this case P_2 is said to be dominant over P_1 with respect to color, and P_1 is called the recessive parent.

Populations P_1, F_1, and P_2 are genetically uniform; they consist of 100 per cent A_1A_1, or A_1A_2, or A_2A_2 organisms. By contrast, populations B_1, F_2, and B_2 are genetically heterogeneous. These populations segregate into two or three classes, namely, white, pink, and red organisms. In other words, in these populations the phenotypes of P_1, F_1, and P_2 reappear in various proportions. Therefore, the B_1, F_2, and B_2 populations are referred to as segregating populations, while the three phenotypically and genotypically uniform populations P_1, F_1, and P_2 are called nonsegregating.

Genotypes and Phenotypes in Quantitative Inheritance

An essential step from qualitative Mendelian genetics to biometrical genetics is taken when Mendel's letter symbols are made to represent quantities rather than qualities, measures or test scores rather than visual impressions. This approach is illustrated in Figure 4-1. The values given for each population are average scores on some test. It can be seen that the position each population occupies along the single dimension of the measuring scale is fully explained by assuming that gene A_1 contributes 5 units to the test score, while gene A_2 contributes 10 units to it. For example, since F_1 organisms are of the type A_1A_2, their

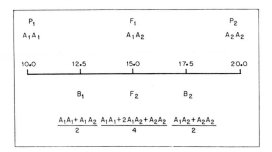

FIG. 4-1. Numerical example illustrating connection between Mendelian genotypes and quantitative phenotypes.

phenotype is $(5 + 10) = 15$. Or, since the B_1 population consists of 50 per cent A_1A_2 and 50 per cent A_1A_1 organisms, the average phenotype of this population is $(10 + 15)/2 = 12.5$.

Dominance and Interaction

It is customary to refer to the position on a measuring scale midway between the positions occupied by the two parents as "mid-parent" (M).

$$M = (P_1 + P_2)/2 = (A_1A_1 + A_2A_2)/2 = A_1 + A_2 \quad (4\text{-}1)*$$

Many computations are facilitated if the mid-parent is taken as the point of origin of the measuring scale (Fig. 4-2,a). On such a scale, $M = 0$, and P_1 lies at a distance $(-a)$ and P_2 at a distance $(+a)$ from M.

In Figure 4-1, F_1 occupied the mid-parent position. However, this was only a special case. The value of the heterozygote

* In this paper, depending on the context, letter symbols such as P_1, F_2 etc. will designate populations, or the average measurement for the population. In Formula 4-1 the letter symbols, obviously, stand for population averages.

$A_1A_2(F_1)$ may be larger or smaller than that expected from summing the values for A_1 and A_2. Often, when alleles of a gene interact, a component d (for dominance) is added. This is shown in Figure 4-2,b, and stated in formula 4-2.

$$F_1 = A_1 + A_2 + d = -a + a + d = d \quad (4\text{-}2)$$

The component d can be positive, or it can be negative. Its effect is to shift the value of F_1 away from the mid-parent toward one of the two parents. The parent toward which F_1 is shifted is said to be dominant, while the other parent is called recessive. In Figure 4-2,b, P_2 is dominant over P_1.

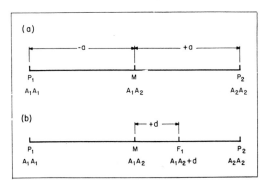

FIG. 4-2. Diagram illustrating the meaning of *a, d,* and *M* in quantitative genetics.

A useful measure of dominance (D) is given by the ratio

$$D = \frac{d}{a} \quad (4\text{-}3)$$

D varies as d varies; as shown in Table 4-2.

TABLE 4-2 NUMERICAL INDEX OF VARIOUS DEGREES OF DOMINANCE

d	D	DEGREE OF DOMINANCE
0	0.0	no dominance
a/2	0.5	partial dominance
a	1.0	complete dominance
1.5a	1.5	overdominance, heterosis, hybrid vigor

In this table, d is positive, and a, the distance between the mid-parent and either parent, is the unit of measurement (i.e., $a = 1.0$). $D = 0$ indicates that F_1 coincides with the mid-parent and that dominance is absent. $D = 1.0$ indicates that F_1 coincides with one of the parents and that dominance of this parent over the other parent is complete. Finally, $0 < D < 1.0$ indicates intermediate or partial dominance, and $D > 1.0$ indicates "hybrid vigor." In this case the F_1 value is larger (or smaller) than either of the parental values. These relationships are shown in Figure 4-3.

It will be noted that in quantitative genetics the term *dominance* is more inclusive than in qualitative genetics. In qualitative genetics only one special case is considered, when P_1 (or P_2) $= F_1$ and, thus, $D = 1.0$. In biometrical genetics, D can assume many other values as shown in Table 4-2 and Figure 4-3.

In biometrical genetics, dominance is inferred from the relative positions of P_1, F_1, and P_2 on a measuring scale (Fig. 4-3). This has an important consequence: the same data may lead to diametrically opposite interpretations with regard to dominance, depending on the scale on which the measurements have been made. A numerical example will make this point clear. Listed in Table 4-3 are the mean measurements for the three nonsegregating populations. Also given are the square roots and logarithms of these means. As can be seen, on the raw-score scale, P_1 is dominant over P_2 (d is negative); on the

square-root scale neither parent is dominant ($d = 0$), and on the logarithmic scale P_2 is dominant over P_1 (d is positive). From this it is evident that, to avoid arbitrariness in the interpretation of data, criteria for the selection of a measuring scale need to be adopted. Two such criteria were

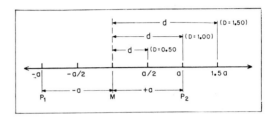

FIG. 4-3. Diagram illustrating various degrees of dominance.

proposed by Mather (1949) and will be discussed below.

Mather's Criteria

Mather's first criterion of an adequate scale is based upon certain relationships between the average phenotypes of the segregating and the nonsegregating populations. These relationships will be discussed first.

The phenotypes of the three nonsegregating populations P_1, F_1, and P_2 cannot be predicted; they have to be established empirically. However, if the phenotypic values of these populations are known, the means for the segregating populations B_1, F_2, and B_2 can be predicted. This is possible because, as can be seen from Table 4-1 and Figure 4-1, these three populations are composed of known proportions of P_1,

TABLE 4-3   EFFECT OF SCALE TRANSFORMATION ON DOMINANCE

SCALE	P_1	F_1	P_2	M	d
Raw-score scale	4.00	16.00	36.00	20.00	-4.00
Square-root scale	2.00	4.00	6.00	4.00	0.00
Logarithmic scale	0.60	1.20	1.54	1.08	$+0.12$

TABLE 4-4   NUMERICAL EXAMPLE TO ILLUSTRATE SELECTION OF ADEQUATE SCALE

SCALE	P_1	B_1	F_1	F_2	B_2	P_2
Raw-score scale	4.00	8.00	16.00	13.80	24.00	36.00
Square-root scale	2.00	2.83	4.00	3.71	4.90	6.00
Logarithmic scale	0.60	0.90	1.20	1.14	1.38	1.56

F_1, and P_2 organisms. The expected average phenotypes of the segregating populations can be computed by means of the following formulas:

(A) $B_1 = (P_1 + F_1)/2 = (-a + d)/2$ (4-4)

(B) $B_2 = (F_1 + P_2)/2 = (a + d)/2$ (4-5)

(C) $F_2 = (P_1 + 2F_1 + P_2)/4$
$= (-a + 2d + a)/4 = d/2$ (4-6)

The relationships stated in these formulas are presented graphically in Figure 4-4.

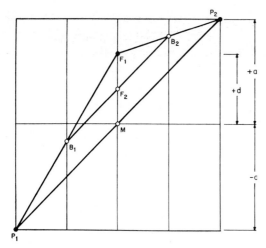

FIG. 4-4. "Genetic triangle": graphic representation of one of Mather's scaling criteria.

The mean values for the nonsegregating populations form the corner points of a triangle which is inscribed in a square. P_1 forms the lower left corner point of the square, P_2 the upper right. The mean measurement for F_1 is entered on the vertical line which bisects the square. It lies at a distance d above the mid-parent. Only partial dominance of P_2 over P_1 is indicated, since d is smaller than a (Fig. 4-2,b. The expected population mean for B_1 lies on the mid-point of P_1F_1 (see Formula 4-4); the expected mean for B_2 lies on the mid-point of F_1P_2 (Formula 4-5). F_2 is at a distance $d/2$ above the mid-parent (Formula 4-6). Incidentally, it can be seen that F_2 lies midway between B_1 and B_2. This relationship is stated in Formula 4-7. It can be readily deduced from relationships A, B, and C.

(D) $(B_1 + B_2)/2 = (-a + d + d + a)/2/2$
$= d/2 = F_2$ (4-7)

A measuring scale on which relationships A, B, and C hold fulfills Mather's first criterion of an adequate scale. By way of illustration, in Table 4-4 means for the segregating populations were added to the table of means presented in Table 4-3. By substituting the original mean measurements (4.00, 8.00, etc.), the square-root values (2.00, 2.83, etc.), and the logarithmic means (0.60, 0.90, etc.) in Formulas 4-4, 4-5, and 4-6, it can be seen that only on the logarithmic scale are the three equations true. Thus the logarithmic scale would be chosen for purposes of data analysis.

Whatever scale is chosen, observed and expected mean measurements are likely to differ because of errors of sampling. However, it is possible to evaluate the significance of such discrepancies. Formulas 4-4, 4-5, and 4-6 can be restated in the form of null hypotheses, as follows:

(A) $\qquad 2B_1 - P_1 - F_1 = 0 \qquad$ (4-8)

(B) $\qquad 2B_2 - P_2 - F_1 = 0 \qquad$ (4-9)

(C) $\quad 4F_2 - 2F_1 - P_1 - P_2 = 0 \quad$ (4-10)

Standard errors (SE) for A, B, and C are given by the following formulas in which SE^2 stands for s^2/N:

$$SE_A = \sqrt{4SE^2{}_{B_1} + SE^2{}_{P_1} + SE^2{}_{F_1}} \qquad (4\text{-}11)$$

$$SE_B = \sqrt{4SE^2{}_{B_2} + SE^2{}_{P_2} + SE^2{}_{F_1}} \qquad (4\text{-}12)$$

$$SE_C = \sqrt{16SE^2{}_{F_2} + 4SE^2{}_{F_1} + SE^2{}_{P_1} + SE^2{}_{P_2}}$$
$$(4\text{-}13)$$

If A, B, and C do not deviate significantly from zero, the critical ratios A/SE_A, B/SE_B, and C/SE_C will not be significant, and the discrepancies between expected and obtained mean measurements for B_1, B_2, and F_2 will be attributed to errors of sampling rather than to inadequacy of the measuring scale chosen.

In order to be considered adequate, a measuring scale must satisfy yet a second criterion proposed by Mather (1949). According to this criterion, variation in the nonsegregating populations must be independent of the mean measurement of the population; this is, $s^2{}_{P_1} = s^2{}_{P_2} = s^2{}_{F_1}$. Theoretically, the total variation in any population, $s_t{}^2$, is due to genetic factors, environmental factors, and an interaction of the two:

$$s_t{}^2 = s_g{}^2 + s_e{}^2 + s^2{}_{gxe} \qquad (4\text{-}14)$$

By definition, nonsegregating populations are genetically uniform. Thus, in these populations, $s_g{}^2 = 0$, and all observed variation consists of $s_e{}^2$ and $s^2{}_{gxe}$. In essence, Mather's second criterion of an adequate scale demands that the latter component, $s^2{}_{gxe}$, be eliminated. This often can be achieved by scale transformation. In practice the criterion is considered to be satisfied if the variances of P_1, F_1, and P_2 do not differ significantly among each other.

Segregation

The preceding sections dealt with the Mendelian concept of dominance and the way it was broadened to apply also to phenomena of quantitative inheritance. This section is devoted to segregation, another Mendelian concept. It will show how segregation manifests itself in quantitative inheritance.

So far it was assumed that if one strain differed from another strain in a given quantitative trait this was due to a difference in one gene pair only. However, there is evidence to indicate that many quantitative traits are determined by more than one gene pair. In P_1 the gene pairs controlling a given trait may be $A_1A_1B_1B_1C_1C_1$, rather than simply A_1A_1, and in P_2 the same trait may be due to $A_2A_2B_2B_2C_2C_2$. In both parental strains, genes A, B, and C cooperate in determining the quantitative expression of one and the same trait; the action of A, B, and C is additive.

The concept of additivity is illustrated in Table 4-5. The mean measurements for P_1 and P_2 are -12 and $+12$, respectively. Three allelic pairs of genes are assumed to account for this difference in phenotype. In Model 1, the magnitudes of the phenotypic effects of the three gene pairs are not alike; but, in each strain, all three gene pairs either increase or decrease the expression of the trait—i.e., they are all negative or all positive. In Model 2, genes having negative effects and genes having positive effects are found in the same strain. In Model 3, all gene pairs within a strain have the same effect on phenotype; they have the same magnitude and the same negative or positive sign. In the present discussion of segregation, Model 3 as shown in Table 4-5 will be assumed to exist. Furthermore, it will be assumed that the interaction component d (see discussion of Formula 4-2)

TABLE 4-5   THREE THEORETICAL MODELS OF ADDITIVITY

			PHENOTYPE			
GENOTYPE		MODEL *1*		MODEL *2*		MODEL *3*
P_1 P_2	P_1	P_2	P_1	P_2	P_1	P_2
A_1A_1 A_2A_2	-6	$+5$	-6	$+4$	-4	$+4$
B_1B_1 B_2B_2	-4	$+3$	-10	$+14$	-4	$+4$
C_1C_1 C_2C_2	-2	$+4$	$+4$	-6	-4	$+4$
Phenotypes	-12	$+12$	-12	$+12$	-12	$+12$

is the same whether A_1 interacts with A_2 or B_1 interacts with B_2, and so on—that is, $d_A = d_B = d_C$.

If these assumptions are made, notation of genotypes can be simplified. Genotype $A_1A_1B_1B_1$ can be denoted by 11 11. Or, $A_1A_2B_1B_2$ can be written 12 12. This notation was adopted in Table 4-6. Entered in this table were the genotypes resulting from the crossing of strains that differed in one or two allelic pairs. Also included in this table were the phenotypes corresponding to each genotype and the frequencies with which these genotypes occur in the three segregating populations.

The derivation of the phenotypes entered in Table 4-6 will be explained for the case of two allelic pairs ($k = 2$). The genotype of P_1 is 11 11. Its phenotype is $(-a)$. Thus the phenotypic value of one 1-gene is $-a/4$.

$$\text{One 1-gene} \ldots \ldots -a/4$$

Similarly, the phenotypic value of one 2-gene is $+a/4$.

$$\text{One 2-gene} \ldots \ldots +a/4$$

The genotype of F_1 is 12 12; its phenotype is *d*. Thus the phenotypic value of one heterozygotic pair (12) is $d/2$.

$$\text{One 12-pair} \ldots \ldots d/2$$

Using these values, the phenotype of each genotype can be determined. For example, the phenotypic value of 11 12 is found as follows:

$$11\ 12 = \quad \begin{array}{r} -3a/4 \\ +1a/4 \\ + \ d/2 \\ \hline -a/2 + d/2 \end{array}$$

The information provided in Table 4-6 makes it possible to compute the genetic

TABLE 4-6   RELATIVE FREQUENCIES OF GENOTYPES AND PHENOTYPES IN SEGREGATING POPULATIONS

	GENOTYPE		PHENOTYPE	RELATIVE FREQUENCY OF TYPE IN SEGREGATING POPULATION		
				B_1	F_2	B_1
k = 1	11		$-a$	1	1	
One allelic	12		d	1	2	1
gene pair	22		$+a$		1	1
	11	11	$-a$	1	1	
	11	12	$-a/2 + d/2$	2	4	
k = 2	11	22	$-a/2 + a/2$		1	
Two allelic	12	12	d	1	4	1
gene pairs	22	11	$+a/2 - a/2$		1	
	22	12	$+a/2 + d/2$		4	2
	22	22	$+a$		1	1

TABLE 4-7   BASIC COMPUTATIONS FOR DERIVATION OF EXPECTED GENETIC VARIANCE
IN P_2 POPULATION $(K = 1)$

GENOTYPE	PHENOTYPE	FREQUENCY	fx	fx^2
11	$-a$	1	$-a$	a^2
12	d	2	2d	$2d^2$
22	a	1	a	a^2
		$N = 4$	$\Sigma X = 2d$	$\Sigma X^2 = 2a^2 + 2d^2$

variance, s_g^2, in the segregating populations by means of Formula 4-15.

$$s^2 = \frac{N\Sigma X^2 - (\Sigma X)^2}{N^2} \qquad (4\text{-}15)$$

The basic computations for an F_2 population are illustrated in Table 4-7. In the bottom row of this table are found the values for N, ΣX, and ΣX^2. By substituting these values in Formula 4-15, $s^2_{g_{F_2}}$ is found:

$$s^2_{g_{F_2}} = (2a^2 + d^2)/4 \qquad (4\text{-}16)$$

Formula 4-16 applies only when $k = 1$. A more general formula which applies to any number of segregating gene pairs is

$$s^2_{g_{F_2}} = (2a^2 + d^2)/4k \qquad (4\text{-}17)$$

Computations analogous to those shown in Table 4-7 can be made for the two backcross populations. When this is done, it is found that:

$$s^2_{g_{B_1}} = (a + d)^2/4k \qquad (4\text{-}18)$$

$$s^2_{g_{B_2}} = (a - d)^2/4k \qquad (4\text{-}19)$$

It should be noted that in applying these formulas the sign of d must be considered. For example, when d is negative, $s^2_{g_{B_2}} = (a + d)^2/4\ k$.

The relationships expressed in Formulas 4-17, 4-18, and 4-19 have many important implications. Only a few of them will be discussed below. Before proceeding, however, a very important matter of terminology has to be settled. We have defined k as the number of allelic *gene* pairs differen-

tiating between the parent strains. While this is correct in theory, in practice it is extremely difficult if not impossible to distinguish between the effects of single genes and the effects of groups or blocks of genes segregating together. It is therefore better to speak of "segregating units," "gene blocks," or "units of segregation" instead of genes. The symbol k, as used henceforth, will refer to such units of segregation.

A graphic representation of some of the information contained in Formulas 4-17, 4-18, and 4-19 is given in Figure 4-5. The genetic variance for each of the three segregating populations was plotted as a function of d. It was assumed that P_2 is dominant over P_1 (d is positive), and that k is the same for the three populations. Several points can be noted:

1. In the absence of dominance ($d = 0$), the variance in the two backcross populations is the same and is half the size of the variance in the F_2 population. However, with dominance ($d \neq 0$), the variance of the backcross to the dominant parent is smaller than the variance of the backcross to the recessive parent.

2. The variance of B_1, the backcross to the recessive parent, increases as a function of an increase of d; as $s^2_{g_{B_1}}$ increases, $s^2_{g_{B_2}}$ decreases. The genetic variance of the dominant backcross reaches a minimum ($s^2_{g_{B_2}} = 0$) when $d = a$, that is, when the mean measurement of F_1 equals that of P_2.

3. Contrary to a widespread misconception, the expected genetic variance of F_2 is

not always the largest among the three segregating populations. The relative size of the variances of these three populations is a function of d.

Formulas 4-17, 4-18, and 4-19 indicate definite limits set to the detection of genetic variance. It can be seen that genetic variance is inversely related to the number

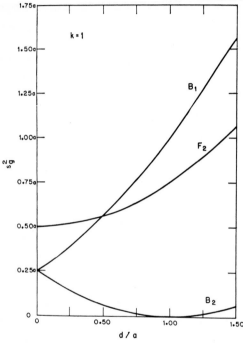

FIG. 4-5. Relation between a, d, and the expected genetic variance, s_g^2 in segregating populations.

of segregating units controlling the character. Genetic variance, s_g^2, decreases as k increases. This suggests that frequently genetic variance will be so small relative to environmental variance that it will be impossible to detect. This point will be elaborated here.

In the discussion of Mather's second criterion it was shown that, on a properly selected scale, the total variance in a segregating population, s_t^2, consists of genetic variance and environmental variance.

$$s_t^2 = s_g^2 + s_e^2 \qquad (4\text{-}20)$$

The nonsegregating populations furnish an estimate of s_e^2. If N's in the nonsegregating populations are equal, the usual procedure is to use the average variance of these populations as a measure of environmental variance.

$$s_e^2 = (s^2_{P_1} + s^2_{F_1} + s^2_{P_2})/3 \qquad (4\text{-}21)$$

If N's in the nonsegregating populations differ, a weighted average of their variances is more meaningful.

The task before us is to demonstrate that the total variance observed in a segregating population, s_t^2, actually is composed of s_e^2 and s_g^2, as indicated by Formula 4-20. This can be accomplished by an F-test.

$$F = (s_g^2 + s_e^2)/s_e^2 = s_t^2/s_e^2 \qquad (4\text{-}22)$$

While this sounds simple in theory, in practice one can expect to demonstrate genetic variation only in rare instances. Suppose, in an experiment, the standard deviation in the nonsegregating populations, s_e, is found to equal a. Moreover, suppose dominance exists and a = d = 1.00. Under these conditions, what are the chances to demonstrate that variation in the F_2 generation has a genetic (s_g^2) and an environmental (s_e^2) component?

Using Formula 4-17, we first compute s_g^2, the expected genetic variance in the F_2 generation for various values of k (Table 4-8, column 2). Next, we add s_e^2 to s_g^2, thus obtaining the expected total variation in the F_2 generation (Table 4-8, column 3). Finally, by substituting these values in Formula 4-22, we obtain F (Table 4-8, column 4). We find that as k increases F decreases.

With 100 and 300 degrees of freedom, F must be 1.45 to be considered significant at the 1 per cent level. Thus, in this hypothetical case, the genetic component in

TABLE 4-8   NUMERICAL EXAMPLE ILLUSTRATING
LIMITATIONS SET ON DETECTION OF GENETIC
VARIANCE s_g^2, BY THE NUMBER OF
SEGREGATING UNITS, K

k	s_g^2	$s_t^2 = s_g^2 + s_e^2$	$F = s_t^2/s_e^2$
1	0.750	1.750	1.750
2	0.375	1.375	1.375
3	0.250	1.250	1.250

$s^2_{t_{F_2}}$ could be demonstrated when $k = 1$, but it could not be detected with $k > 1$.

In this example, s_e was assumed to equal a. Actually, in behavioral experiments, environmental variation, as measured by the standard deviation in the nonsegregating populations, is quite frequently larger than a. But even with $s_e = a$, and with a relatively large number of subjects ($^{100}\!/_{300}\ df$), genetic variation could not be demonstrated if k were larger than one. Thus one has reason to be pessimistic when it comes to detecting genetic variation in behavioral experiments. Empirical studies have borne out this view. Yet, some authors were puzzled by their inability to demonstrate segregation in the F_2 generation. Actually, as was shown, this is what should have been expected.

From Formulas 4-15 through 4-19 it follows that the genetic variance of a segregating population is related to k, the number of allelic segregating units that differentiate between the parent strains. This fact makes it possible to determine k, provided the genetic variance of the segregating populations can be estimated.

We will discuss first the estimation of k from information provided by the backcross populations. From Formulas 4-18 and 4-20 it follows that:

$$s^2_{t_{B_1}} - s_e^2 = (a + d)^2/4k \qquad (4\text{-}23)$$

Thus,

$$k_{B_1} = (a + d)^2/4(s^2_{t_{B_1}} - s_e^2) \qquad (4\text{-}24)$$

Similarly,

$$k_{B_2} = (a - d)^2/4(s^2_{t_{B_2}} - s_e^2) \qquad (4\text{-}25)$$

Theoretically, Formulas 4-24 and 4-25 should result in the same estimate of k. In practice, however, it is recommended to use the estimate obtained from the backcross to the recessive parent because, as has been shown in Figure 4-5, the genetic variance of the backcross to the dominant parent can become very small. Thus, errors of sampling affect it proportionally more than the larger variance of the backcross to the recessive parent.

The numbers of allelic pairs of genes differentiating between the parent strains can also be estimated from F_2 data. From Formulas 4-17 and 4-20 it follows that

$$s^2_{t_{F_2}} - s_e^2 = (2a^2 + d^2)/4k$$

Thus,

$$k_{F_2} = (2a^2 + d^2)/4(s^2_{t_{F_2}} - s_e^2) \qquad (4\text{-}26)$$

In the preceding sections a genetic model was adopted which imposes restrictions on the interpretation of data. The genetic situation represented by Model 3 in Table 4-5 was assumed to exist. In practice, however, it is much more likely that the genotypic situation corresponds to that represented by Model 2. One important consequence of basing the analysis of data on Model 3 rather than on Model 2 must be mentioned.

It can be shown that genetic variance, s_g^2, is at a minimum in segregating populations resulting from the crossing of pure strains of the type represented by Model 3. Genetic variance is intermediate when the genetic situation conforms to Model 1, and it is largest when the genotypic situation conforms to Model 2. This means that the genetic variance observed in experiments ($s_t^2 - s_e^2$) tends to be larger than the theoretical genetic variance computed by using Formulas 4-17, 4-18, and 4-19.

This, in turn, means that estimates of k based on Formulas 4-24, 4-25, and 4-26 tend to underestimate k. These estimates are minimum estimates. For example, if k is computed to be two, it may be concluded that at least two segregating units differentiate between the parent strains. The num-

FIG. 4-6. Activity wheel with cover removed.

ber of such units may be larger, but it is unlikely that it is smaller.

The concepts and methods discussed on the preceding pages were developed by geneticists who, for the most part, worked with plant material. The methods have not been applied to any extent by psychologists, and, lacking empirical studies, it cannot be determined how useful these methods will prove to be for behavior genetics. Many experimental studies will have to be under-

taken before this will be known. Four such experiments are presented in detail below.

EXPERIMENTS WITH MICE

Inheritance of Spontaneous Activity in Mice

In several pilot studies we had found that inbred strains of mice tend to differ in the amount of spontaneous running in activity wheels. Some strains are very active in this situation; others are slow and sluggish. The purpose of this breeding experiment was to find out whether activity was dominant over sluggishness, or vice versa, and how many pairs of allelic segregating units differentiated between an active and a sluggish strain.

• MATERIALS AND METHOD

Mice in this laboratory are being weaned when they are about 30 days old. Litter mates of the same sex are kept together for the next 30 days. At the age of 2 months, each mouse is transferred to an individual cage and assigned to an experimental group. Testing occurs when the animal is 70 to 100 days old. All animals are maintained on Rockland Mouse Diet and, except during testing, have free access to food and water.

The present study was conducted with A/Jax mice (P_1), C57B1/10 mice (P_2), and various crosses between them. The symbols given in Table 4-1 will be used in referring to these crosses.

The activity wheels used in our laboratory are 6″ in diameter and weigh 285 grams. The running surface is made of $\frac{1}{4}$″ wire mesh and is 3″ wide. Revolutions run are counted photoelectrically. The wheel is shown in Figure 4-6. During actual testing a cover is placed over the front side of the wheel.

A mouse put into an activity wheel for

the first time does not know what to do. It has to learn how to run in it. Pilot studies indicated that about six hours of training are needed for a mouse to become proficient in wheel running. Thereafter, running scores still tend to increase, but only slightly. In this study, mice were prerun on two consecutive days for three hours each day. After this pretraining the test proper started. Each mouse was tested in four 90-minute sessions spread over four days. The total number of revolutions run by a mouse in these 360 minutes constituted its score.

• RESULTS

Choice of a measuring scale. Distributions of running scores for the six experimental populations are given in Table 4-9. Data for males and females were pooled because no differences were found between the sexes. A check was made to determine whether F_1 hybrids resulting from the crossing of P_1 females with P_2 males differed from the reciprocal crosses $P_2 \times P_1$. No difference was found, and thus the data for reciprocal crosses were pooled in the F_1 population.

Three kinds of scores are listed in the left-hand columns of Table 4-9: raw scores, square-root scores, and log scores. The raw scores represent thousands of revolutions run in six hours; the square-root and log scores were obtained by transforming the raw scores. Listed at the bottom of Table 4-9 are the means and variances for each

TABLE 4-9 SPONTANEOUS ACTIVITY TEST

THOUSANDS OF REVOLUTIONS			POPULATION					
RAW SCORE	SQUARE-ROOT SCORE	LOG SCORE	P_1	B_1	F_1	F_2	B_2	P_2
7	2.65	0.85	2	1				
8	2.83	0.90	4	2				
9	3.00	0.95	8	0		4		
10	3.16	1.00	17	6	3	7	4	6
11	3.32	1.04	18	13	2	8	3	7
12	3.46	1.08	7	12	6	11	10	7
13	3.60	1.11	3	9	6	14	17	12
14	3.74	1.15	6	17	4	17	23	25
15	3.87	1.18	2	14	14	15	19	20
16	4.00	1.20	3	5	10	17	21	21
17	4.12	1.23		4	9	9	9	13
18	4.24	1.26		3	5	4	6	2
19	4.36	1.28		0	6	5	2	1
20	4.47	1.30		1	2	4	2	1
21	4.58	1.32			1			

			P_1	B_1	F_1	F_2	B_2	P_2
N			70	87	68	115	116	114
Raw Score		$\bar{X}$	11.0	12.1	15.4	14.3	14.6	14.4
		s^2	4.30	5.84	6.75	7.28	4.39	4.08
Square-Root Score		$\bar{X}$	3.3043	3.7655	3.9056	3.7608	3.8115	3.7800
		s^2	0.0945	0.1046	0.1139	0.1298	0.0763	0.0742
Log Score		$\bar{X}$	1.0338	1.1171	1.1810	1.1470	1.1608	1.1535
		s^2	0.006586	0.006930	0.005914	0.007246	0.004066	0.004129

population as computed using each of the three measuring scales.

Tests A, B, and C (Formulas 4-8–4-13) were applied to the data. The results of these tests are shown in Table 4-10. As can be seen, neither the raw-score scale nor

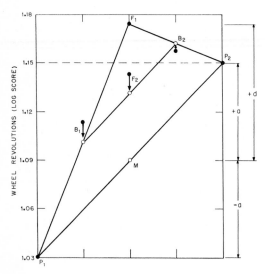

FIG. 4-7. Spontaneous activity test: observed and expected population means.

the square-root scale satisfies Mather's first criterion of scale adequacy. On both scales the B_1 population (Test A) deviates significantly from its expected position midway between P_1 and F_1. Only the log scale was found to be adequate. On this scale

the observed mean values for B_1, B_2, and F_2 do not deviate significantly from expected values. Mather's second criterion is less well satisfied by the logarithmic scale. The variance of P_1 is larger than the variance of P_2 since $s^2_{P_1}/s^2_{P_2}$ results in an $F = 1.60$. With 69 and 113 degrees of freedom, an F-ratio of 1.60 indicates a difference in variance which is significant at the .02 level. In spite of this shortcoming, the logarithmic scale was adopted for further analysis of the data.

Before proceeding, some of the values basic to the analysis of the data were computed and collected in Table 4-11. They include: a, that is, half the distance between P_1 and P_2; d, that is, the distance between the mid-parent, M, and F_1; s_e^2, that is, the weighted average of the variances for the nonsegregating populations.

Dominance. The results are shown in Figure 4-7. The mean values for the nonsegregating populations form the three corner points of the triangle. The *expected* mean values for B_1, F_2, and B_2 are indicated by circles. The *observed* mean values for these populations are shown as filled-in circles, and an arrow points from observed mean to expected mean measurements.

As can be seen, the P_2 strain is dominant over P_1. More precisely, we deal with

TABLE 4-10   MATHER'S SCALING TESTS APPLIED TO SPONTANEOUS ACTIVITY TEST DATA

TEST	RAW-SCORE SCALE	t	SQUARE-ROOT SCALE	t	LOG SCALE	t
A	-2.2 ± 0.6551	3.36	$.3211 \pm 0.0885$	3.62	$.0194 \pm 0.02235$	0.87
B	-0.6 ± 0.5352	1.12	$-.0626 \pm 0.0704$	0.89	$-.0129 \pm 0.01793$	0.72
C	1.0 ± 1.2280	0.81	$.1477 \pm 0.1636$	0.71	$.0387 \pm 0.03855$	1.00

TABLE 4-11   SPONTANEOUS ACTIVITY TEST: SUMMARY OF DATA NEEDED FOR GENETIC ANALYSIS

$a = .059850$	$d = .087350$	$s_e = .072750$	$d/a = 1.46$
$a^2 = .003582$	$d^2 = .007630$	$s_e^2 = .005293$	$s_e/a = 1.22$

behavioral overdominance, or hybrid vigor, since the F_1 mice significantly ($t_{F_1} - {}_{P_2}$ = 2.48, P < .02) outperform both parent strains. Stated in formal terms, d is positive and larger than a; D, that is, d/a = 1.46.

Additional evidence for dominance of P_2 over P_1 is obtained from a comparison of the two backcross variances (see discussion of Fig. 4-5). The variance of B_1, the backcross to the recessive parent, is significantly larger (F = 1.70, P < .01) than the variance of B_2, the backcross to the dominant parent.

Segregation. Before entering into the rather intricate discussion of the statistical demonstration of segregation, an inspection of Table 4-9 may be helpful. It will be noted that the B_1 population covers the entire range of its two parent populations P_1 and F_1. This indicates that the B_1 population contains, as expected, a group of mice which, with respect to running, resembles P_1 mice, and another group which resembles F_1 mice. The B_2 population also covers the range of its parent populations F_1 and P_2. On the other hand, the F_2 population does not cover the entire range of P_1, F_1, and P_2. In particular, low-scoring animals are missing. This may be due to an error of sampling, but it may also indicate a differential viability within the F_2 population; it is possible that animals which would score low in this test do not survive to testing age.

Inspection of the variances given in the bottom row of Table 4-9 shows that, contrary to expectation (see Fig. 4-5 and related discussions), $s^2_{B_1}$ is smaller than $s^2_{F_2}$ although this difference is not significant. Equally unexpected is the very small variance of $s^2_{B_2}$. Actually, we cannot know whether this variance is small or whether the environmental variance, $s_e^2 = .005293$, was inflated by some factors which were

not properly controlled. All in all, these unexpected features suggest extreme caution in the interpretation of the results of the following analysis.

First, we compare $s^2_{t_{B_1}}$ and $s^2_{t_{F_2}}$ with s_e^2 (see discussion of Formulas 4-20–4-22 and Table 4-8):

$$s^2_{t_{B_1}}/s_e^2 = (s^2_{g_{B_1}} + s_e^2)/s_e^2 = 1.31$$

$$F_{.05}(86/249df) = 1.33$$

$$s^2_{t_{F_2}}/s_e^2 = (s^2_{g_{F_2}} + s_e^2)/s_e^2 = 1.37$$

$$F_{.05}(114/249df) = 1.30$$

The obtained F-ratios barely reach significance and thus only suggest that $s^2_{t_{B_1}}$ and $s^2_{t_{F_2}}$ contain a genetic component s_g^2.

The next question concerns k, the number of segregating allelic units. Using Formulas 4-24 and 4-26, one finds that $k_{B_1} = 3.31$, and $k_{F_2} = 1.89$. This suggests that wheel running is a character controlled by not less than two and, probably, not many more than three segregating units.

Inheritance of Exploratory Behavior

• MATERIALS AND METHOD

In this study we used the same two strains of mice as in the preceding experiment, namely, A/Jax (P_1) and C57B1/10 (P_2), and the reader should refer to the discussion of that experiment for details on materials and method.

Mice placed in a novel environment will behave as if exploring it. To measure such activity we used a four-compartment maze. As the animal moved from one unit of the maze to another, it interrupted a light beam and activated a photorelay and counter. The score for an animal consisted of the total count registered in a 10-minute period of testing. The apparatus is shown in Figure 4-8. Obviously, during actual testing the maze was covered.

• RESULTS

Choice of a measuring scale. Distributions of scores for the six populations of

FIG. 4-8. Exploration maze with cover removed.

mice are shown in Table 4-12. No differences were found between the sexes, and the data for males and females were there-

fore pooled. As there was no difference between reciprocal crosses in the F_1, data for P_1 x P_2 and P_2 x P_1 mice were also pooled.

Table 4-12 presents grouped data. All computations, however, were performed with ungrouped data. This explains the difference between the means recorded at the bottom of this table and the means that can be computed using the grouped data shown. Mice were tested 10 at a time. Variance due to significant differences among these replications was removed from total variance. The variances shown in Table 4-12 represent the thus corrected values.

Both criteria of Mather for an adequate scale were found to be met by the raw-score scale. Tests A, B, and C were applied, and it was found that neither A, B, nor C differed significantly from zero (see bottom row of Table 4-12). Also, the

TABLE 4-12   EXPLORATORY BEHAVIOR TEST

RAW SCORES	P_1	B_1	F_1	F_2	B_2	P_2
55–64	1			1		
65–74	2			0		
75–84	3	3	1	0		1
85–94	4	4	1	2	3	1
95–104	5	13	1	15	2	5
105–114	8	13	3	10	5	4
115–124	6	17	11	18	7	13
125–134	4	9	9	10	5	10
135–144	4	6	13	16	13	14
145–154	3	6	4	10	9	12
155–164		3	6	8	1	7
165–174		6	5	5	6	5
175–184			3	3	3	3
185–194			2	2	3	0
195–204			1		0	3
205–214					1	1
215–224						1
N	40	80	60	100	58	80
$\bar{X}$	110.9	121.6	143.8	130.9	142.4	140.4
s^2	502	556	603	644	688	678

$$A = -11.5 \pm 7.1 \qquad B = 0.6 \pm 8.1 \qquad C = -15.3 \pm 12.8$$

TABLE 4-13   EXPLORATORY BEHAVIOR TEST: SUMMARY OF DATA NEEDED FOR GENETIC ANALYSIS

$a = 14.75$	$d = 18.15$	$s_e = 24.78$	$d/a = 1.23$
$a^2 = 217.56$	$d^2 = 329.42$	$s_e^2 = 613.88$	$s_e/a = 1.68$

variances of P_1, F_1, and P_2 did not differ significantly among each other. Thus the raw-score scale was adopted for further analysis. Some of the values necessary for further analysis were computed and collected in Table 4-13. Environmental variance, s_e^2, represents the weighted average of the variances for the nonsegregating populations.

Dominance. Figure 4-9 is a graphic presentation of the results. It is constructed like Figures 4-4 and 4-7. The F_1 hybrids do not differ from P_2 ($t = 0.79$), but differ significantly ($t = 6.92$) from P_1. Thus P_2 is dominant over P_1, but overdominance is not indicated in this instance.

Contrary to expectation, the variance of B_1, the backcross to the recessive parent, is smaller than the variance of B_2, the backcross to the dominant parent (see discussion of Fig. 4-5). Also, the variance of B_1 is smaller than the variance of F_2 (Fig. 4-5) in spite of dominance ($d = 1.23$ a). However, $s^2_{B_1}$ does not differ significantly from $s^2_{B_2}$ or $s^2_{F_2}$ and thus does not invalidate the genetic model on which these analyses are based.

Segregation. Neither $s^2_{t_{B_1}}$ nor $s^2_{t_{F_2}}$ is significantly larger than s_e^2. Thus it cannot be demonstrated that in these populations the total variance is composed of genetic variance, s_g^2, and environmental variance, s_e^2 (see discussion of Formulas 4-20–4-22 and Table 4-8). This finding precludes further analysis. However, it should be pointed out that, because of the relatively large environmental variance ($s_e = 1.68$ a), detection of more than one segregating unit ($k > 1$) would have been impossible anyhow. And that at least one

segregating unit differentiates between the parent strains can be assumed without analysis.

Inheritance of Climbing

° MATERIALS AND METHOD

The same two strains of mice, A/Jax (P_1) and C57B1/10 (P_2), and crosses between them were used (see discussion

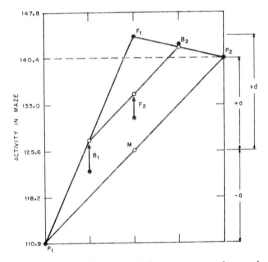

FIG. 4-9. Exploratory behavior test: observed and expected population means.

of materials and method under "Inheritance of Spontaneous Activity in Mice"). In this test which was developed by Dr. Emil Fredericson (unpublished) the mouse is placed on a small $2'' \times 1\frac{1}{2}''$ wire mesh platform on top of a 3-foot high aluminum pole. One side of the pole is covered with $\frac{1}{4}''$ wire mesh which makes it possible for the mouse to climb down the pole (Fig. 4-10). The time spent by the mouse on the pole is measured in seconds. Mice which do not descend within half an hour are removed from the pole. Thus the highest score obtainable in this test is 1800 seconds.

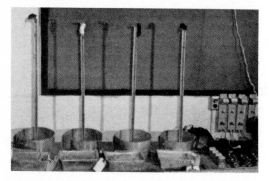

FIG. 4-10. Pole climbing test.

- RESULTS

The results of this study can be summarized in a few short paragraphs. Because a time limit was set, and because many animals did not descend from the pole within this time limit, it was not possible to compute means or variances. This in turn made it impossible to apply the usual tests for segregation. But inferences concerning dominance relationships can be drawn.

Table 4-14 presents distributions of scores for the six populations tested. Instead of means, medians are given in this table. These medians were used to draw Figure 4-11. As explained in the discussion of Mather's first criterion, Figure 4-11 is a graphic representation of certain expected relationships among segregating and non-segregating populations (Formulas 4-4–4-6). It can be seen that, in general, these expectations are well borne out by the results of this study. The median for B_2 falls exactly between F_1 and P_2 (Formula 4-5). The median for F_2 is exactly at a distance

TABLE 4-14   POLE CLIMBING TEST

TIME ON POLE IN SECONDS	POPULATION					
	P_1	B_1	F_1	F_2	B_2	P_2
0–50	2	11	22	8	20	46
51–150	3	23	35	29	44	43
151–250	6	16	17	16	24	32
251–350	8	11	17	18	11	23
351–450	12	13	6	5	10	10
451–550	4	6	9	10	4	10
551–650	6	2	6	6	5	2
651–750	2	2	3	5	4	2
751–850	2	3	3	5	1	2
851–950	2	6	2	3	1	5
951–1050	5	2	1	3	2	2
1051–1150	2	1	0	0	1	0
1151–1250	3	0	1	5	0	0
1251–1350	0	3	2	5	0	1
1351–1450	3	1	0	1	0	2
1451–1550	1	2	1	2	0	3
1551–1650	2	2	0	3	0	0
1651–1750	1	2	1	1	1	0
1751–1850	25	15	3	19	7	10
N	89	121	129	144	135	193
Median	825	345	194	370	185	173

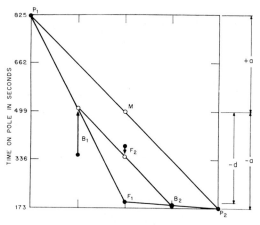

FIG. 4-11. Pole climbing test: observed and expected medians for populations.

$d/2$ from M and F_1 (Formula 4-6). Only the B_1 population is not midway between P_1 and F_1 (Formula 4-4); but, using nonparametric tests, it can be shown that, as a group, B_1 mice are significantly faster than P_1 mice and significantly slower than F_1 mice. Inspection of Table 4-14 and Figure 4-11 clearly indicates dominance of P_2 over P_1. The tendency to descend from the pole rapidly is dominant over late descent.

As mentioned above, the usual tests for segregation cannot be applied because the particular measure used precludes computation of variances. However, close inspection of the frequency distributions shown in Table 4-14 suggests segregation. For example, the B_1 population consists of many low-scoring animals, but also of a considerable number of mice which did not descend from the pole within the time limit. Thus, as expected, the B_1 population appears to be composed of fast F_1 and slow P_1 mice. Similarly, the F_2 population con-

discussion of materials and method under "Inheritance of Spontaneous Activity in Mice"). In this test the mouse is placed in an $8'' \times 3'' \times 3''$ tunnel. One end of the tunnel is closed. The other end opens into an open area, a rectangular box, $12'' \times 6'' \times 8''$, without a lid. The time the mouse spends in the tunnel before emerging into the center of the open box is measured in seconds. The maximum time allowed is 1800 seconds. Figure 4-12 shows an earlier

FIG. 4-12. Emergence-into-open field test: during actual testing runway is covered.

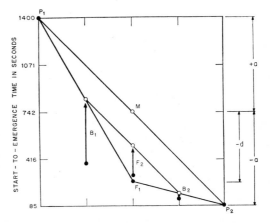

FIG. 4-13. Emergence-into-open field test: observed and expected medians for populations.

sists of low-scoring animals and a large proportion (13 per cent) of animals which remained on the pole longer than 1800 seconds. The F_2 score distribution suggests that the F_2 population segregated into fast F_1 and P_2 and slow P_1 animals. Using goodness-of-fit tests, more refined analyses of these frequency distributions are possible. However, the techniques will not be described here. We will be satisfied with having demonstrated dominance of P_2 over P_1 with regard to the trait measured.

Emergence into Open Field

• MATERIALS AND METHOD

A/Jax mice (P_1), C57B1/10 mice (P_2), and crosses between them were used (see

model of the apparatus used. In this earlier apparatus, the tunnel in which the mouse was placed was longer.

• RESULTS

Score distributions for the six populations of mice tested are given in Table 4-15. As in the preceding test, the use of a time limit made it impossible to compute means and variances. Medians were computed instead and are given in Table 4-15. The results are represented graphically in Figure 4-13. Dominance of P_2 over P_1 is clearly indicated. F_1 animals resemble P_2 in that they do not hesitate to emerge into an open field. On the other hand, 40 per cent of the P_1 animals do not enter the open space within the half-hour of testing.

TABLE 4-15   EMERGENCE-INTO-OPEN FIELD TEST

START-TO-EMERGENCE TIME IN SECONDS	POPULATION					
	P_1	B_1	F_1	F_2	B_2	P_2
0–50	1	14	13	51	40	46
51–150	2	19	19	23	44	42
151–250	2	9	12	18	18	33
251–350	5	22	10	18	19	12
351–450	1	15	8	15	7	4
451–550	2	8	6	14	9	2
551–650	3	10	6	12	3	1
651–750	4	11	5	12	5	2
751–850	3	7	3	3	2	1
851–950	0	5	2	4	1	0
951–1050	3	5	2	4	1	0
1051–1150	3	2	0	3	1	0
1151–1250	4	2	0	0	0	1
1251–1350	2	2	1	1	1	0
1351–1450	3	1	0	1	0	0
1451–1550	2	0	1	3	0	0
1551–1650	4	1	0	0	0	0
1651–1750	1	1	0	3	0	0
1751–1850	30	11	2	10	3	5
N	75	145	90	195	154	149
Median	1400	407	260	281	134	85

The median for the B_1 animals does not lie midway between P_1 and F_1, but, as a group, B_1 do differ significantly from both P_1 and F_1. The median for the B_2 population is very close to its predicted position on the measuring scale, and the median for the F_2 population probably does not differ significantly from its predicted position.

Because variances are not available, segregation cannot be demonstrated statistically.

DISCUSSION

The purpose of this chapter was to present some concepts of biometrical genetics and to show that they can be applied to the study of inheritance of behavior. Two phenomena of inheritance, dominance and segregation, were singled out for discussion. Four examples of genetically determined behavior traits were given. In each case it was possible to specify the dominance relationships existing between the two strains of mice used in these studies. However, only in the case of spontaneous running in activity wheels was it possible to make some tentative statements with regard to segregation.

In order to demonstrate dominance, all one needs to do is to show that certain specifiable relationships exist among the *means* of segregating and nonsegregating populations. The mean measurements for these populations do not depend on the number of allelic gene pairs differentiating between the parent strains; and thus, theoretically, the mean for a population can be established with any desired degree of accuracy by increasing the number of organisms tested and by thus decreasing the standard error of the mean. On the other hand, to demonstrate segregation, one has to show that certain relationships exist among the *variances* of segregating and nonsegregating populations. Here the experimenter has no full control over the situation. The variance of a segregating population is composed of environmental variance and genetic variance. The environmental component can be made small by careful control of all known environmental sources of variation, but in practice it cannot be reduced to zero. The genetic component depends on the number of allelic gene pairs differentiating between the parent strains: the larger the number of these gene pairs, the smaller the genetic component of variance becomes, and there is nothing the experimenter can do about that. When the genetic component of variance becomes very small compared with the environmental component, then its presence cannot be established, and segregation cannot be demonstrated.

In two of the four studies presented above, measures were used which did not permit the computation of means and variances. Medians were computed instead, and, using these medians, it was possible to characterize the dominance relationships existing between the two parent strains tested. Lacking estimates of variation, no inferences could be drawn with regard to segregation.

We believe that our empirical findings have one major implication for the methodology of future psychogenetic research. Experimenters who in the past have concerned themselves mainly with demonstrating differences between the mean performance of experimental and control groups tend not to put too much effort into reducing the number of uncontrolled factors which conceivably influence performance and thus increase the so-called error variance. The reason for this is that, if the error variance is large, all that needs to be done, is to increase the number of subjects in one's groups. This reduces the standard error of the difference, and a difference between groups can be demonstrated if it is present at all. Actually, often the procedure of reducing the standard error of the difference by increasing the number of organisms in one's groups may prove to be less costly than the control of all factors that potentially may inflate the error variance. This procedure may be adopted even in genetic research if all that we care to study are dominance relationships between strains because, as was pointed out above, dominance relationships are established by comparisons of means. If, however, segregation is to be studied, a meticulous control of error variance becomes imperative because, as was explained at some length, genetic variation cannot be detected in the presence of a large error variance.

By presenting and discussing one particular experimental design, we hope not to have created the false impression that psychogenetic research need be restricted to the study of the three segregating and three nonsegregating populations which were used in our experiments. On the contrary, there are many questions which cannot be answered using the design presented here. To name but one, using this design one could not decide whether actually the P_1 strain differs from the P_2 strain in the way assumed by Model 3 (see Table 4-5 and related discussion). However, there are ways to get a better picture about the real genotypic situation, and some of them have been explored by geneticists.

After this glimpse at the quantitatively most elegant and most advanced field of biology, some readers may want to gain more direct knowledge of it by turning directly to the writings of geneticists. We would feel rewarded if a few went even farther and joined the growing number of those who now work in the here-described borderland of behavioral and genetic research. We can only hope that psychogenetics will show hybrid vigor and provide another unifying link in the growing edifice of life sciences.

REFERENCES

CASPARI, E. 1958. "Genetic Basis of Behavior," in *Behavior and Evolution*, ed. by ROE, A., and SIMPSON, G. G. New Haven, Yale University Press.

FALCONER, D. S. 1960. *Introduction to Quantitative Genetics*. New York, Ronald.

FULLER, J. L., and THOMPSON, W. R. 1960. *Behavior Genetics*. New York, Wiley.

HALL, C. S. 1951. "The Genetics of Behavior," *Handbook of Experimental Psychology*, ed. by STEVENS, S. S. New York, Wiley, pp. 304–329.

MATHER, K. 1949. *Biometrical Genetics*. London, Methuen.

ZIRKLE, C. 1951. "The Knowledge of Heredity Before 1900," *Genetics in the Twentieth Century*, ed. by DUNN, L. C. New York, Macmillan.

5

ALCOHOL PREFERENCE OF MICE

David A. Rodgers

Gerald E. McClearn

The purpose of this report is to summarize the results to date of a project that has been exploring the genetic, physiological, and environmental aspects of voluntary alcohol consumption of the mouse. These results will be considered in the context of previous research on alcohol consumption of animals and humans.

We wish to emphasize at the outset that the present research is not directly concerned with the problem of human alcoholism, even though it is hoped that the findings may contribute toward an ultimate understanding of alcoholism. The variability that we have observed among different strains of one species, the mouse, should be adequate warning against the a priori assumption that the results apply across species even moderately separated on the phylogenetic scale. The question of whether the relationships found in the mouse are also characteristic of humans is an empirical one and can only be answered by research on the human. The thorough exploration of determinants of alcohol

preference in the mouse, with the attendant advantages of a high degree of control of the experimental situation, may nevertheless be both a fruitful and an economical source of hypotheses concerning the mechanisms of alcohol preference in other species. It is also an interesting area of investigation by itself.

In the present report, we will briefly summarize the characteristics of alcohol as a food substance and as a drug, will review previous research findings concerning the inheritance of alcohol preference, will present our own findings concerning inheritance of alcohol preference in the mouse, will review previous experimental findings concerning the physiological determinants of alcohol preference, and will present our own findings concerning physiological determinants of alcohol preference in the mouse.

ALCOHOL: FOOD SUBSTANCE AND DRUG

Ethanol is a naturally occurring alcohol usually formed by bacterial action on sugar solutions. Small but measurable quantities are normally present in the body. Hirsh (1949) reports that the brain contains .0004 per cent alcohol, the blood contains .004 per cent, and the liver contains .0026

The original researches reported here were supported by National Science Foundation Grants No. G4574 and No. G9936.

The animals were obtained from the inbred strains maintained by the Cancer Research Genetics Laboratory, Berkeley, California.

per cent. Bacteria present in the large intestine produce alcohol; in rare instances, apparently in intoxicating quantity. The following newspaper account appeared recently concerning a 46-year-old native of Hokkaido, Japan:

O's troubles began two decades ago. After eating anything, his breath began to smell of alcohol, and his face became red. It was embarrassing. But "O" didn't bother much about it until last year when the symptoms became so bad, he couldn't walk straight after a meal. Dr. Sasaki, bacteriologist at the university, said he discovered a yeast fungus growing in the patient's stomach. The yeast fermented everything he ate (*San Francisco Chronicle*, 1959).

Ethanol is totally miscible with water and enters the blood stream by simple diffusion through the walls of the stomach and intestines. It can safely be injected directly into the blood stream in appropriate concentrations. Once in the blood it distributes itself relatively uniformly throughout the body fluids (Lester and Greenberg, 1952), although some differences in concentration are reported (cf. Carpenter, 1940). When oxidized to carbon dioxide and water, it releases approximately 7.1 large calories per gram. Different investigators (Morgan *et al.*, 1957; Gillespie and Lucas, 1958) have estimated that from 75 per cent to 100 per cent of these calories are physiologically utilizable. The initial step in the metabolism of ethanol is its conversion to acetaldehyde in the presence of alcohol dehydrogenase (ADH). Some investigators (cf. The American Foundation, 1955) posit that other enzymes may also bring about this conversion. The reaction takes place primarily in the liver, although there is evidence that some alcohol is metabolized in the brain, kidney, and other organs (cf. Bartlett and Barnet, 1949; Lester and Greenberg, 1952;

The American Foundation, 1955). The catabolic pathways as currently understood are short and direct (Fig. 5-1), involving few intermediate steps and few enzyme and vitamin systems. Under normal conditions the rate of conversion of alcohol to acetaldehyde is the limiting one in the rate of utilization of the alcohol (cf. Newman, 1947).

In contrast to the relatively short catabolic pathways, the anabolic pathways by which alcohol could be converted into semipermanent body tissue are long and involved. Ethanol is converted to acetaldehyde at a relatively constant rate once it enters the blood stream (Newman, 1947; Bartlett and Barnet, 1949) and is therefore stored in the body (fluids) only so long as is necessary for the conversion to take place. The rate of conversion is presumed to depend primarily upon the amount of ADH in the liver.

Bartlett and Barnet (1949) studied the rate of oxidation of radioactive alcohol in rats. Following administration of an oral dose of 1 g. per kilogram body weight, they found that 75 per cent of the alcohol had been oxidized to carbon dioxide at the end of five hours and that 90 per cent was oxidized at the end of 10 hours. Very little was incorporated into semipermanent body tissue, a result that might be expected in view of the marked difference in complexity of the catabolic and anabolic pathways.

The characteristics of alcohol metabolism suggest that as a food substance ethanol would have value as a relatively immediate source of calories but little value as an anabolic building block. As will be considered later, it may also have high value as a source of calories that places minimal wear and tear on enzymatic and vitamin systems, but low value as a source of replenishment of those systems. If, as Richter has hypothesized (1942–1943), animals make "wise" choices in their free selection of foodstuffs, then these characteristics of alcohol might be related to the differential preference that animals show for alcohol and might make it a preferred food for some animals under some circumstances.

the action of certain inhibiting centers in the brain (cf. Grenell, 1957). Increasing amounts of alcohol produce progressively mild to marked behavioral disorganization, stupor, and eventually death. These effects depend on the presence of ethanol in the

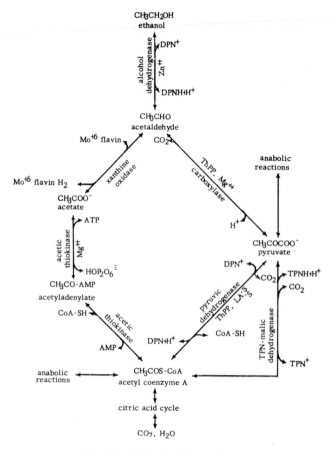

FIG. 5-1. Ethyl alcohol metabolism.

In addition to its characteristics as a food, ethanol also has properties as a drug. Although the mechanisms of its narcotic action are not well understood, it is presumed to act directly on the central nervous system, perhaps by interference with synaptic transmission or cell metabolism. Paradoxically, alcohol in moderate amounts is subjectively experienced as a stimulant, presumably because it selectively depresses

blood stream and therefore at least superficially bear an inverse relationship to its utilization as a food. As the alcohol is metabolically consumed, the drug effects disappear. If alcohol preference is based on its drug action, then such preference would be unrelated, or possibly even negatively related, to the ability of the subject to utilize alcohol as a calorie source. This latter possibility suggests the popular hypothesis that alcohol is an attractive poison, that it is a depressant taken because it is subjectively experienced as a stimulant, and that alcohol preference is a "perverse" appetite rather than an appetite based on ethanol's metabolic utility. Williams' genetotrophic theory of alcoholism (1951) posits that alcohol preference is perverse in this sense, although his theory does not state that the appetite for alcohol is based on its drug effects.

In addition to its narcotic and nutritional properties, alcohol may have other pharmacological characteristics that are important in determining alcohol preference. For example, Gross (1945) suggests that alcohol acts directly on the pituitary to alter the output of pituitary hormones. Fleetwood (1955) reports that alcohol operates in some way to eliminate certain blood fractions associated with resentment and tension. The mode of the action is unclear. Similarly, other mechanisms could be involved in alcohol action and preference. It may even be found that mechanisms important in determining alcohol preference in one group of subjects are not important in another group of subjects; there may be partial truth in Lemere's blunt assertion that " . . . each alcoholic drinks for his own special reasons" (1956, p. 202).

INHERITANCE OF ALCOHOL PREFERENCE

A variety of biochemical mechanisms seems almost certainly to be involved in determining alcohol preference. Furthermore, it seems probable that there are genetically determined differences in these mechanisms and thereby in alcohol preference. Much of the early work on such genetic differences concerned the inheritance of alcoholism, which is one form of extreme preference for ethanol. More recently, following Richter and Campbell's method (1940) of measuring consumption in a free-

choice situation, the genetics of alcohol preference in animals has been explored. Evidence from these studies will be reviewed as a background for our own investigations of the genetic basis of alcohol preference in the mouse.

Humans have demonstrated some preference for ethanol in one form or another since prehistoric times (cf. Hirsh, 1949) and undoubtedly have shown marked individual differences in such preference from the beginning. Such individual variability has long suggested the possibility that genetic factors might play an important role in determining differences in preference. Writing in 1828, MacNish (1828, p. 26) observes, "Drunkenness appears to be in some measure hereditary. We frequently see it descending from parents to their children. This may undoubtedly often arise from bad example and imitation, but there can be little question that, in many instances at least, it exists as a family predisposition." As Bleuler has properly emphasized (1955a, 1955b), there are many difficulties in isolating genetic from environmental contributions to variance in studies of human behavior. However, after extensive investigations of family histories in the United States and Switzerland, he concludes that both genetic and environmental factors are important in producing differences in susceptibility to alcoholism. Kaij (1957) draws the same conclusion, that both hereditary and environmental factors are important, after examining the drinking habits of a group of identical and fraternal twins. Roe, however, casts some doubt on the relative importance of genetic factors in her study (1944) of the adult adjustment of foster-reared children whose natural parents were alcoholic. She found no greater incidence of alcoholism in a sample of 36 such adults than in a foster-reared control group whose natural parents were not alcoholic. Some caution is necessary in the interpretation of her results because mean age of her subjects, 32, is relatively young for the onset of alcoholism and because her sample size is relatively small. However, her data provide no suggestive evidence that her results would be substantially altered by a larger or more mature group.

Several investigations suggest the existence of genetically determined differences in alcohol preference in subhuman species. Emerson *et al.* (1952) found marked species differences in preference for a 10 per cent ethanol solution versus water. Deer mice and hamsters showed the most marked preference for alcohol. Sprague-Dawley rats and cotton rats showed relatively low preference for alcohol under conditions of adequate diet. These investigators also found species differences in the effects of nutritional supplements on alcohol preference. Mardones, Segovia, and Hederra (1950, 1953) selectively bred rats for high and low alcohol preference under conditions of dietary deficiency of their Factor N_1, a thermostable yeast fraction presumably of the B-complex family. They obtained a significant parent-offspring correlation of alcohol preference of +.416 in the third to seventh generations of selection. Reed (1951) found some significant differences in alcohol consumption among six different strains of rats of varying degrees of inbreeding. These results suggest genetic differences in preference. Using two sublines of Wistar rats and three strains of mice (dba, C3H, and a commercial albino strain), Williams, Berry, and Beerstecher (1949a) report strain differences in alcohol preference and in the effect of nutritional deficiency on preference. The significance of their results is somewhat obscured by their failure to report statistical tests of significance of differences, by the fact that

close genetic control was maintained in only one of the strains tested (dba mouse), and by their report that considerable variability was observed in all other strains. Their results, nevertheless, suggest that differences in genetic constitution contribute significantly to the variance of alcohol preference. Mirone has used several strains of mice (C57, dba, CF_1, Swiss) in nutritional studies of alcohol intake (1952, 1957, 1958, 1959) but has not commented on strain differences. Her results, however, in conjunction with the results obtained by Williams *et al.* (1949a) suggest that strain differences in the mouse may exist.

GENETICS OF ALCOHOL PREFERENCE OF MICE

As previously reported (McClearn and Rodgers, 1959, 1961; Rodgers and McClearn, 1959), we have carried out a series of studies that establish the existence of stable strain differences in alcohol preference in the mouse and demonstrate that preference can be systematically altered by manipulation of genotype. These data along with further data that confirm and extend the earlier findings will be presented. The following studies have been made: (1) test of strain differences in alcohol preference, using available inbred strains (Fig. 5-2); (2) tests of genetic transmissibility of alcohol preference to first-generation hybrid offspring, using one high-preference strain crossed with four low-preference strains (Fig. 5-2); (3) test of some maternal effects, using one high-preference strain reciprocally crossed with a low-preference strain (Fig. 5-3); (4) test of effect of one kind of heterozygosity, using reciprocal crosses of two low-preference strains (Fig. 5-3); (5) test of postnatal maternal effects on alcohol preference, using offspring of a high-preference strain and of a low-preference strain cross-fostered by mothers of the opposite strain (Fig. 5-4); (6) attempt to obtain an analysis of the genetic mechanism, using F_1, F_2, and backcross generations derived from crosses of a high-preference strain with a low-preference strain (Fig. 5-5); (7) test of variability of alcohol preference in a genetically heterogeneous population consisting of double-cross animals of four low-preference strains (Fig. 5-6); (8) test of variability of alcohol preference in a genetically heterogeneous population consisting of double-cross animals of three low-preference strains and one high-preference strain (Fig. 5-6); (9) test of alcohol preference in the first generation selectively bred from the animals of the genetically heterogeneous double-cross group containing the high-preference genome (Fig. 5-7).

The animals were housed for testing in individual cages with a standard laboratory ration available ad lib. They were offered an ad-lib choice between water and a 10 per cent ethanol solution from standard drinking tips extending through the cage tops. Daily consumption records were kept for a two-week period. In the initial study, the positions of the drinking bottles were reversed after the sixth and tenth days. In subsequent studies, the positions were reversed every third day.

Significant strain differences in alcohol preference were found. The C57BL/Crgl strain shows higher mean preference than the other strains; the latter in the initial study do not differ significantly from each other in mean preference (Fig. 5-2). Since bottle leakage, as measured in bottles set up in empty cages, can amount to approximately 15 per cent of the normal fluid intake of a mouse, the alcohol intake of the low-preference strains may be almost zero and the plain-water intake of the C57BL strain may be correspondingly lower than is indicated in Fig. 5-2.

All F_1 generations derived from crosses of the high-preference C57BL strain with the low-preference strains (Fig. 5-2) show mean preference intermediate between those of the parent strains and somewhat below the mid-parent value. Data from Figure 5-3 support the otherwise questionable intermediacy of the C57BL $\times$ C3H/2Crgl cross shown in Figure 5-2.

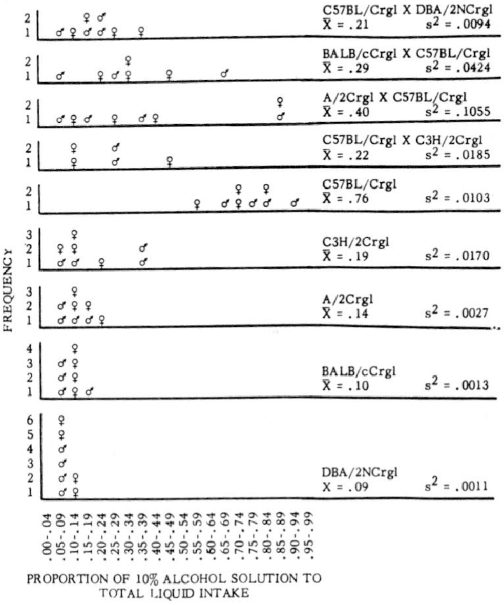

FIG. 5-2. Alcohol preference of parent strains and F_1 animals.

Comparison of preference of F_1's from the C57BL $\times$ C3H/2 cross with preference of F_1's from the reciprocal C3H/2 $\times$ C57BL cross shows no significant difference (Fig. 5-3). These results tend to rule out the possibility that alcohol preference is a characteristic attributable solely to maternal effects.

Mean alcohol preference of the F_1's from crosses of the C3H/2 and A/2Crgl strains is low (Fig. 5-3), as is that of the two parent strains (Fig. 5-2). This finding indicates that heterozygosity alone does not always produce intermediate alcohol preference, by demonstrating that animals with a high degree of heterozygosity can consistently show low preference for alcohol under the test conditions we have used. This finding is confirmed by further studies (e.g., Fig. 5-6). One female from the C3H/2 × A/2 cross shows a deviantly high alcohol preference. It is not apparent whether this deviance is due to genetic mutation, to genetic variability in the parent strains in spite of their generations of inbreeding, or to some environmental factor that uniquely affected this particular ani-

served in an occasional C57BL reared by a C57BL mother (Fig. 5-5), so that the explanation would not seem to lie in strain differences in maternal behavior or nutrition. Either genetic or experimental differences or an interaction between the two could be responsible. Breeding tests are being carried out to see if the low preference can be transmitted.

In an initial study (results shown in Figure 5-5) we found A mice reared by their own mothers have low mean alcohol preference and very little variability in

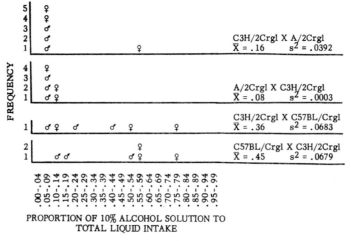

FIG. 5-3. Alcohol preference of indicated F_1's.

mal. We now have breeding tests under way to determine whether the high preference of this animal is genetically transmissible.

C57BL young fostered from birth to weaning by mothers of the low-preference A/Crgl strain do not differ significantly in mean preference from C57BL young reared by C57BL mothers (Fig. 5-4). Both groups show the high mean preference characteristic of the strain. One male reared by an A mother deviates markedly from the strain pattern, showing almost complete alcohol avoidance. No explanation is readily available. The same deviation has been ob-

preference. In the present foster-rearing control group of A mice reared by A mothers (Fig. 5-4), the mean alcohol preference is significantly higher (p < .01) than in the group shown in Figure 5-5. No ready explanation is available for this difference. All of the "deviantly" high-preference animals of the foster-rearing study are females, so that cyclical variability might be responsible. We have not yet critically examined this possibility, although evidence of such variability is strikingly absent in the first study. The deviant behavior of the control group remains unexplained at present. However, it does not obscure the results of the foster-rearing study (Fig. 5-4); nor does it materially affect earlier conclusions on strain differences. Mean preference of the control group is still relatively low and is substantially below that of the C57BL strain. The mean preference of the A young fostered by the C57BL mothers is actually somewhat below that of the control group but does not differ significantly from that of either the control group or the group shown in Figure 5-5. The conclusion seems war-

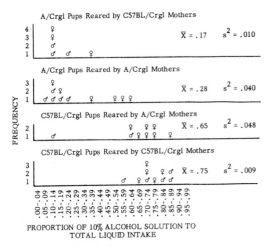

FIG. 5-4. Effect of foster rearing on alcohol preference.

ranted that strain differences in alcohol preference are not due to strain differences in maternal behavior or nutrition during the period between birth and weaning.

The mean alcohol preferences of parent, F_1, F_2, and backcross generations of the C57BL strain crossed with the A strain follow the pattern expected of a genetically transmitted characteristic in which alcohol preference as here measured is either additive or incompletely recessive to alcohol avoidance (Fig. 5-5). The F_1 and F_2 mean preferences are intermediate and below the mid-parent value. The mid-parent value, however, is contained within the 95 per

cent confidence interval of the F_1 mean, so that the possibility of straight additivity cannot at present be ruled out. The mean preferences of the two backcross generations differ significantly from each other in the expected directions, the F_1 cross to the C57BL parent showing the higher mean preference. The variance of the F_2's is,

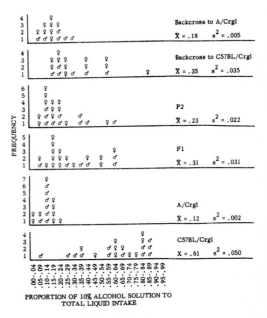

FIG. 5-5. Alcohol preference of C57BL/Crgl and A/Crgl mice and of F_1. F_2, and backcross generations.

contrary to expectation, smaller than, although not significantly different from, that of the F_1's. Consequently, the computation of heritability; partitioning of additive, dominance, and epistatic effects; and estimation of the probable number of genes involved, using conventional genetic models, is impossible. Further data are necessary before a comprehensive genetic analysis can be made. The present results favor a polygenic interpretation.

Greater variability of preference was found in the larger group of C57BL S's used for this study (Fig. 5-5) than was found in the initial study (Fig. 5-2). One animal shows almost total abstention, and a number show low to intermediate preference. In this (Fig. 5-5) as well as in previous two studies (Figs. 5-2, 5-3), the F_1 groups tend to show considerable variability in preference. Such variability indicates either that the animals are not well buffered against differential environmental effects or that appreciable genetic variability remains in the parent strains. All

in-strain variance or whether environmental variability is predominantly responsible.

Three double-cross groups were derived from the same four inbred strains, one of which was the high-preference C57BL. These groups all show an expected wide range of preference, skewed toward the high-preference end of the distribution, with median preference over the three groups being relatively low at .24 (Fig.

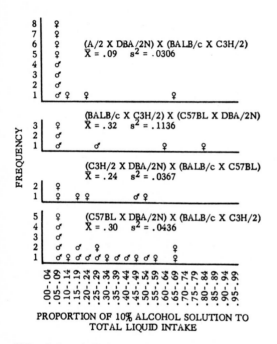

FIG. 5-6. Alcohol preference of double-cross generations.

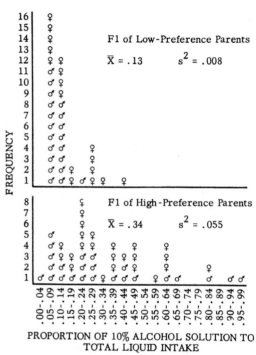

FIG. 5-7. Alcohol preference of first generation of selective breeding from double-cross animals of C57BL, DBA/2N, C3H/2, and BALB/c ancestors.

strains used have had rigorous brother-by-sister inbreeding for from 17 to 100 generations. The C57BL, for example, had been inbred for 38 generations at the time the data in Figure 5-5 were collected. Lerner (1954) has argued, however, that appreciable heterozygosity may still remain even after such a long history of inbreeding. Loeb, King, and Blumenthal's results (1943) support his argument. Further investigations may reveal whether such genetic variability accounts for our observed with-

5-6). No mouse from these groups could have received more than one-half of its genotype from the C57BL ancestor, and the probability of receiving this much is diminishingly small. The average received would be one-fourth. No animal in these groups could be homozygous for C57BL genes not carried by the other strains. It is therefore not surprising that few high-preference animals are found in this group.

The double-cross group containing no genetic material from a high-preference strain shows consistently low preference except for one markedly deviant animal (Fig. 5-6). The high preference of this one animal, a female, may be due to an unusual recombination of genetic material from the low-preference strains or to unusual environmental or developmental factors. It is being bred to determine whether or not the high preference can be genetically transmitted.

Further evidence that alcohol preference can be genetically manipulated is provided by data from the first-generation selective breeding of the double-cross groups containing the C57BL genome (Fig. 5-7). The offspring from high-preference parents show significantly higher mean alcohol preference than those from low-preference parents. Such a response to selection suggests a genetic basis for the difference in phenotype. The high-preference parents (mean preference = .58) produce offspring of high, intermediate, and low preference, with the predominant number falling in the intermediate range (Fig. 5-7). In contrast, the low-preference parents (mean preference = .08) produce mostly low-preference offspring.

Among the offspring of the low-preference parents, almost all of the S's showing intermediate preference are females (Fig. 5-7). As was suggested by a previous study (Fig. 5-4), these data raise the possibility that cyclical variations characteristic of the female elevate preference of some S's. However, relatively few animals are involved, and more investigation will be necessary to evaluate such a possibility.

Conclusions

The several studies completed to date represent a beginning exploration of the genetics of alcohol preference of the mouse. A genetically transmissible high preference

for 10 per cent alcohol solution in comparison to water, under conditions of otherwise normal diet, has been demonstrated in the C57BL strain. Additional high-preference sublines are being developed, containing genetic material from the C57BL, C3H/2, BALB/cCrgl, and DBA/2NCrgl strains. The A, A/2, BALB/c, and DBA/2N have been identified as low-preference strains under the test conditions. It has not yet been possible to determine the additivity, dominance, and epistatic contributions; to compute the heritability; or to estimate the number of genes involved in transmission of alcohol preference. The complexity of the results suggests that several genes are involved. The results from reciprocal crosses and foster rearing indicate that maternal effects do not play a prominent role in determining alcohol preference in the strains studied.

PHYSIOLOGICAL FACTORS INFLUENCING ALCOHOL PREFERENCE

With the clear establishment of genetic differences in alcohol preference and the identification of high- and low-preference strains, it becomes possible to examine the particular physiological mechanisms that mediate the appetite for alcohol.

Previous research has indicated that a number of organ systems may influence alcohol preference. Various investigators have found suggestive evidence implicating the thyroid, pancreas, pituitary-adrenal system, gastric system, and liver. Carbohydrates, fats, amino acids, vitamins, and previous alcohol consumption have all been shown to affect alcohol preference. These findings will be briefly reviewed as a background for our own work on physiological determinants of alcohol preference of mice.

Thyroid involvement has been examined by several investigators. Zarrow and Rosenberg (1953) found that the goitrogen

propyl thiouracil increased alcohol preference of Sprague-Dawley rats. Thyroidectomy had no effect on preference, and
thyroxine given with the propyl thiouracil
failed to decrease, and perhaps increased,
the effect of the goitrogen. Decreased food
intake and weight loss accompanied the
treatment. Control rats fed restricted
amounts of food comparable to those consumed by the treated rats showed a parallel
but less marked increase in alcohol preference. Zarrow and Rosenberg conclude that
propyl thiouracil acts independently of the
thyroid and that the thyroid itself is not
directly involved in increasing alcohol preference. Richter (1957a, 1957b) found that
thyroid powder, thyroxine, and tri-iodothy-
ronine decreased alcohol preference of Norway rats, whereas thyroidectomy tended to
increase preference. The ingestion of alcohol by hyperthyroid animals had adverse
effect on their adrenals, liver, and kidneys.
Iida found that antithyroid treatment did
not induce alcohol appetite in mice (1957).
Mirone (1957) found that iodine deficiency
decreased alcohol preference of C57BL
mice. These results suggest that thyroid
activity may limit but not stimulate alcohol
appetite. The site or mechanism of action
of the propyl thiouracil and of the thyroid
derivatives is not yet clear.

The results obtained by Forsander, Kohonen, and Suomalainen (1958) suggest the
possibility of pancreatic involvement in
alcohol preference. These investigators report an increase in alcohol preference in
rats fed N-sulfaninyl-N'-n-butylcarbamide
("Nadisan") and in rats injected with
insulin. Alcohol consumption of rats injected with alloxan dropped to zero.

Gross (1945) posits that many symptoms
of alcoholic intoxication and of chronic
alcoholism are due to the direct effect of
ethanol on the pituitary and the indirect
effect, through the pituitary, on other organ
systems. The possibility of pituitary involvement in alcohol preference has been
examined in several studies. Special attention has been given to pituitary hormones
affecting the adrenal system. Research on
these two systems, the pituitary and the
adrenals, will therefore be considered together. Iida (1957) found a small increase
in alcohol preference of saline-fed mice
when they were injected with desoxycorti-
costerone acetate or cortisone in small
doses. Large doses decreased the preference. Administration of ACTH, posterior
pituitary hormones, and desoxycorticos-
terone had no effect on preference. Non-
adrenalectomized mice fed saline developed
a slight increased preference for alcohol,
but this increase did not occur in adrenalectomized mice. Of perhaps greater significance than the positive nature of Iida's
findings is their implication that pituitary-
adrenal manipulation had only a small
effect on preference. The maximum alcohol
preference developed by Iida's subjects was
about 5 per cent of total fluid intake. It
therefore seems reasonable to conclude that
the pituitary hormones had relatively little
effect. Sackler and co-workers (1952) report a decrease in alcohol preference in
schizophrenics given histamine, ACH, or
ACTH. Johnston (1954) found that treatment of alcoholics with adrenal cortex
hormones was no more effective in reducing craving than was treatment with
placebos. Both Freeman and Watts (1942)
and Talbot, Bellis, and Greenblatt (1951)
report that prefrontal lobotomy has little
or no effect on alcohol preference of
most human S's, although it may markedly
increase or decrease alcohol consumption of some S's. Since psychosurgery
presumably reduces the impact of external stimuli on the adrenal system, these
results may suggest lack of involvement
of the adrenal system in alcohol pref-

erence. Results of several studies on stressful situations, however, favor the possibility of such involvement. Moore *et al.* (1952) found that periodic sonic stimulation increased alcohol intake in rats. They interpret the increase as a reaction to a stressful situation. Dember and Kristofferson (1955) found that susceptibility to audiogenic seizures was positively related to alcohol preference of rats. They conclude that seizure susceptibility is an indication of tension and that tension increases alcohol preference. Masserman and Yum (1946) found experimental neuroses to increase alcohol preference of cats. Conger (1956) reports that alcohol differentially decreases the avoidance drive in rats. He interprets the results as supporting an anxiety-drive-reduction theory of alcoholism. Tobach (1957) presents data purporting to substantiate a relationship between anxiety and alcohol preference in rats. She found 4 of 66 behavioral measures to relate at the 5 per cent level of chance to alcohol preference. Since 4 such "significant" relationships out of 66 does not exceed chance expectation, however, her results must be discounted pending further confirmation. Milhorat, Diethelm, Fleetwood, and Doty (Diethelm, Doty, and Milhorat, 1945; Milhorat and Diethelm, 1947; Diethelm, Fleetwood, and Milhorat, 1950; Fleetwood, 1955) have identified blood fractions associated with anxiety, tension, and resentment in humans. They identify the "anxiety substance" as having properties similar to nor-epinephrine and the "tension substance" as having properties similar to acetylcholine. Westerfeld and Schulman (1959) have recently pointed out that the "resentment substance" has properties similar to serotonin. Fleetwood (1955) reports that ingestion of alcohol reduces the "tension substance" in the blood, the effect being greater in alcoholics

than in normals. He also reports that ingestion of alcohol reduces the "resentment substance" in alcoholics but has less effect in normals, and that alcohol slightly reduces the "anxiety substance" in both groups. Although these latter studies do not deal directly with alcohol preference, they suggest an interaction between alcohol ingestion and adrenal activity and tend to support tension-reduction theories of alcohol preference.

Several investigators (Soeder, 1957; Merkel, 1957; Navratil, 1959) report data suggesting an increase in alcohol preference in humans following gastrectomy. Navratil (1959) presents the hypothesis that the change in alcohol preference is a result of psychological factors. However, the possibility also exists that aspects of digestive function are involved. The possible mechanisms involved or what effect the operation has on them is not clear.

Liver damage and alcoholism have long been closely linked. Incidence of deaths from cirrhosis of the liver is the one variable from which cultural incidence of alcoholism is estimated by the Jellinek formula (1947). The general assumption is that the liver condition is a direct or indirect effect of high alcohol preference and is not a cause of such preference. However, Sirnes (1953) reports that experimentally induced cirrhosis of the liver markedly increases alcohol preference of rats. Mardones (1955) reports that at least some of Sirnes's liver-damaged rats drink alcohol in doses producing drunkenness, doses resulting in blood alcohol levels as high as 3 g. per liter. This rate of intake is strikingly higher than that found in most other experimental studies of animals. The results strongly implicate liver activity as a factor in alcohol preference. Sirnes suggests that the increased preference may be due to the role of thiamin in carbohydrate, fat, and alcohol metabolism. This relationship will be considered in more detail after further experimental work is reviewed. Iida (1957) reports that alcohol preference of mice was increased both by placing NaCl in the drinking fluids and by daily injection of saline. He suggests that the effect was due to disturbed liver activity. The mechanism of action is not apparent, and the observed effect was small. Silkworth and Texon (1950) report data that seem to be in contradiction to Iida's findings. They report a negative relationship between blood chloride level of alcoholic patients and their craving for alcohol. Administration of saline was found to decrease craving. Mirone's finding (1957) that sodium-deficient and potassium-deficient diets did not affect alcohol preference of C57 mice tends to, but does not completely, rule out the possibility that Iida's results were due to increased sodium intake. More investigation seems called for before conclusions are drawn concerning the relationship between chloride or mineral intake and alcohol preference. Liver involvement in such a relationship also remains to be demonstrated.

Rogers, Pelton, and Williams (1955, 1956) and Rogers and Pelton (1957) have explored the effects of various amino acids on alcohol preference, and conclude that preference of both humans and rats is decreased by ingestion of glutamine. No effect was obtained from ingestion of glutamic acid, sodium glutamate, asparagine, or glycine. The basis for the effect of glutamine is not evident.

Beginning with the work of Mardones and Onfrey (1942) and stimulated by Williams' genetotrophic theory of alcoholism (1947, 1951, 1959; Williams, Berry, and Beerstecher, 1949*a*, 1949*b*), a number of investigators (Mardones, Segovia, and Onfrey, 1946; Brady and Westerfeld, 1947;

Mardones, Segovia, and Hederra, 1950, 1953; Beerstecher *et al.*, 1951; Mardones, 1951; Smith, Dardin, and Brown, 1951; Williams, Pelton, and Rogers, 1955; Mirone, 1957) have found that various vitamin deficiencies will increase alcohol preference or that administration of vitamins will decrease preference. The B-complex vitamins seem particularly important. Several investigators (Mardones, 1951; Beerstecher *et al.*, 1951; Mirone, 1957) have demonstrated that thiamin deficiency increases alcohol preference of rats and mice. Other vitamin deficiencies that have been found to increase alcohol preference are deficiencies of riboflavin, pantothenic acid, pyridoxine (Beerstecher *et al.*, 1951), Vitamin B_{12} (Williams *et al.*, 1949*a*), a thermostable yeast fraction presumably of the B-complex family (Factor N_1) (Mardones, 1951; Mardones *et al.*, 1950, 1953), and Vitamin A (Williams *et al.*, 1949*a*). Under certain conditions, notably when other deficiencies exist, investigators have found alcohol preference to be unaffected by the administration of riboflavin, pyridoxine, niacin, inosital, choline, liver extract containing biotin (Mardones *et al.*, 1946), calcium pantothenate (Mardones *et al.*, 1946; Mirone, 1957), thiamin (Mardones *et al.*, 1946; Johnston, 1954), and other vitamins or vitamin combinations (Brady and Westerfeld, 1947; Iida, 1957; Greenberg and Lester, 1957). Mirone found that pyridoxine-deficient diets tended to decrease rather than increase the alcohol preference of C57 mice (1957). In general, it can be concluded that vitamin deficiencies, especially those of the B-complex and particularly that of thiamin can increase alcohol preference. Decrease in alcohol preference is not necessarily produced by increased intake of any single vitamin, however, especially if other critical vitamin deficiencies continue to exist.

Westerfeld and Lawrow (1953) relate the thiamin-deficiency increased preference for alcohol to the role of thiamin in the metabolism of alcohol, carbohydrates, and fats. They point out that less thiamin is required for a given calorie yield from alcohol than is required for an equal yield from fat or sugar, and less is required for fat than for sugar. They compute a yield of 180 calories per thiamin utilization from glucose, 286 calories from stearic acid, and 322 calories from alcohol. Consistent with the explanation that thiamin availability differentially affects appetite for sugar, fat, and alcohol is the finding of Richter and Barelare (1939) that Vitamin-B-deficient rats showed decreased preference for sucrose and increased preference for olive oil. As mentioned, Sirnes (1953) posits that the thiamin-sparing action of alcohol accounts for increased alcohol preference following cirrhosis of the liver. It is conceivable that increase in alcohol preference following other vitamin deficiencies and disturbances of other organ systems may also be due to the relative ease with which the caloric value of alcohol can be realized. Several studies have been made of the relationship between the appetite for alcohol and alcohol's usefulness as a source of calories. Richter (1941, 1953), Gillespie and Lucas (1958), and Morgan and co-workers (1957) have found that alcohol can be used by rats as a calorie source to maintain body weight when it is partially substituted for other foods. Mirone (1952, 1959) reports no adverse effect on weight gain of weanling mice reared on 5 per cent or 10 per cent alcohol as their sole source of fluid. She does not, however, report the effect of alcohol intake on intake of other food. Westerfeld and Lawrow (1953) report that severe food deprivation increases alcohol preference in rats, although moderate food deprivation does not affect pref-

erence. Zarrow and Rosenberg (1953) also report increase of alcohol preference of rats with restricted food intake. These results indicate that alcohol can be used as a source of calories and that restriction of other sources of calories may increase alcohol preference.

The relative availability of specific sources of calories seems to be important in determining alcohol preference. There is some evidence that variation of fat intake has more effect than variation of sugar intake. Mirone (1957) found that a high-fat diet decreased alcohol preference of C57 mice but that a low-fat diet had no effect on preference. Lester and Greenberg (1952) found that rats offered a fat solution as an alternative to alcohol decreased their alcohol consumption. Williams and co-workers (1949a) report that linseed oil reduces alcohol preference of some rats. In general, it would seem that increased fat intake reduces alcohol preference but that decreased fat intake does not necessarily increase preference.

Lester and Greenberg (1952) found that rats offered a sucrose solution in addition to alcohol decreased their alcohol intake. Mardones and co-workers (1955) confirmed this reduction in alcohol intake with their Factor-N_1-deficient rats. It is possible, however, that the decrease in alcohol consumption produced by the presence of a sugar solution does not represent a decrease in alcohol preference so much as it represents a still higher preference for the sugar solution. Mardones *et al.* (1955) found that alcohol preference of their rats was not affected by either a sugar-free diet or free access to solid sugar. Mirone (1957) found that a high-sugar diet did not affect alcohol preference of C57 mice. Lester and Greenberg (1952) report some decrease in alcohol preference in rats offered solid sucrose, although the decrease was considerably less than that produced by a sugar solution. They also report (Greenberg and Lester, 1957) that rats on a low-sugar, high-fat, high-protein diet consume more alcohol than rats on a high-sugar, low-fat, low-protein diet. There thus is contradictory evidence about the effect of sugar intake on alcohol preference. It has been established, however, that most animals studied prefer a sugar solution to an alcohol solution.

The effect of alcohol intake on alcohol preference has been extensively considered, although less extensively examined experimentally. As early as 1819, Brühl-Cramer wrote, "The ingestion of brandy gives birth to what we believe to be the closest cause of the disease [dipsomania], and that again leads to the consumption of brandy" (Cited by Marconi, 1959). There is some evidence that alcohol consumption stimulates alcohol preference of animals. Richter (1957a) reports that two wild rats forced to consume 20 per cent alcohol for six months subsequently showed such high preference for alcohol that they ignored other foodstuffs and soon died. It is possible that the prolonged consumption of alcohol had led to nutritional or organ deficiencies that mediated the increased preference. Laboratory rats did not show the same addiction pattern. Mirone (1957) reports that C57 mice forced to consume 5 per cent alcohol for 11 weeks following weaning showed higher ethanol preference than controls reared on water. She also reports (1952) that a combined group of dba and CF1 mice forced to consume 5 per cent alcohol for 12 or 15 months following weaning showed higher preference than controls reared on water. These results provide support for the assumption that alcohol preference is increased by the ingestion of alcohol.

Many issues remain to be clarified con-

cerning the physiological determinants of alcohol preference in the various species studied. Vitamin deficiency, and especially thiamin deficiency, can apparently increase alcohol preference in rodents. The evidence to date supports the hypothesis that such increase in preference is related to the comparative ease with which the caloric content of the alcohol can be utilized. Further work testing such a relationship seems warranted. Alcohol intake apparently increases alcohol appetite. The mode of action is unclear, and would also seem to be a promising area for further study. Perhaps related to the effects of both vitamin deficiencies and previous alcohol consumption is the effect of liver malfunction on alcohol preference. More study of the role of the liver, and especially the role of alcohol dehydrogenase contained in the liver, would seem desirable. The influence of tension and resentment as possibly mediated by acetylcholine and serotonin, respectively, needs further study as a factor influencing alcohol preference. Further study of the role of the thyroid in limiting alcohol appetite might clarify nutritional or tension-resentment mechanisms involved in alcohol preference, or might suggest still other mechanisms. These are among the more important and promising leads suggested by research to date on physiological determinants of alcohol preference. They by no means exhaust the possibilities, however. In fact, few organ and metabolic systems have been clearly ruled out as having no effect on alcohol preference.

Since there is a large variety of mechanisms possibly involved in alcohol preference, maximum standardization of metabolic variables, through the use of inbred strains, becomes highly desirable. In the following material we will present our exploratory findings to date concerning the nature of, and physiological mechanisms related to, alcohol preference of inbred strains of mice.

PHYSIOLOGICAL DETERMINANTS OF ALCOHOL PREFERENCE OF MICE

We are carrying out four series of studies in the exploration of physiological mechanisms influencing alcohol preference of the mouse. One series is concerned with the

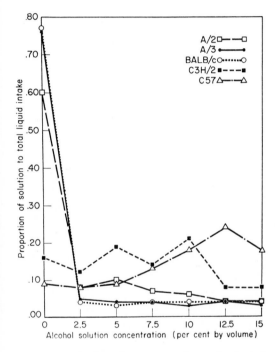

FIG. 5-8. **Preferred concentration of alcohol solution.**

strength of the alcohol preference or aversion of the different strains. Data from three studies will be presented. A second series is concerned with the effect of forced alcohol intake on alcohol preference. Data from two studies will be presented. A third series is concerned with the effect of anterior telencephalic lesions on alcohol aversion.* Data from two studies will be presented.

* Gilbert M. French is collaborating in these studies.

presented. The fourth series is concerned with the utilization of alcohol as a nutritional substance. Data from three studies will be presented.

The first study on strength of alcohol preference or aversion was performed to determine the concentration of alcohol most preferred by the C57BL strain and to determine whether the strains showing low preference for a 10 per cent solution would also show low preference for other concentrations. For three weeks, animals from five strains were allowed a choice of water or six concentrations of alcohol ranging from 2.5 per cent to 15 per cent. Bottle positions were changed every third day. The animals were housed three to a cage, four cages per strain. From Figure 5-8 it can be seen that the C57BL preference peaks at 12.5 per cent, a higher concentration than preferred by any other strain. The BALB/c and A/3Crgl show almost total avoidance of all alcohol concentrations. The A/2 show a slight acceptance of the very low concentrations, although their predominant preference is for water. The C3H/2 tend to avoid the highest concentrations but show relatively uniform preference for all solutions containing 10 per cent or less alcohol. As can be seen from Figure 5-9, the C3H/2 animals show a progressive shift with time toward preference for higher concentration. Their preference during the third week is primarily for the 10 per cent solution, whereas during the first two weeks they showed highest preference for the 5 per cent solution. The results establish the C3H/2 as an intermediate-preference strain under these test conditions. The study also tentatively indicates that the aversion of the A/2 animals for weak alcohol solutions is not as great as is that of the BALB/c and A/3 animals (Fig. 5-8). By demonstrating that strain differences are associated with several degrees of alcohol preference, the study tends to confirm the previous suggestion that alcohol preference is determined by a multiple-gene or a multiple-allele system or by both.

The strength of the C57BL preference for alcohol was tested by offering five S's a choice between a 10 per cent ethanol

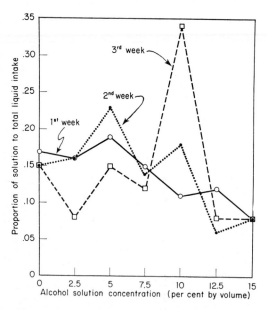

FIG. 5-9. Concentration of alcohol solution pre-ferred by C3H/2.

solution, a 15 per cent sucrose solution, and water. The sugar and alcohol solutions are approximately equal in caloric value. The animals without exception showed marked preference for the sugar solution, with a mean daily intake of 13.8 ml. This far exceeded their average intake of alcohol, 1.2 ml., and of water, also 1.2 ml., in the choice situation, and was more than double their usual intake of liquid when only water was present. The results indicate that the normal alcohol preference of the mice is not strong as compared to their pref-erence for a sucrose solution.

The high preference of animals for a sugar solution was used to test the degree of alcohol aversion of the low-preference

strains. In this study, sugar was added to the alcohol. Mice from nine strains were allowed a choice between water and a 10 per cent alcohol solution containing either 0, 2, 4, 8, or 16 g. of sucrose per 100 cc. of solution. Bottle positions were changed daily. The condition of sugar content was changed every third day. The particular sequence of sugar concentrations was randomly determined and was different for each mouse of a given strain but was

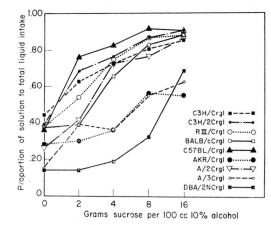

FIG. 5-10. Effect of sucrose content on prefer-ence for 10 per cent alcohol.

parallel across strains. Five mice per strain were tested, and average preference for each concentration versus water was de-termined (Fig. 5-10). For these same animals, relative preferences for a 2 per cent sucrose solution versus water and for a 15 per cent sucrose solution versus water were also determined, to assess possible strain differences in preference for sucrose. All strains except the AKR/Crgl showed greater than 90 per cent preference for a 15 per cent sugar solution versus water, and all strains except the A/3 showed better than 80 per cent preference for a 2 per cent sugar solution versus water, indicating that the strains have a pronounced preference for sugar even in concentrations as low as

2 per cent. From Figure 5-10 it can be seen that all strains will consume substantial amounts of alcohol solution if it contains sufficient sugar. There are marked strain differences in preference for the alcohol-sugar combination, however. The most pronounced differences are apparent when 10 per cent alcohol contains 2 per cent sucrose. The differences appear to be due in part to differences in preference for sucrose, since a significant correlation of $+.49$ is obtained between strain means for preference for 2 per cent sugar solution versus water and strain means for preference for 10 per cent alcohol containing 2 per cent sugar versus water. More work is necessary to clarify these relationships. However, the results indicate that the aversion to alcohol is weak in many of the nonpreferring strains, since it can be overcome with relatively small concentrations of sugar. The DBA/2N, AKR, and A/3 show the most pronounced aversion to the sweetened alcohol solutions (Fig. 5-10). As in the previous study, these results also suggest that either a multiple-allele system or a multiple-gene system is involved in determining alcohol preference.

In general, the results of the studies so far completed on strength of alcohol preference and aversion indicate that there is a graded sequence of preference represented by the different strains and that neither the preference for nor the aversion to 10% concentration of alcohol is strong relative to the preference for a sucrose solution.

To test the effect of forced alcohol intake on the aversion shown by the low-preference strains, adult animals of four strains were forced to consume 10 per cent alcohol for 14 days, were tested for alcohol preference in a choice situation for 14 days, were forced to consume alcohol solution for 53 more days, and were again tested for

alcohol preference. Control animals were maintained on water during the forced alcohol periods. The preferences following the 53-day period of forcing are shown in Figure 5-11. The results indicate that the

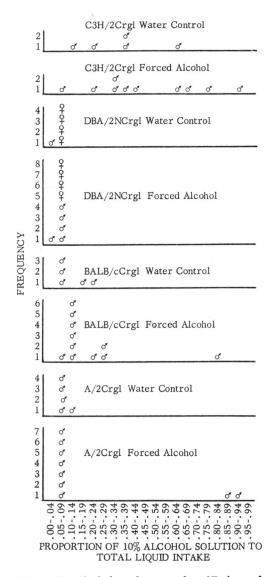

FIG. 5-11. Alcohol preference after 67 days of forced alcohol consumption.

preference of most animals is unaffected by enforced alcohol consumption but that a few may develop a marked taste for alcohol as a result of the forcing. The 53-

day period of forcing was no more effective than the 14-day period. Only in the DBA/2N strain did the forcing fail to produce any high-preference animals. Both the control and experimental animals of the C3H/2 group show a mean preference in the intermediate range, again suggesting that the C3H/2 is an intermediate-preference strain. The results of the study suggest that the effect of forced alcohol intake

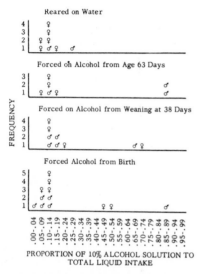

FIG. 5-12. Alcohol preference of BALB/c after indicated periods of forced alcohol consumption. Animals tested at age 116 days.

on preference may be an all-or-none phenomenon. If so, it would seem likely that changes in organ systems or other metabolic systems might mediate the change and that simple "habituation" could not account for the difference.

To explore further the effect of forced intake on alcohol preference, a more extensive study was made with the low-preference BALB/c strain. The animals were divided into four groups at birth. The first group was forced to consume alcohol from birth, via the mothers' milk or the drinking bottles; the second group was forced from

weaning at 38 days; the third group was forced from 63 days of age; and the fourth group was provided water without alcohol until testing. Testing was done at 116 days of age. Results, shown in Figure 5-12, indicate, as in the previous study, that a few animals are markedly affected by being forced to consume alcohol but that preference of most of the animals is not elevated over that of the controls reared on water. Within the limits of the present design, age at onset and duration of forced consumption seem to have relatively little differential effect at least on BALB/c mice. The results clearly contradict the assumption that forced alcohol intake will elevate alcohol preference of all or even most S's. As in the previous study, they suggest the operation of some all-or-none factor. More investigation is required before the exact nature of the effect can be specified.

A study was undertaken to determine whether lesions in the anterior telencephalon would reduce the alcohol aversion of low-preference mouse strains. Approximately the anterior third of the cerebrum, including the olfactory bulbs, was removed bilaterally from animals of the low-preference A and BALB/c strains. One group of control animals underwent all operative procedures except for the removal of brain tissue. Another group underwent all operative procedures except for skull opening and removal of brain tissue. In addition, two animals were given relatively small bilateral lesions, and one animal received a unilateral lobectomy of the frontal pole. Alcohol preference was tested following recovery from the operations (Fig. 5-13). The standard testing procedure was altered in one respect: the bottle positions were changed only once, at the end of the first week of the two-week preference run. It had been noted in a preliminary pilot study that the brain-damaged mice tended to show perseveration of position choice for the first day following a change of bottle position. A single position change was therefore used, to minimize the effect of perseveration while still assessing the possible effect of position habit. From Figure 5-13 it can be seen that the bilateral operation clearly increases alcohol preference of the experimental animals above that of the controls.

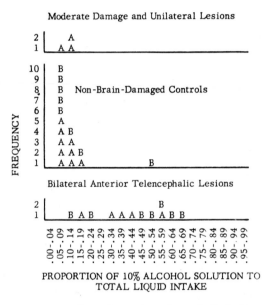

FIG. 5-13. Effect of anterior telencephalic lesions on alcohol preference. A indicates A/Crgl; B indicates BALB/cCrgl.

Neither mild damage nor unilateral lobectomy elevated preference. Daily consumption records indicate that position habit and perseveration do not account for the elevation.

To test the possibility that the increased preference of the operates was associated primarily with a loss of olfactory acuity and a subsequent loss of ability to discriminate the alcohol solution from water, a second group of animals of the A strain underwent removal of the olfactory bulbs. Control animals received anesthesia but had no surgery. The olfactory operates show intermediate preference (Fig. 5-14), but are not significantly different from the controls, which also show intermediate preference. The moderate preference of the controls is consistent with the data from the foster-rearing study (Fig. 5-4), but inconsistent with other data on the A strain (Figs. 5-5, 5-13), and prevents conclusive interpretation of the present results. The possibility that the effect of the operations is due to loss of olfactory acuity cannot be dismissed at present.

The last series of studies to be reported concerns the utilization of alcohol as a nutritional substance. An initial study was made of the effects of food deprivation on alcohol preference. Animals from five

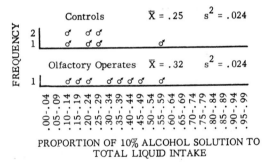

FIG. 5-14. Effects of removal of olfactory bulbs on alcohol preference of A/Crgl mice.

different strains were tested for alcohol preference for one week on a standard diet. During the following two weeks, each S was fed the same diet, but in a daily amount equal (to the nearest half gram) to one-tenth of its predeprivation body weight. Alcohol preference was measured during the two weeks of deprivation. The median weight at the end of the two weeks was 85 per cent of the initial body weight. From Figure 5-15 it can be seen that the C57BL animals tended to increase their intake during deprivation but that the preferences of the other strains either were unaffected or decreased during deprivation. The decreases of the C3H/2 and A/3 strains are not, however, statistically significant. In spite of the small number of animals used, the C57BL increase between Weeks 1 and 3 is significant beyond the .01 level of chance. These results indicate marked strain differences in the effect of food deprivation on alcohol preference and suggest that deprivation is most likely to increase consumption of animals already showing high preference. Further evidence on these relationships is provided by the following study.

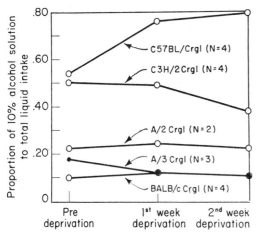

FIG. 5-15. Effect of food deprivation on alcohol preference.

To test whether strain differences in alcohol preference were related to ability to utilize alcohol as a calorie source, animals from six strains were maintained on a 10-per-cent-of-body-weight-per-day deprivation schedule for three weeks. During the first two weeks, approximately half of the animals were given water, and the other half were given 10 per cent alcohol as a drinking fluid. During the third week, they were allowed a choice of water or 10 per cent alcohol solution. Weight loss was measured daily. Because we have previously found a high mortality rate among

animals dropping appreciably below 80 per cent of initial body weight during deprivation, S's in the present study were taken off of the deprivation schedule for two days if they dropped below 80 per cent. They were then returned to the deprivation schedule. Weight losses of the water-fed and the alcohol-fed groups are

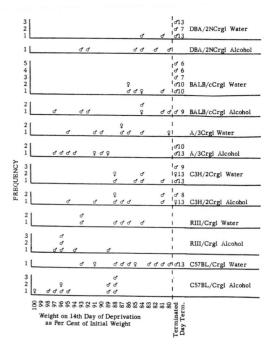

FIG. 5-16. Effect of forced alcohol consumption on weight retention during 14 days of food deprivation.

shown in Figure 5-16. Alcohol preferences during the third week of deprivation are shown in Figure 5-17. The results indicate marked strain differences in ability to utilize alcohol to maintain body weight. The C3H/2 and A/3 animals show approximately as much weight loss on alcohol as on water. The C57BL and the RIII/Crgl both maintain weight better on alcohol than on water, the differences being statistically significant at beyond the .01 level and the .05 level for the two strains, respectively, using the rank test of the differences between two averages. The greater weight losses of the BALB/c animals and of the DBA/2N animals cn water closely approach but fail to reach the .05 level of significance. Ability to maintain body weight was not related to the absolute amount of alcohol consumed. Previous studies concerning the physiological utilization of alcohol have been somewhat inconsistent (Morgan *et al.*, 1957; Gillespie and Lucas, 1958). Perhaps there are genetically determined differences in ability to utilize alcohol. Other mechanisms might account for the present results, however. For example, it may be that the strains differ in activity level following water and alcohol consumption. A strain made more active by alcohol would require more calories and would therefore show an apparent inability to utilize the caloric content of the alcohol, whereas a strain made less active by alcohol might show an apparent utilization of alcohol amounting to even more than 100 per cent of its caloric value. These possibilities were not explored in the present study, but will need clarification before final conclusions concerning the present results can be drawn.

From Figure 5-17, it can be seen that the normally low-preference strains do not have a marked increase in preference as a result of three weeks of food deprivation, although some individuals in these strains do show moderate alcohol consumption. In most strains, confirming previous results on nondeprived animals, the effect of forced alcohol intake on preference is not pronounced (Fig. 5-17). In only two strains, the C57BL and the DBA/2N, is the difference between the forced alcohol and the water groups significant. The C57BL show increased preference following alcohol consumption. The DBA/2N show a significant decrease in preference ($p < .05$), not apparent in Figure 5-17 because of width of

interval, even though the alcohol consumption figures are so low as to be seriously affected by bottle leakage. The C57BL are the highest preference strain and the DBA/2N, in this study as well as others (Figs. 5-2, 5-10, 5-12, 5-18), are the lowest preference strain. Again the data suggest that

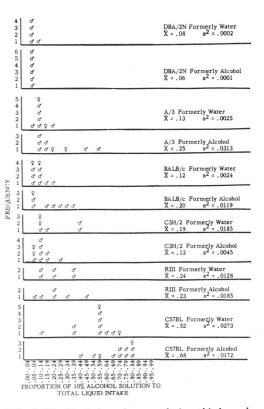

FIG. 5-17. Alcohol preference during third week of deprivation.

forced alcohol intake affects high-preference animals and low-preference animals differently and confirms that there are strain differences in the effect of forced alcohol intake on alcohol preference.

No clear relationship is demonstrated between strain differences in alcohol preference and ability to maintain weight on alcohol. However, further investigation of a possible relationship seems called for, since the two strains that showed highest

under conditions of food deprivation and alcohol dehydrogenase activity in the liver. Maternal effects have been ruled out as primary sources of strain differences in preference. The identification of several levels of preference under certain conditions suggests that alcohol preference is determined by either a multiple-gene system or a multiple-allele system or both.

Much further work remains to be done to clarify the genetic and physiological mechanisms underlying differences in alcohol preference in the mouse. While work to date has been exploratory and has involved relatively small numbers of animals, it has begun to clarify some of the mechanisms involved, and lays the groundwork for more thorough investigation. It has clearly demonstrated the value of using inbred strains in the study of alcohol preference and the feasibility of using alcohol preference as a phenotype of mouse behavior.

REFERENCES

THE AMERICAN FOUNDATION. 1955. "Alcoholism," in *Medical Research: A Mid-Century Survey*, Vol. 2. *Unsolved Clinical Problems: In Biological Perspective*. Boston, Little, Brown, pp. 517–574.

BARTLETT, G. R., and BARNET, H. N. 1949. Some observations on alcohol metabolism with radioactive ethyl alcohol. *Quart. J. Stud. Alcohol*. 10: 381–397.

BEERSTECHER, E., JR., REED, J. G., BROWN, W. D., and BERRY, L. J. 1951. The effects of single vitamin deficiencies on the consumption of alcohol by white rats. *Univ. Texas Publications*, No. 5109, pp. 115–138.

BLEULER, M. 1955a. "Familial and Personal Background of Chronic Alcoholics," in *Etiology of Chronic Alcoholism*, ed. by DIETHELM, O. Springfield, Ill., Thomas, pp. 110–166.

BLEULER, M. 1955b. " A Comparative Study of the Constitutions of Swiss and American Alcoholic Patients," in *Etiology of Chronic Alcoholism*, ed. by DIETHELM, O. Springfield, Ill., Thomas, pp. 167–178.

BRADY, R. A., and WESTERFELD, W. W. 1947.

Effect of B-complex vitamins on voluntary consumption of alcohol by rats. *Quart. J. Stud. Alcohol*. 7: 499–505.

CARPENTER, T. M. 1940. The metabolism of alcohol: a review. *Quart. J. Stud. Alcohol*. 1: 201–226.

CONGER, J. J. 1956. Reinforcement theory and the dynamics of alcoholism. *Quart. J. Stud. Alcohol*. 17: 296–305.

DEMBER, W. N., and KRISTOFFERSON, A. B. 1955. The relation between free-choice alcohol consumption and susceptibility to audiogenic seizures. *Quart. J. Stud. Alcohol*. 16: 86–95.

DIETHELM, O., DOTY, E. J., and MILHORAT, A. T. 1945. Emotions and adrenergic and cholinergic changes in the blood. *A. M. A. Arch. Neurol. & Psychiat*. 54: 110–115.

DIETHELM, O., FLEETWOOD, M. F., and MILHORAT, A. T. 1950. "The Predictable Association of Certain Emotions and Biochemical Changes in the Blood," in *Life Stress and Bodily Disease*. Baltimore, Williams & Wilkins.

EMERSON, G. A., BROWN, R. G., NASH, J. B., and MOORE, W. T. 1952. Species variation in preference for alcohol and in effects of diet or drugs on this preference. *J. Pharmacol. & Exper. Therap*. 106: 384 (Abstract).

FLEETWOOD, M. F. 1955. "Biochemical Experimental Investigations of Emotions and Chronic Alcoholism," in *Etiology of Chronic Alcoholism*, ed. by DIETHELM, O. Springfield, Ill., Thomas, pp. 43–109.

FORSANDER, O., KOHONEN, J., and SUOMALAINEN, H. 1958. Physiological alcohol consumption. *Quart. J. Stud. Alcohol*. 19: 379–387.

FREEMAN, W., and WATTS, J. W. 1942. *Psychosurgery*. Springfield, Ill., Thomas.

GILLESPIE, R. J. G., and LUCAS, C. C. 1958. Metabolic availability of energy of ingested ethyl alcohol. *Canad. J. Biochem*. 36: 307–317.

GREENBERG, L. A., and LESTER, D. 1957. "Vitamin Deficiency and the Etiology of Alcoholism," in *Alcoholism, Basic Aspects and Treatment*, ed. by HIMWICH, H. E. Am. A. Advancement Sc., Publication No. 47, pp. 67–71.

GRENELL, R. G. 1957. "Some Effects of Alcohols on the Central Nervous System," in *Alcoholism, Basic Aspects and Treat-*

ment, ed. by HIMWICH, H. E. *Am. A. Advancement Sc.,* Publication No. 47, pp. 7–17.

GROSS, M. 1945. The relation of the pituitary gland to some symptoms of alcoholic intoxication and chronic alcoholism. *Quart. J. Stud. Alcohol.* 6: 25–35.

HIRSH, J. 1949. *The Problem Drinker.* New York, Duell, Sloan & Pearce.

IIDA, S. 1957. Experimental studies on the craving for alcohol: I. Alcoholic drive in mice following administration of saline. *Jap. J. Pharmacol.* 6: 87–93.

JELLINEK, E. M. 1947. *Recent Trends in Alcoholism and in Alcohol Consumption.* New Haven, Hillhouse Press.

JOHNSTON, M. 1954. The treatment of alcoholics in an outpatient clinic with adrenal cortex hormones and vitamin B₁. *Quart. J. Stud. Alcohol.* 15: 238–245.

KAIJ, L. 1957. Drinking habits in twins. *Acta Genet. Med.* 7: 437–441.

LEMERE, F. 1956. What causes alcoholism? *J. Clin. & Exper. Psychopath.* 17: 202–206.

LERNER, I. M. 1954. *Genetic Homeostasis.* New York, Wiley.

LESTER, D., and GREENBERG, L. A. 1952. Alcoholism, 1941–1951: A survey of activities in research, education and therapy: III. The status of physiological knowledge. *Quart. J. Stud. Alcohol.* 13: 444–452.

LESTER, D., and GREENBERG, L. A. 1952. Nutrition and the etiology of alcoholism. The effect of sucrose, fat, and saccharin on the self-selection of alcohol by rats. *Quart. J. Stud. Alcohol.* 13: 553–560.

LOEB, L., KING, H. D., and BLUMENTHAL, H. T. 1943. Transplantation and individuality differentials in inbred strains of rats. *Biol. Bull.* 84: 1–112.

MCCLEARN, G. E., and RODGERS, D. A. 1959. Differences in alcohol preference among inbred strains of mice. *Quart. J. Stud. Alcohol.* 20: 691–695.

MCCLEARN, G. E., and RODGERS, D. A. 1961. Genetic factors in alcohol preference of laboratory mice. *J. Comp. Physiol. Psychol.* 54: 116–119.

MACNISH, R. 1828. *The Anatomy of Drunkenness,* 2nd ed. Glasgow, W. R. M'Phun.

MARCONI, J. T. 1959. The concept of alcoholism. *Quart. J. Stud. Alcohol.* 20: 216–235.

MARDONES R., J. 1951. On the relationship between deficiency of B vitamins and alcohol intake in rats. *Quart. J. Stud. Alcohol.* 12: 563–575.

MARDONES, J. 1955. "Craving" for alcohol. *Quart. J. Stud. Alcohol.* 16: 51–53.

MARDONES R., J. and ONFRAY B., E. 1942. Influencia de una substancia de la levadura (elemento del complejo vitamínico B?) sobre el consumo de alcohol en ratas en experimentos de autoselección. *Rev. Chil. Hig. Med. prev.* 4: 293–297.

MARDONES R., J., SEGOVIA M., N., and HEDERRA D., A. 1950. Herencio del alcoholismo en ratas. I Comportamiento de la primera generación de ratas bebedoras, colocadas en dieta carenciada en factor N₁. *Bol. Soc. Biol. Santiago.* 7: 61–62.

MARDONES R., J., SEGOVIA M., N., and HEDERRA D., A. 1953. Heredity of experimental alcohol preference in rats: II. Coefficient of heredity. *Quart. J. Stud. Alcohol.* 14: 1–2.

MARDONES R., J., SEGOVIA-RIQUELME, N., HEDERRA D., A., and ALCAINO G., F. 1955. Effect of some self-selection conditions on the voluntary alcohol intake of rats. *Quart. J. Stud. Alcohol.* 16: 425–437.

MARDONES, J., SEGOVIA, N., and ONFRAY, E. 1946. Relationship between the dose of Factor N and the alcohol intake of rats under self-selection conditions. *Arch. Biochem.* 9: 401–406.

MASSERMAN, J. H., and YUM, K. S. 1946. An analysis of the influence of alcohol on experimental neuroses in cats. *Psychosom. Med.* 8: 36–52.

MERKEL, K. L. 1957. Alkoholismus bei Lungentuberkulösen: Versuch einer medizinisch-psycholigischen Studie im Heilstättenmilien. *Bietr. Klin. Tuberk.* 116: 653–676.

MILHORAT, A. T., and DIETHELM, O. 1947. Substances in blood of patients during emotional states. Effect on isolated rabbit intestine. *Fed. Proc.* 6: 165–166 (Abstract).

MIRONE, L. 1952. The effect of ethyl alcohol on growth, fecundity, and voluntary consumption of alcohol by mice. *Quart. J. Stud. Alcohol.* 13: 365–369.

MIRONE, L. 1957. Dietary deficiency in mice in relation to voluntary alcohol consumption. *Quart. J. Stud. Alcohol.* 18: 552–560.

MIRONE, L. 1958. The effect of ethyl alcohol

on growth and voluntary consumption of alcohol by successive generations of mice. *Quart. J. Stud. Alcohol.* 19: 388–393.

MIRONE, L. 1959. Water and alcohol consumption by mice. *Quart. J. Stud. Alcohol.* 20: 24–27.

MOORE, W. T.; MOORE, B. M.; NASH, J. B., and EMERSON, G. A. 1952. Effects of maze running and sonic stimulation on voluntary alcohol intake of albino rats. *Texas Rep. Biol. & Med.* 10(1): 59–65.

MORGAN, A. F., BRINNER, L., PLAA, C. B., and STONE, M. M. 1957. Utilization of calories from alcohol and wines and their effects on cholesterol metabolism. *Am. J. Physiol.* 189(2): 290–296.

NAVRATIL, L. 1959. On the etiology of alcoholism. *Quart. J. Stud. Alcohol.* 20: 236–244.

NEWMAN, H. W. 1947. Some factors influencing the rate of metabolism of ethyl alcohol. *Quart. J. Stud. Alcohol.* 8: 377–384.

REED, J. G. 1951. A study of the alcoholic consumption and amino acid excretion patterns of rats of different inbred strains. *Univ. Texas Publications,* No. 5109, pp. 144–149.

RICHTER, C. P. 1941. Alcohol as food. *Quart. J. Stud. Alcohol.* 1: 650–662.

RICHTER, C. P. 1942–1943. Total selfregulatory functions in animals and human beings. *Harvey Lect.* 38: 63–103.

RICHTER, C. P. 1953. Alcohol, beer, and wine as foods. *Quart. J. Stud. Alcohol.* 14: 525–539.

RICHTER, C. P. 1957a. "Decreased Appetite for Alcohol and Alcoholic Beverages Produced in Rats by Thyroid Treatment," in *Hormones, Brain Function, and Behavior,* ed. by HOAGLAND, H. New York, Academic Press, pp. 217–220.

RICHTER, C. P. 1957b. "Loss of Appetite for Alcohol and Alcoholic Beverages Produced in Rats by Treatment with Thyroid Preparations," in *Alcoholism, Basic Aspects and Treatment,* ed. by HIMWICH, H. E. *Am. A. Advancement Sc.,* Publication No. 47, pp. 59–65.

RICHTER, C. P., and BARELARE, B. 1939. Further observations on the carbohydrate, fat, and protein appetite of Vitamin B deficient rats. *Amer. J. Physiol.* 127: 199–210.

RICHTER, C. P., and CAMPBELL, K. H. 1940. Alcohol taste thresholds and concentrations of solution preferred by rats. *Science.* 91: 507–508.

RODGERS, D. A., and McCLEARN, G. E. 1959. Genetic factors in alcohol preference in laboratory mice. *Am. Psychologist.* 14: 396 (Abstract).

ROE, A. 1944. The adult adjustment of children of alcoholic parents raised in foster-homes. *Quart. J. Stud. Alcohol.* 5: 378–393.

ROGERS, L. L., and PELTON, R. B. 1957. Glutamine in the treatment of alcoholism: a preliminary report. *Quart. J. Stud. Alcohol.* 18: 581–587.

ROGERS, L. L., PELTON, R. B., and WILLIAMS, R. J. 1955. Voluntary alcohol consumption by rats following administration of glutamine. *J. Biol. Chem.* 214: 503–506.

ROGERS, L. L., PELTON, R. B., and WILLIAMS, R. J. 1956. Amino acid supplementation and voluntary alcohol consumption by rats. *J. Biol. Chem.* 220: 321–323.

SACKLER, R. R., SACKLER, M. D., CO TUI, MARTÍ-IBÁÑEZ, F., and SACKLER, A. M. 1952. On tolerance to and craving for alcohol in histamine-treated schizophrenics. *Psychiatric Quart.* 26: 597–607.

San Francisco Chronicle. His stomach brewed its own hangover. July 9, 1959, p. 18.

SEGOVIA-RIQUELME, N., VITALE, J. J., HEGSTED, D. M., and MARDONES, J. 1956. Alcohol metabolism in "drinking" and "nondrinking" rats. *J. Biol. Chem.* 223: 399–403.

SILKWORTH, W. D., and TEXON, M. 1950. Chloride levels in the blood of alcoholic patients in relation to the phenomenon of craving. *Quart. J. Stud. Alcohol.* 11: 381–384.

SIRNES, T. B. 1953. Voluntary consumption of alcohol in rats with cirrhosis of the liver: a preliminary report. *Quart. J. Stud. Alcohol.* 14: 3–18.

SMITH, J. A., DARDIN, P. A., and BROWN, W. T. 1951. The treatment of alcoholism by nutritional supplement. *Quart. J. Stud. Alcohol.* 12: 381–385.

SOEDER, M. 1957. Trunksucht nach Magenresektion. *Nervenarzt.* 28: 228–229.

TALBOT, B., BELLIS, E. C., and GREENBLATT, M. 1951. Alcoholism and lobotomy. *Quart. J. Stud. Alcohol.* 12: 386–394.

TOBACH, E. 1957. Individual differences in behavior and alcohol consumption in the rat. *Quart. J. Stud. Alcohol. 18:* 19–29.

WESTERFELD, W. W., and LAWROW, J. 1953. The effect of caloric restriction and thiamin deficiency on the voluntary consumption of alcohol by rats. *Quart. J. Stud. Alcohol. 14:* 378–384.

WESTERFELD, W. W., and SCHULMAN, M. P. 1959. Some biochemical aspects of the alcohol problem. *Quart. J. Stud. Alcohol. 20:* 439–451.

WILLIAMS, R. J. 1947. The etiology of alcoholism: a working hypothesis involving the interplay of hereditary and environmental factors. *Quart. J. Stud. Alcohol. 7:* 567–587.

WILLIAMS, R. J. 1951. *Nutrition and Alcoholism.* Norman, Okla., University of Oklahoma Press.

WILLIAMS, R. J. 1959. Biochemical individuality and cellular nutrition: prime factors in alcoholism. *Quart. J. Stud. Alcohol. 20:* 452–463.

WILLIAMS, R. J., BERRY, L. J., and BEERSTECHER, E., JR. 1949a. Biochemical individuality: III. Genetotrophic factors in the etiology of alcoholism. *Arch. Biochem. 23:* 275–290.

WILLIAMS, R. J., BERRY, L. J., and BEERSTECHER, E., JR. 1949b. Individual metabolic patterns, alcoholism, genetotrophic diseases. *Proc. Nat. Acad. Sc., Washington, D.C. 35:* 265–271.

WILLIAMS, R. J., PELTON, R. B., and ROGERS, L. L. 1955. Dietary deficiencies in animals in relation to voluntary alcohol and sugar consumption. *Quart. J. Stud. Alcohol. 16:* 234–244.

ZARROW, M. X., and ROSENBERG, B. 1953. Alcoholic drive in rats treated with propyl thiouracil. *Am. J. Physiol. 172:* 141–146.

6

ROLE OF INHERITANCE IN DETERMINATION
OF SEXUAL BEHAVIOR PATTERNS

Robert W. Goy

Jacqueline S. Jakway

NATURE AND EVOLUTIONARY SIGNIFICANCE OF PATTERNS OF SEXUAL BEHAVIOR

The relationship between the genotype of an animal and its display of sexual behavior constitutes a comparatively new area of investigation. Like any other character involved in "fitness," sexual behavior is of selective importance in evolutionary development. All other aspects of fertility being equal, the individual most successful in mating will make the greatest genic contribution to the succeeding generation, and the genes of the sexually successful will become more and more frequently represented in a population. Should a mutation occur which results in advantageous morphologic, physiologic, or behavioral characteristics, the advantage is most likely to be lost or held to a low equilibrium value, if by virtue of its pleiotropic nature it has a detrimental effect on mating behavior. On the other hand, disadvantageous mutations may become widespread if they pleiotropically augment mating success. Thus the extent to which the genotype affects sexual behavior and the relationships between sexuality and other inherited behavioral traits (such as aggression) are problems of basic theoretical as well as practical concern.

Sexual behavior is customarily treated as a pattern of independently identifiable components arranged in a temporal sequence. For the male, mating behavior is usually described in terms of rates or duration of particular activities such as sniffing, mounting, and intromission in mammals; mounting and treading in birds; or wing vibrations in insects. The length of time from the introduction of the female to the first ejaculation is frequently employed. Use of rates and duration in quantitation of the female sexual responses such as mounting or receptive stance has been made. In mammals, the temporal relationships of the elements of sexual behavior to the estrous period is often used. Little attention has been given to the order or sequence in which the elements appear in the pattern. Sequence has, however, been shown to be an important species difference in ducks (K. Lorenz, 1958) and may well be profitably studied in genetical investigations of other groups.

A considerable body of literature has been devoted to the separability of the individual components or elements of the

96

mating pattern (Young, 1961). In most cases, neither the genetic nor the physiological basis for division into components has been elucidated, and the division is based on purely functional considerations. However, Bastock (1956) found that a single gene affects the performance of only one element in the mating behavior pattern of the male *Drosophila,* and Jakway (1959) and Goy and Jakway (1959) showed a separation in the inheritance of elements of the sexual behavior pattern of the male and the female guinea pig. The extent to which behavioral components are genetically independent remains to be empirically determined for the majority of species.

In addition to the composite nature of sexual behavior, a wide variety of sexual activities exist. Ford and Beach (1951) in a broad cross-cultural and cross-species survey point out that although heterosexual coitus is the dominant mode of expression basic tendencies toward homosexual activity, autogenital stimulation, and interspecific sexual behavior exist throughout the mammalian scale. The authors conclude, particularly for the human and primates, that the frequency and form of these varieties of sexual behavior are in part a consequence of the species heredity and in part the result of early experience. In the fundamental mammalian heritage of every individual is a capacity to respond as both a male and a female to a wide range of stimuli. In the opinion of Ford and Beach, the extent of genotypic control over sexual behavior is largely confined to the endowment of an individual with those tendencies or capacities characteristic of the species.

GENETIC STUDIES OF INTERGENERIC AND INTERSPECIFIC VARIATIONS IN SEXUAL BEHAVIOR

The differences between species or genera represent a much broader source of genetic variance than can ever be encountered within a species, and the problem of interspecific crosses is no longer of interest purely for the tabulation of successes. Recently, interest has been directed to the possibility of studying "primitive" behavioral types (Poulsen, 1950). Presumably, recombination permits inferences about the behavior displayed by the common progenitors of the two species. In Poulsen's study of a cross between a domestic duck and a domestic goose, the hybrid male did not display sexual behavior even when injected with relatively large amounts of male hormone. Thus, in at least one instance, the failure of interspecific hybrids to propagate may be attributed to an inadequacy in sexual behavior, since no other aspects of infertility could be determined. Much more data would be needed, of course, to demonstrate that the genes for components of sexual behavior were nonallelic in the two parental species. That interpretation is, however, tenable.

In pheasant-turkey hybrids, an intergeneric cross, Asmundson and F. W. Lorenz (1955) reported that neither eggs nor semen were obtained and that mating behavior was never observed. Failure of a hybrid to display mating behavior was reported by Huxley (1941) in an intergeneric cross between an Amherst (*Chrysolophus amherstiae*) and Impeyan (*Lophophorus impeyans*) pheasant. The hybrid observed, a male, showed "no trace of sexual interest."

In a study of the sexual behavior of platyfish and swordtails, two sympatric species of fishes, Clark, Aronson, and Gordon (1954) partitioned the precopulatory behavior into components. They found that some elements in the behavior of the platyfish were absent in the swordtail, and that the reverse was true as well. This variation was greater, then, than has ever been found within a species. Despite parental differences in the precopulatory pattern as well as in mating duration, Clark and co-workers were able to obtain interspecies hybrids of F_1, F_2, and backcross generations. Although formal genetic analysis was impossible, evidence was obtained for "dominance" and "recessive" relationships in some components. In general, however, the action of many genes or genetic factors, each of small effect, appeared to be involved in the determination of the components of male sexual behavior studied.

In an extensive survey, Spieth (1952) compared the mating behavior of 101 species and subspecies of the *Drosophila.* Differences in mating behavior corresponded well to the existing taxonomic groupings. The common elements of sexual behavior permitted the reconstruction of the "primitive" or ancestral type, and in addition, the observation was confirmed that closely related species displayed nearly identical patterns of mating behavior.

Even when closely related species appear to differ greatly (that is, by the presence or absence of a particular component), the difference may be one of threshold of excitation. Thus, Manning (1959a, 1959b) in a study of *melanogaster* and *simulans* has shown that the behavioral elements of "scissoring" normally absent in *melanogaster* males, and present in *simulans,* can be made to appear in the *melanogaster* behavior sequence if sluggish females are used as the sexual stimuli. Correspondingly, "scissoring" increases in frequency and duration of occurrence in the mating display of *simulans* tested with sluggish females.

K. Lorenz (1958) has recently shown that male hybrids between different species of ducks retain the ability to display sexual behavior, but that the different components of courtship may not be arranged in an orderly fashion. Occasionally components

not seen in either parental line appear in the hybrids. To our knowledge this is the only evidence available demonstrating a genotypic modification of the temporal relations between the behavioral components.

Hinde (1956) has studied the courtship and copulatory behavior of different species of finches and their hybrids, in addition to other aspects of behavior. He concludes that in each instance in which the complex behavioral patterns are highly similar within the parental species a similar genetic substrate exists. When the parental species differ markedly in a particular trait, the hybrid tends to resemble one parent ("dominance"), or the behavior does not appear at all. The latter alternative seems to be more characteristic of the relatively distant intergeneric crosses previously reported than for crosses between closely related species.

Manning (1959b) noted phenotypic dominance of the *simulans* male courtship pattern in crosses between that and the closely related *melanogaster* species of *Drosophila.* One aspect of this study is especially noteworthy. Strong sexual isolation exists between these two species to the extent that mature males (3 days old) rarely display full courtship behavior toward females of the other species. This discrimination appears to be built up or to mature gradually since males of both species display courtship behavior quite indiscriminately during the first day of life to most moving objects of the right size, including other males. By maturity, however, hybrid males display the same discrimination for females as that characteristic of the parental *simulans.* Hybrid females are courted successfully only by *melanogaster* males. Further genetic analysis would be most interesting in this particular case to determine the degree and type of genetic linkage present between these two aspects of courtship, i.e., between the pattern of behavioral elements and the discriminatory process.

Ehrman (1960) demonstrated that crosses between subspecies of *Drosophila paulistorum* can produce hybrids which fail to display mating behavior. From matings of Amazonian males with Andean-South-Brazilian females, the male hybrids were sexually sluggish regardless of the type of female placed with them, and the females never displayed receptive postures when courted by hybrid males or males of either parental subspecies. The genetic constitution of the hybrids appears to result in inadequate vigor of sexual behavior, but its effects on the discriminatory process are difficult to evaluate. Strong sexual isolation normally exists between the parental lines.

The problem of courtship discrimination has received considerable attention in studies on *Drosophila* (Spieth, 1947, 1949) and appears to be a function of the female as often as it is a function of the male. Thus Streisinger (1948) showed that the high sexual isolation existing between *melanogaster* and *pseudoobscura* tends to break down or be greatly reduced when the males are tested with etherized females. Spieth (1951) found that among 14 naturally occurring strains of *Drosophila* isolation was maintained by a definite intra-strain balance between the sexes with respect to sexual "drive" and discrimination. Frequently the "balance" was of such a nature that a strain was characterized by sexually sluggish males and highly receptive females. In such instances, the females were observed to maintain the sexual isolation of the strain by displaying a high degree of courtship discrimination toward males of their own strain. Moreover, in strains characterized by active males, the same relationship between high sexual drive and high discrimination was found.

GENETIC STUDIES OF INTRASPECIFIC VARIATIONS IN SEXUAL BEHAVIOR

The study of intraspecific differences in sexual behavior which are attributable to genotypic factors requires somewhat different considerations from those we have been employing, primarily because the genetic variance is not so great. It must be realized in the search for genetic bases for sexual behavior patterns that there is variation from individual to individual, and that the performance of a subject varies from test to test. The phenotype of a particular gene complex will be expressed as a continuum within experimentally definable limits.

Genetically Heterogeneous Populations

That the limits of the phenotypic expression of elements in sexual behavior are set by the genome is strongly suggested by the consistency of individual differences found in genetically heterogeneous populations. Table 6-1, modified from the data presented by Young *et al.* (1939), shows that number of hours in heat during 11 consecutive estrous cycles were remarkably constant for individual female guinea pigs. There is a relatively good correlation between the performance on the first recorded estrus and the mean over-all estrous period. Unpublished data from the University of Nebraska (Jakway and Sumption, personal communication) from a series of 30-minute mating observations of 10 boars demonstrate characteristic individual patterns of behavior. This is illustrated by Table 6-2 which shows that in rate of nuzzling each animal performed quite consistently during each of six observations with an estrous sow. A similar demonstration of the consistency of individual differences for male guinea pigs is presented by Young in Chapter 7 of this book. Grunt and Young (1952) have shown that differences be-

TABLE 6-1   LENGTH OF HEAT IN HOURS DURING CONSECUTIVE ESTROUS CYCLES IN THE GUINEA PIG

ANIMAL	CYCLE											MEAN
	1ST	2ND	3RD	4TH	5TH	6TH	7TH	8TH	9TH	10TH	11TH	
1045	19.5	20.0	15.5	31.0	26.0	24.5	26.5	14.0	10.5	18.0	11.0	19.7
1251	16.0	12.5	15.5	13.5	14.0	5.0	22.0	12.5	15.5	12.5	11.5	13.7
1274	13.5	6.0	8.0	7.5	5.0	9.0	10.0	10.5	8.5	9.5	8.5	8.7
1073	10.0	8.5	8.5	3.0	11.0	5.0	8.5	8.5	10.0	9.5	9.0	8.3
1509	10.0	6.5	16.0	9.0	5.0	10.0	6.5	6.0	6.5	8.0	8.0	8.3
1120	8.0	7.0	6.5	9.0	4.0	9.0	8.0	8.0	7.0	8.0	7.5	7.4
1315	7.5	9.0	8.0	6.5	11.0	7.5	7.5	6.0	6.5	5.5	5.5	7.3
1521	4.5	6.0	5.5	9.5	4.0	8.0	7.0	10.0	9.5	5.5	8.5	7.1
1063	0.0	0.0	0.0	2.0	0.0	5.0	—	0.0	0.0	3.5	0.0	1.1
1230	0.0	0.0	0.0	0.0	2.0	0.0	5.5	3.5	0.0	7.5	—	1.8

tween high- and low-drive male guinea pigs persist after castration and are not related to the quantity of androgen injected. This finding demonstrates that some inherent or constitutional factor other than amount of endogenous hormone accounts for the differences between high- and low-drive males. Studies demonstrating highly consistent individual differences between cows in the intensity of estrus have also been reported (Rottensten and Touchberry, 1957). In repeated observations of the sexual behavior of 102 bulls of several

TABLE 6-2   FREQUENCY OF NUZZLING DISPLAYED BY BOARS DURING CONSECUTIVE OBSERVATIONS LASTING 30 MINUTES

ANIMAL	OBSERVATION						MEAN
	1ST	2ND	3RD	4TH	5TH	6TH	
1	32	35	23	26	9	26	25.2
3	12	7	23	31	21	26	20.0
4	17	39	5	16	12	21	18.3
2	20	2	23	16	27	21	18.2
7	2	9	27	41	5	19	17.2
11	7	8	15	21	13	26	15.0
6	16	11	9	29	5	15	14.2
10	20	8	8	21	6	6	11.5
8	4	10	4	15	16	10	9.8
9	7	23	7	3	3	7	8.3

breeds, Fraser (1957, 1960) noticed that individuals were consistent in the time required to achieve copulation. Such studies of individuals never conclusively demonstrate genetic influence, but are merely suggestive.

Further evidence of the role of inheritance in genetically heterogeneous populations is obtained from the study of family relationships. Wood-Gush and Osborne (1956) studied sex drive in cockerels from a subline of Brown Leghorns. The inbreeding coefficient of their stock was about 25 per cent. They found significant differences between sire families in a measurement of mating frequency, suggesting a genetical basis for degree of sex drive. Craig, Casida, and Chapman (1954) in a pedigree study established the hereditary nature of low libido in a commercial strain of rats. In comparing breeds of domestic sheep, Hafez (1951, 1952) found that the ewes differed in intensity of sexual drive as measured by their pursual of males. No such breed differences were detected among the rams. Asdell (1946) observed that estrous ewes of the Merino breed were notably restless, while Dorset ewes assumed a stance characteritsic of that breed. Breed differences in both disposition and in sexual drive among bulls are described by Fraser (1957, 1960). These differences were particularly striking among animals four years of age and older. After the fourth year the interval to copulation in minutes was significantly greater in beef bulls (24.91) than in dairy bulls (12.80).

Using behavioral criteria Burger (1952) determined the duration of components of the estrous cycle in two breeds of swine. The length of diestrus, during which the female shows no interest in the boar and consistently refuses his attentions, was not significantly different in the two breeds. The length of proestrus, during which the female shows interest in the male but will not accept service, and the duration of metestrus, or waning estrus, were also essentially similar in the two breeds. On the other hand, the mean duration of full estrus in the Large Black breed (62.57 hours) was significantly longer than in the Large White breed (47.60 hours). Within the breeds the correlation coefficient for duration of estrus between sisters was also highly significant. We will later discuss the inheritance of duration of estrus, as induced by a standard hormonal dosage, in spayed guinea pigs.

Further use of the genetically heterogeneous population has been made by the use of selection techniques. Following the 1956 work reported above, Wood-Gush (1960) obtained progeny from the four top-scoring and four low-scoring cockerels. The differences in mating frequency between the "high" and "low" strains persisted in the F_1 generation and the F_2 group, as well. Data from the F_3 generation were inconclusive because of illness in the flock. In five generations of selective breeding for strength of sex drive, Rasmussen (1952) derived two strains of rats. Both males and females of the high-sex-drive strain crossed an electrified grid six times more frequently to reach an animal of the opposite sex than did animals of the low-drive strain.

Genetically Homogeneous Populations

One difficulty in the use of pedigree and selective breeding studies lies in the fact that each animal is genetically unique in the experiment. An approach to this problem revolves about the ability of the investigator to test groups of animals who are identical in genotype and are, in this sense, experimental replicates. Such animals are available to the experimenter from three sources. First, there are monozygotic litter mates. Secondly, there are members of highly inbred strains, and thirdly, the first-generation (F_1) progeny of animals from two highly inbred strains. Animals from highly inbred strains are both virtually identical in genotype and maximally homozyous. Assuming that all genotypes in a population reproduce uniformly, Pearl (1914), Fish (1914), and Jennings (1916), by direct methods, and Wright (1921), using path coefficients, demonstrated that following a system of brother-sister matings the percentage of heterozygosity in a population is infinitesimal by the thirtieth generation. Wright showed that the correlation between offspring of a mating would be 0.989 by the fifteenth generation. Should there be a selective advantage for heterozygosity, however, no system of inbreeding is likely to result in complete homozygosity (Hayman and Mather, 1953). As a consequence of the uniform homozygosity of highly inbred strains, F_1 progeny of two such strains are equally uniform in genotype but, in contrast to the inbred individuals, are maximally heterozygous. Monozygotic litter mates, on the other hand, are genetically identical, but the percentage of homozygosity depends upon the degree of inbreeding of the parents.

Observations on the similarity of sexual behavior of monozygotic animals have been made only rarely. Olson and Peterson (1951) reared a set of Milking-Shorthorn-identical-triplet bulls in the same environment. They were brought into service with considerable effort at 13.5 months of age. All three were stubborn and lacked interest in serving. This is a marked deviation from the normal pattern in dairy bulls, which are ordinarily exceedingly sexually active. One such bull has been induced to furnish up to 19 ejaculates in two hours (Hale and Almquist, 1960). Most impressive data come from Bane's (1954) seven-year study of six pairs of monozygous twin bulls. Although all were of the Swedish Red and White breed, the pairs came from different herds of noninbred stock. They consequently represented six different genotypes. Despite dietary differences between siblings during rearing, there was very little difference between brothers in sexual performance. There were, however, both quantitative and qualitative differences between pairs.

By using highly inbred strains of laboratory animals the mating behavior of large numbers of subjects of presumably identical genotype has been studied. By this means it has been possible not only to identify a particular pattern of behavior with a specific genotype but to study the extent of the phenotypic variations permitted by a single genotype under standard conditions of testing.

Some phenotypic variation exists within genetically identical groups even though experimenters adhere to rigid standards in rearing and in observations. We have no reason to believe that the limits of variation in any measure of sexual performance are comparable for all genotypes. While one genotype may engender an extremely stereotyped sexual pattern, another may permit greater plasticity. Although no extensive study has been made of sexual behavior in a large number of highly inbred strains from one species, comparisons of guinea pig Strains 2 and 13 are partially supportive. Within a given sample, males of Strain 13 tend to have higher coefficients of variation in measures of sexual activity than do those from Strain 2 (Jakway, 1959). On the other hand, during the past seven years there has been less variation between samples of Strain-13 males than of Strain-2 males (Valenstein, Riss, and Young, 1955; Jakway, 1959). For females, variation resembles that described for the males, with Strain 13 exhibiting greater variation within samples and smaller variations between samples. Thus the plasticity or range of phenotypic variability of an individual's sexual behavior may be determined by genetic factors. Additional discussion will be given to the problem of plasticity in a later section of this paper.

Fredricson *et al.* (1955) demonstrated in two inbred strains of mice that there were hereditary differences in the relationship of sexual to aggressive behavior. In C57BL/10 males, sexual behavior was capable of abolishing or delaying aggressive behavior. In males of the BALB/C Strain, aggressive behavior was dominant over sexual activity. Levine (1958) found that two inbred strains of mice differed materially in mating success. When a male CBA/JAX (F_{77}) and male ST/JAX (F_{34}) were caged with a single female, ST progeny far outnumbered those from CBA. Siegel (1959) tabulated courts, mounts, treads, and complete matings of White Plymouth Rock cocks from three inbred lines and two single-line crosses. He found highly significant line differences in each of the sex-drive factors. Smith (1956) described an inbred line of *Drosophila subobscura* in which the males were characterized by an unusually low degree of mating success. Evans (1928) found a strain of inbred albino rats in which the males copulated much less frequently than males from a genetically heterogeneous stock. A quantitative study of elements of the male pattern of sexual behavior in Strain-2 and Strain-13 guinea pigs was made by Valenstein and co-workers (1954). The inbred strains were compared with a stock of heterogeneous animals. Strain-2 males achieved a slightly higher sex-drive score than Strain 13 and were characteristically more active in the lower measures (sniffing, nuzzling, and abortive mounting) of the behavioral complex. The mean sex-drive score for animals from the heterogeneous stock was higher than that for either inbred strain. It is most noteworthy for our purposes that the inter-individual variance was much higher in the heterogeneous group than in either inbred strain. Spayed females of the same inbred strains were found by Goy and Young (1957a) to differ in responsiveness to injections of estradiol benzoate and progesterone in the display of estrous behavior. Once estrus was induced, the strains differed both in amounts of male-like mounting and in strength of the lordosis response to stroking.

In an early attempt to establish inbred strains of swine, Hodgson (1935) noted the gradual accumulation of a number of reproductive abnormalities. Among these was the eventual refusal of boars to mate with their sisters although they performed readily with other females. Such a finding could be explained either by (1) genetically controlled restriction of the range of stimuli adequate to elicit sexual behavior in the boar or (2) a genetically influenced decrease in the quality of receptivity displayed by the particular females.

Genetic Analyses Using Inbred Strains

In none of the above studies were the experiments designed to elucidate the genetic mechanisms. Nor in most were the females and males of the same or similar genotype studied concurrently. A more systematic genetic analysis of sexual behavior has been carried out by Bastock (1956). Her study involving a yellow mutation in *D. melanogaster* demonstrated that the locus for yellow had a pleiotropic effect which quantitatively reduced a single component of the male courtship behavior. In the yellow population the mutation appeared to facilitate receptivity in females. Outcrossing yellow stock with wild produced a stock differing from the wild only at the yellow locus. In this stock, female receptivity was not facilitated, but the male behavior remained depressed. Bastock concluded that high female receptivity had been selected for in the yellow stock as a compensation for the male deficiency. For our purposes, in addition to the compensatory balance of the male and female patterns, the demonstration that different genes are actually involved in the behavior of the male and female is noteworthy.

In the Endocrine Laboratory at the University of Kansas an attempt has been made to study the genetic mechanisms involved in the inheritance of patterns of sexual behavior. Two highly inbred strains of guinea pigs and their crosses have been examined. Strains 2 and 13 have been maintained by brother-sister matings from 1906 to 1933 and from 1940 until the present time. During the 1933–1940 interval they were maintained by within-strain random matings (Wright, 1922; Riss, 1955). The number of generations of inbreeding exceeds considerably the theoretical requisite (Wright, 1921) to reach homozygosity. Should vigor in phenotypic traits of high adaptive value depend upon heterozygosity, homozygosity may even yet be incomplete.

It has been found that within the two strains the pattern of sexual behavior is relatively stable for both males (Valenstein, Riss, and Young, 1954, 1955) and

TABLE 6-3   RATE OF ABORTIVE MOUNTING IN INBRED AND CROSSBRED MALE GUINEA PIGS

GROUP	ABORTIVE MOUNTS PER *15* SECONDS						
	.01–.15	*.16–.30*	*.31–.45*	*.46–.60*	*.61–.75*	*.76–.90*	*.91–1.05*
	%	%	%	%	%	%	%
Strain 2			5	40	35	10	10
Strain 13	11	50	33	6			
F_1		30	50	20			
F_2		23	63	10	3		
$F_1 \times 2$		8	24	42	17	8	2
$F_1 \times 13$	10	45	43	2			

Per cent is of each genetic group in each category.

females (Goy and Young, 1957*a*). In addition, the pattern is quite different in the two strains.

In studies designed to reveal the genetic mechanism for sexual behavior in the guinea pig (Jakway, 1959; Goy and Jakway, 1959), F_1 and F_2 hybrids, as well as F_1 backcrosses to the two strains, were obtained. Males from inbred Strain 2 had a higher frequency of ejaculation, a shorter latency to ejaculation, higher frequencies of intromission and mounting, and were generally more active than males from Strain 13. For the females, those from Strain 2 displayed a shorter latency to estrus, a longer duration of estrus, a less vigorous lordosis, and a lower frequency of mounting than the females from Strain 13. In addition, for the females strain differences in temporal relationships between the peak of mounting activity and the peak of heat were demonstrated. Strain-2 females displayed a low peak of mounting prior to the peak of heat. For Strain 13, the peak of mounting coincided with the peak of heat.

Among the males, crosses between these strains indicated a common mode of inheritance for mounting and general activity on the one hand and intromission and ejaculation on the other. The sluggish Strain-13 pattern displayed phenotypic

dominance in rate of mounting and general sexual activity, as illustrated in Table 6-3. In the F_1 generation, frequency of intromission and ejaculation greatly exceeded that in Strain 2, the higher of the parental strains as shown in Table 6-4. This pronounced heterosis magnified the phenotypic dominance of the Strain-2 traits. Values from the F_2 and backcross generations supported the interpretation of Strain-2 dominance. The occurrence of heterosis prevented estimates of genetic independence for these traits displaying a common mode of inheritance. For mounting and general activity, either pleiotropy or close linkage of nonsegregating genes is suggested by the consistent correlation between the quantitative expression of those components in both the pure strains and the hy-

TABLE 6-4   DISPLAY OF EJACULATIONS IN INBRED AND CROSSBRED GUINEA PIGS

GROUP	PER CENT DISPLAYING EJACULATION
Strain 2	50
Strain 13	39
F_1	100
F_2	57
$F_1 \times 2$	62
$F_1 \times 13$	52

TABLE 6-5   TEMPORAL RELATIONSHIPS BETWEEN MOUNTING AND RECEPTIVITY IN
INBRED AND CROSSBRED GROUPS OF FEMALE GUINEA PIGS

GROUP	N	A MEAN LATENCY IN HOURS TO THE PEAK OF MOUNTING	B MEAN LATENCY IN HOURS TO THE PEAK OF RECEPTIVITY	DIFFERENCE BETWEEN A AND B
Strain 2	26	5.60	6.10	0.50
Strain 13	34	7.93	7.68	−0.25
F_1	24	6.10	6.58	0.48
F_2	40	6.04	6.49	0.45
$F_1 \times 2$	40	5.56	6.12	0.56
$F_1 \times 13$	55	7.08	7.13	0.05

brids. In F_2 and backcross generations a recombination of separately inherited traits resulted in a restitution of parental types in addition to the maintenance of the newly created classes.

In the study of the females, spayed animals with exogenous hormones were used. Of the measures studied, latency to estrus and duration of estrus proved to be correlated manifestations displaying phenotypic dominance of the Strain-2 values. Both the vigor of the lordosis and the frequency of mounting displayed intermediate inheritance but differed from one another by the number of genes involved. The vigor of the lordosis appeared to be due to the action of a single or very few genes without dominance. In contrast, the frequency

of mounting was not restored to the parental values in the first backcross generations, indicating the action of more than a few genetic factors. The temporal relationship between the peak of mounting and the peak of heat displayed clear phenotypic dominance of the Strain-2 values, and is particularly interesting as an example of the genetic control over the temporal relations between the elements of the sexual behavior pattern. Data illustrative of this temporal relationship are presented in Table 6-5.

Heterosis was not observed in the quantitative manifestations of any of the female components. A suggestion of heterosis was found in considering combinations of components in the F_1 where a large proportion

TABLE 6-6   DISTRIBUTION OF PHENOTYPIC COMBINATIONS OF VIGOR (V) AND RESPONSIVENESS (R)
IN GROUPS OF INBRED AND CROSSBRED FEMALE GUINEA PIGS

GROUP	HIGH V HIGH R	HIGH V LOW R	INTERMEDIATE V LOW R	INTERMEDIATE V HIGH R	LOW V HIGH R	LOW V LOW R
	%	%	%	%	%	%
Strain 2				11.5	88.5	
Strain 13	6.9	66.5	27.6			
F_1	21.7	4.3	21.7	39.1	13.0	
F_2	17.0	14.9	12.8	27.7	21.3	6.4
$F_1 \times 2$	4.2		6.3	31.2	45.8	12.5
$F_1 \times 13$	18.2	34.5	23.6	16.4		7.3

Per cent is of each genetic group in each category.

of the females (21.7 per cent) displayed a high degree of responsiveness to the hormone and a high degree of vigor in the expression of the sexual components (Table 6-6). Such a new combination of components might well represent optimal fitness. In contrast, a new combination appeared in 6.4 per cent of the F_2 population which might represent minimal fitness insofar as the values within the parental population are concerned. This combination was characterized by both low responsiveness to the hormone and low vigor of the components.

GENETIC BASIS FOR SEXUAL DIMORPHISM OF MATING BEHAVIOR

These data obtained from the guinea pig permit certain conclusions not previously recognized. However, the tentative nature of these conclusions must be emphasized.

Disregarding for the moment the sex of the individual involved, it is possible to compare the modes of inheritance of the various behavior traits studied. In addition, some inference may be made as to whether the number of genetic factors influencing any two traits is the same or different. Thus any two traits may differ in the degree of dominance manifested or in the number of genetic factors operating or both. The basic obstacle to deriving conclusions from such comparisons arises from the sexual dimorphism of the traits. The difficulty is made obvious by giving as an example a comparison of the modes of inheritance of egg production in hens with rate of comb growth in cocks. So long as the modes of inheritance are distinct, no difficulty in interpretation is encountered. On the other hand, when the modes of inheritance appear identical, any interpretation of the traits as pleiotropic manifestations is unwarranted without much more extensive

genetical analysis than we have undertaken for sexual behavior.

Primary among the remaining obstacles to interpretation is the matter of method of measurement. For example, if in a study on the inheritance of body size all males are measured for height and all females are weighed, no difficulty is encountered in interpretation if the modes of inheritance are identical. The problem in this instance lies in the interpretation of differing modes of inheritance. For our data on sexual behavior, particularly for mounting behavior, a decision must be made regarding the extent to which the divergent methods of measurement determine the divergent modes of inheritance.

When each of the male behavior traits is compared with each of the female behavior traits, the results suggest that the genetic basis for male behavior is distinct and separate from that for female behavior. In our investigations, only frequency of ejaculation and intromission rate in the male were parallel in mode of inheritance to any of the female traits (latency and duration of estrus). Although both displayed phenotypic dominance of the Strain-2 values, the male traits differed from the female traits in (1) the manifestation of heterosis and (2) a greater degree of polygenicity.

For mounting behavior in males, the Strain-13 values displayed phenotypic dominance. Among females, inheritance was intermediate. In addition, more genetic factors appear to contribute to the determination of mounting displayed by females than by males. This evidence alone does not permit the interpretation of different sets of alleles for male and female mounting behavior because of the different methods of measurement employed. Supportive evidence is available however. Between the inbred strains, the quantitative manifestation of mounting is exactly opposite in the two sexes. Males from Strain 2 mount more than males from Strain 13, whereas females from Strain 2 mount less than females from Strain 13. In an outbred stock of guinea pigs, males mount more than either of the inbred strains, but females are intermediate (Valenstein, Riss, and Young, 1954; Jakway, 1959; Goy and Jakway, 1959; Goy and Young, 1957a, 1957b). Treatment of females with testosterone propionate results in the display of mounting which more closely resembles that displayed by males and differs importantly from mounting normally displayed by females with respect to its frequency and time of occurrence (Phoenix *et al.*, 1959). In contrast, estradiol does not appreciably stimulate mounting in the male (Antliff and Young, 1956). Consideration of these facts supports the conclusion that the mounting displayed by the estrous female is determined by genetic factors relatively independent from those determining mounting in the male.

We suggest that two complete sets of alleles exist for the components of male and female sexual behavior. Both sets are found in every individual, but each set normally finds expression only in one sex. Within each set all genes are neither linked nor on the same chromosome, for they assort independently to establish new combinations in the F_2 and backcross generations. From the genetical viewpoint, sexual behavior is a sex-influenced trait in which the transmission of the genetic complement is the same for both sexes but expressivity is modified by the sexual milieu. The view that two patterns of sexual behavior are represented in the individual genome has previously been suggested for the rat purely on the basis of behavioral evidence (Beach, 1945) as well as for most species of mammals (Ford and Beach, 1951).

In previous reports (Goy and Young,

1957a; Goy and Jakway, 1959) attention was directed to the finding that the vigor of male sexual behavior was inversely related to the vigor of lordosis displayed by females from the same genetic group. A comparable relationship was found in *Drosophila* for the yellow mutant strain studied by Bastock (1956) and for a number of naturally occurring strains studied by Spieth (1951). The F_1 hybrid males obtained from the Strain-2 $\times$ Strain-13 cross in guinea pigs displayed a pattern of sexual behavior that was close to that of an outbred stock (Stock T) in terms of vigor. Hybrid females, however, displayed lordoses that were intermediate in vigor to those of the inbred strains and more vigorous than those of the outbred stock. We therefore conclude, as did Bastock, that the more vigorous receptive responses of the inbred females are a compensatory balance resulting from selection during the establishment of the strains.

The reason selection operates on female behavior traits in these instances is not understood. There is no question but that the degenerative effects of inbreeding on the male behavior necessitate compensation if reproduction is to continue. Possibly the vigor of male sexual behavior depends more on the degree of heterozygosity than on the presence or absence of specific alleles, whereas the latter are more important to the vigor of female sexual behavior. Certainly within the range of heterozygosity and allelic combinations studied in the guinea pig this generalization is valid.

The relative unimportance of specific alleles to male sexual behavior is suggested by the variety of ways in which success in mating may be achieved. Some males mount frequently but have few intromissions; others, equally successful, mount less frequently and have relatively more frequent intromissions. In addition, mating success for the male requires considerable modification in the pattern to conform to varying environmental conditions. Thus a considerable degree of plasticity remains in the quantitative and qualitative relationships between the behavioral components. As Caspari (1958) has suggested for other types of behavior, selection may favor high modifiability of the male pattern. For the female, success in mating requires only a lordosis above a certain level of vigor elicitable by a more specific type of stimulation.

Three additional types of plasticity in phenotypic expression of sexual behavior require comment. First, a relatively wide range of objects exist which provide sexual stimulation but differ in their capacity to elicit the response (Beach, 1942b; Walton, 1950). That the range of such stimuli is genetically determined is postulated by Ford and Beach (1951) and strongly suggested by studies on isolating mechanisms. The specificity of the adequate stimuli tends to increase with maturity in most of the species studied from insects to man, but the relative contributions of experiential and genetic factors have not been assessed.

The second type of plasticity to environmental change is not directly associated with the stimulus object. Rearing animals in isolation, or in situations in which the opportunity for sexual stimulation is relatively restricted, has been shown to be detrimental to the adult sexual performance of lower mammals (Valenstein *et al.*, 1955; Valenstein and Goy, 1957; Goy and Young, 1957b; Zimbardo, 1958) and fish (Shaw, Ch. 8, this book). The results so far obtained with the guinea pig suggest that highly inbred and homozygous strains are more variable in this respect than animals from genetically heterozygous backgrounds. If, as Lerner (1954) says, a heterozygous animal is superior to the homozygous in "buffering" against environmental change,

it would be instructive to study these types of plasticity in both homozygous strains and their maximally heterozygous F_1 progeny.

To date, the only information we have bearing on the problem of variability and heterozygosity pertains to interindividual variation. For male guinea pigs, maximal heterozygosity in the F_1 is associated with a decrease in variability of sexual behavior in comparison with the parental strains. A similar relationship was not generally found for the female guinea pig, however, and confirmatory evidence from other strain crosses as well as from other species is needed.

The third type of plasticity of sexual responses is seen in the temporary inversion of sexual behavior displayed by individuals of both sexes. The frequency with which such inversions may be observed led Ford and Beach to postulate that the fundamental mammalian heritage is a bisexuality of the physiological mechanisms underlying reproductive behavior. The failure to find parallel or similar modes of inheritance for male and female traits in the guinea pig, although subject to metrical bias, suggests a similar bisexuality for the genetic factors underlying reproductive behavior. Not to be overlooked is the fact that the induction of masculine behavior in females of most mammalian species represents one of the simplest illustrations of the effect of the genotype on sexual behavior. As Fuller (1951) has pointed out, a female dog injected with androgen behaves like a male dog and not like a male from some other species.

The view elaborated here in no way suggests that the capacity of an individual to display the behavior of the opposite sex is equal to that of its own sex. Careful assessment of the capacity to display heterotypical behavior has long been a subject of study (Ball, 1939, 1940; Beach, 1942*a*, 1945, 1948; Beach and Rasquin, 1942). Recently it has been shown in genetically heterogeneous guinea pigs (Phoenix *et al.*, 1959) that the extent to which the potentiality for display of male characteristics may be realized in the female is in part a product of fetal endocrine factors. The degree to which a genetic female responds as a male is increased by altering the fetal endocrine environment to a sufficient degree to produce hermaphroditism. Although masculine behavior can be induced in normal spayed females treated with testosterone, the limit of expression is lower than in castrated males and hermaphrodites similarly treated, and the rate of response to the injected androgen is slower. Theoretically, the genic potentiality for behavior of the female type is present in the male, but historically it has been more difficult to produce behavioral feminization of males than masculinization of the female by use of heterologous hormones (Young, 1961). Despite the fact that within a few hours of birth the male guinea pig will exhibit lordosis, a full expression of this trait has never been induced in the adult. The induction of female behavior in males of lower mammals frequently requires specialized environmental manipulations that tend to raise the level of sexual excitation in the male.

CONCLUSIONS

The experiments reviewed above demonstrate that a hereditary basis for sexual behavior exists which is susceptible to genetic manipulation. Genetic alteration of the phenotype for sexual behavior has been demonstrated for invertebrates, fish, birds, and lower mammals. Although not supported by direct evidence in every phylogenetic group, the following conclusions appear tenable.

Genetic differences between species or larger taxonomic groupings account for variations in the form or nature of the behavioral elements comprising the pattern of sexual behavior. Within a species or species group, the form or pattern of sexual behavior is relatively uniform, and genetic variance accounts largely for variation in the quantitative aspects of components (i.e., frequency, duration, or intensity of expression). Of particular interest is the demonstration that the genetic mechanisms determining the quantitative expression of various components are relatively independent. This genetic separability of the components is true for the elements of both male and female sexual behavior. Moreover, the genetic factors determining the quantitative expression of components of male sexual behavior appear to be relatively independent from those influencing female sexual behavior. Genetic manipulations have been reported which affect only one component of the sexual behavior of males and do not alter any observable component of female behavior.

Genetic factors have been shown to be important in determining the limits of variability or plasticity of the sexual response within a species. The particular genetic factor or set of factors limiting (1) intraindividual variation, (2) stimulus-object range which elicits sexual behavior, and (3) inversions of the sexual pattern cannot be stated for any species at the present time. Certain types of environmentally produced changes as well as interindividual variability appear to be accentuated by homozygosity and diminished by heterozygosity. Degree of heterozygosity also is related directly to the vigor of male sexual behavior for the relatively restricted range of heterozygosity studied in the guinea pig. It is possible that a similar relationship between heterozygosity and vigor of sexual

VALENSTEIN, E. S., and GOY, R. W. 1957. Further studies of the organization and display of sexual behavior in male guinea pigs. *J. Comp. & Physiol. Psychol. 50:* 115–119.

VALENSTEIN, E. S., RISS, W., and YOUNG, W. C. 1954. Sex drive in genetically heterogeneous and highly inbred strains of male guinea pigs. *J. Comp. & Physiol. Psychol. 47:* 162–165.

VALENSTEIN, E. S., RISS, W., and YOUNG, W. C. 1955. Experiential and genetic factors in the organization of sexual behavior in male guinea pigs. *J. Comp. & Physiol. Psychol. 48:* 397–403.

WALTON, A. 1950. Patterns of male sex behaviour. *Proc. Soc. for the Study of Fertility* (Great Britain), Edinburgh Conference. *1:* 40–44.

WOOD-GUSH, D. G. M. 1960. A study of sex drive of two strains of cockerels through three generations. *Animal Behav. 8:* 43–53.

WOOD-GUSH, D. G. M., and OSBORNE, R. 1956. A study of differences in the sex drive of cockerels. *Brit. J. Animal Behav. 4:* 102–110.

WRIGHT, S. 1921. Systems of mating. II. The effects of inbreeding on the genetic composition of a population. *Genetics. 6:* 124–143.

WRIGHT, S. 1922. The effects of inbreeding and crossbreeding on guinea pigs. I. Decline in vigor. II. Differentiation among inbred families. *U.S. Dept. Agric. Bull.,* No. 1090, pp. 1–63.

YOUNG, W. C. 1961. "The Hormones and Mating Behavior," in *Allen's Sex and Internal Secretions,* 3rd ed., ed. by YOUNG, W. C. Baltimore, Williams & Wilkins.

YOUNG, W. C., DEMPSEY, E. W., HAGQUIST, C. W., and BOLING, J. L. 1939. Sexual behavior and sexual receptivity in the female guinea pig. *J. Comp. Psychol. 27:* 49–68.

ZIMBARDO, P. G. 1958. The effects of early avoidance training and rearing conditions upon the sexual behavior of the male rat. *J. Comp. & Physiol. Psychol. 51:* 764–769.

PART II

INSTINCTUAL BEHAVIOR

7

PATTERNING OF SEXUAL BEHAVIOR

William C. Young

It has long been a matter of record that the behavior brought to expression by the gonadal hormones depends on the character of the soma or, perhaps better, on the character of the tissues which mediate this behavior. This conclusion seems first to have been stated by Goodale in an article published in *Genetics* in 1918. He was impressed by the failure of ovaries implanted into capons to feminize their behavior and stated: " . . . the character of the sexual reactions seems to depend upon the substratum, while the gonad merely determines that it shall be given expression." Nineteen years later, Ball (1937) reported that estrogen increased the masculine behavior of male rats rather than feminizing them and concluded that gonadal hormone in adults merely activates a pattern already present. About the same time, after noting the lack of relationship between the ovarian condition and the character of heat in the guinea pig, Young *et al.* (1938) reached a similar conclusion. In their words, ovarian hormones possess a potentiality of action

The experiments reviewed in this chapter were supported in part by Research Grant No. M504 from the National Institute of Mental Health, U.S. Public Health Service, and in part by grants from the Committee for Research in Problems of Sex, National Academy of Sciences—National Research Council.

which is limited by the responsiveness of the soma on which they act. By 1952 the closeness of the relationship between the character of the soma and the action of male hormone was demonstrated. It had been learned that male guinea pigs, when tested repeatedly with estrous females, tend to display relatively uniform patterns of behavior (Table 7-1). When animals of these types were castrated and, after an interval, given equal amounts of testosterone propionate, their behavior returned to the precastrational levels (Grunt and Young, 1952).

With this background of information, it soon became apparent that an investigator desirous of ascertaining the determinants of these and other patterns of mating behavior would have to direct his attention not so much to the hormones but rather to a search for factors which influence the character of the tissues on which the hormones act.

Using the guinea pig, this has been done, and we have identified factors such as age (Wilson and Young, 1941; Riss *et al.*, 1955), the genetical background (Valenstein, Riss, and Young, 1954; Goy and Young, 1957*a*), and contact with other animals (Valenstein, Riss, and Young, 1955; Valenstein and Young, 1955; Goy and

TABLE 7-1   SEXUAL BEHAVIOR SCORES OF INTACT MALE GUINEA PIGS IN SUCCESSIVE TESTS
AT INTERVALS OF 4 TO 7 DAYS*

| ANIMAL | SCORE | | | | | | | | | | MEAN |
	1	2	3	4	5	6	7	8	9	10	
103T	15.3	8.8	12.0	10.8	8.8	15.4	14.0	17.3	13.5	16.0	12.9
631T	10.4	12.7	14.0	8.8	9.7	9.3	10.9	12.0	9.6	13.3	11.1
3400T	11.1	10.4	10.5	9.4	9.8	11.4	9.0	9.5	14.7	12.2	10.8
3L	10.0	8.3	7.0	6.5	3.5	7.3	10.3	6.4	8.7	4.8	7.3
3419L	5.0	5.9	7.7	7.1	6.1	6.4	4.5	5.7	5.9	7.5	6.2
10L	8.6	5.9	7.8	7.0	2.5	6.8	4.8	5.4	4.9	4.0	5.8
1599	2.6	0.6	3.3	5.3	4.6	4.3	2.0	1.8	1.4	3.8	2.8
611T	0.0	2.6	3.6	3.3	2.9	2.6	2.6	2.4	2.2	0.9	2.3
144	1.0	2.6	3.1	1.8	1.6	3.0	1.5	2.0	0.6	1.9	1.8

* The relative uniformity is seen in selected high-drive, intermediate-drive, and low-drive animals.

Young, 1957b) which are influential in shaping the character of other types of behavior as well.

But an important additional step has been taken, and this is an investigation of the effect of a hormone, testosterone propionate, administered prenatally, on the pattern of behavior displayed after the attainment of adulthood. The results from these experiments have recently been reported (Phoenix, *et al.,* 1959).

PRENATALLY ADMINISTERED ANDROGEN AND RESULTANT MATING BEHAVIOR

When pregnant guinea pigs were injected intramuscularly with 5 mg. of testosterone propionate (Perandren propionate) on Day 10 and 1 mg. daily from Day 11 to Day 68 of the gestation period, the following effects on structure and behavior were produced:

1. All the females became hermaphroditic with masculinized external genitalia, hypertrophied Wolffian ducts, failure of Müllerian duct-urogenital sinus fusion, and ovarian dysfunction. No mammal that has been studied seems immune to such effects, including the rhesus monkey and man (see Wells and Van Wagenen, 1954; Wilkins

et al., 1958; and the reviews by Black and Bentley, 1959; Burns, 1960). Important features of the ovarian dysfunction are described by Turner (1939) and, for the animals used in the present study, by Tedford and Young (1960).

2. In the females a suppression of the feminine measures of behavior was revealed by decrease in the per cent of tests positive for estrus, the duration of estrus, and the duration of maximum lordosis. A stimulation of the tissues mediating the masculine component of behavior in the female was revealed by the greater amount of male-like mounting behavior.

3. The hermaphroditic females had become more responsive to the androgen, testosterone propionate, than ovariectomized, normal females.

4. The effects on the females receiving the androgen prenatally were permanent, whereas any measurable effects on the mothers into whom the hormone had been injected or on normal females treated with testosterone propionate from Day 1 to Day 80 postnatally were transitory.

5. The sexual behavior of the male siblings was not affected by the treatment. When tested after the attainment of adult-

hood, their behavior was not significantly different from that of the untreated controls.

6. The answer to a question that was not within the scope of the initial investigation is now being sought. This has to do with the portion of the embryonic and fetal periods during which testosterone propionate must be administered in order to produce the effects described above. When 40 mg. of the hormone were given between Days 15 and 30 of gestation, no effects were detected on the behavior displayed as adults. However, when the treatment was continued (1 mg. daily) until Days 40, 45, and 55, progressive effects were found; the behavior of the animals treated from Day 30 to Day 65 was not different from that of the hermaphrodites tested in the first study (Goy, Bridson, and Young, 1961). Thus far, therefore, it seems that the "critical" period is relatively late rather than early in the 66- to 70-day embryonic and fetal periods.

EFFECT OF ANDROGEN ON DEVELOPING GENITAL TRACTS

The full significance of these results has yet to be revealed, but they do enable us to assign the place of genetical, experiential, and hormonal factors in the determination of patterns of reproductive behavior displayed during adulthood. As the individual develops during the embryonic and fetal periods, genetical and hormonal factors participate in the organization of the tissues which will later mediate mating behavior. Even if no other information existed, the action of genetical factors would be revealed by the circumstances that animals developing in the same environment are born as either males or females. The action of hormonal factors during these periods is demonstrated by the experimental data reviewed above. After birth, in the guinea

pig, there is no evidence that gonadal hormones organize patterns of behavior, but there is abundant evidence that genetical and experiential factors are interacting at this time.[*] The importance of the genetical factor is revealed by the existence of strain differences (Valenstein, Riss, and Young, 1954; Goy and Young, 1957a), and the importance of contact with other animals is evident from the experiments of Valenstein, Riss, and Young, 1955; Valenstein and Young, 1955; Goy and Young, 1957b, particularly in the male and for the masculine component of the pattern in the female.

In addition to answering the question which stimulated the investigation we have reviewed, the results have a place in a broader context. An analogy between the action of hormones on the tissues mediating mating behavior and their action on the genital tracts should be noted. The embryonic and fetal periods, when the genital tracts are exposed to the influence of an as yet unidentified morphogenic substance, presumably a fetal gonadal hormone, are periods of differentiation. Under the influence of this substance (or substances), the Wolffian duct system develops to become the epididymis, ductus deferens, and seminal vesicles of the adult male, and the Müllerian duct system develops to become the Fallopian tube and uterus of the adult female. After the attainment of adulthood, these structures again become the target organs of hormonal substances; but in this phase the hormones are activational rather than organizational, and they stimu-

[*] The subject is discussed at length by Young (1960) in a review. Results reported by Kagan and Beach (1953) and by Beach (1958) led to the conclusion that isolated male rats exhibit normal sexual behavior and therefore that contact with other animals is not necessary for the maturation of this behavior. Zimbardo (1958), on the other hand, reported that the sexual behavior of male rats reared in part-time cohabitation was superior to that of rats raised in isolation or segregation.

late growth, secretion, motility, and, in the uterus, the changes necessary for nidation. Our data suggest that for the neural tissues mediating mating behavior, corresponding relationships exist. The embryonic and fetal periods are periods of organization or "differentiation" in the direction of masculinization or feminization. Adulthood, when gonadal hormones are being secreted, is the period of activation; neural tissues are the "target organ," and mating behavior is brought to expression.

An extension of the analogy comes from a comparison of processes involved in the development of the genital tract (Burns, 1942, 1949, 1960; Jost, 1947, 1953, 1957; Wells, Cavanaugh, and Maxwell, 1954; Witschi, Nelson, and Segal, 1957) with those involved in the development of the tissues mediating mating behavior. In the case of the latter (Phoenix *et al.* 1959), testosterone propionate administered prenatally affected the behavior of the male but slightly, whereas the effects on the female were profound. In the female there was a heightened display of the masculine component of the sexual behavior pattern and a suppression of the feminine components. In studies on the genital tracts the effects on the male were relatively slight. There was some hypertrophy of the prostate and seminal vesicle and some increase in size of the penis (Greene, 1942), but in none of these tissues was it great. Within the female, on the other hand, the Wolffian duct system was stimulated to reach a stage never seen in a normal female (Dantchakoff, 1938*a*, 1938*b*, 1938*c*; Greene, 1942; Turner, 1939), and locally, when a fetal testis was implanted into a female fetus, Jost (1953, 1957) reported that there was an inhibition of the Müllerian duct on that side. In our animals, as we have noted, there was a failure of fusion of the uterus with the urogenital sinus.

EFFECT OF HORMONAL FACTORS ON MASCULINE AND FEMININE BEHAVIOR PATTERNS

Against this background, it seems appropriate to ask if this action of fetal morphogenic substances is limited to the genital tracts and to the neural tissues mediating mating behavior? Is it beyond the realm of possibility that these substances participate in the establishment of other behavioral differences between males and females? I am thinking especially of differences in behavior such as those described by Yerkes (1943) and Hebb (1946) in male and female chimpanzees. The male is revealed to be a fighter and a bluffer (who can also be bluffed), the female as treacherous and harder than the male to bluff consistently. Differences between the sexes are also seen in the play configuration of preadolescent children (Erickson, 1951), and there must be many more examples. Could not hormonal factors acting during the prenatal period contribute to this basic masculinity or femininity and therefore be partly responsible for the differences between the sexes?

The question is timely because of the position taken by the Hampsons and based on their many studies with Money (Hampson, 1955; Hampson and Money, 1955; Money and Hampson, 1955; Money, Hampson, and Hampson, 1955, 1956). In a review Hampson and Hampson (1960) have discussed psychologic sex and gender role and concluded:

. . . an individual's gender role and orientation as boy or girl, man or woman does not have an innate, preformed instinctive basis as some have maintained. Instead the evidence supports the view that psychologic sex is undifferentiated at birth—a sexual neutrality in the place of the Freudian bisexuality—and that the individual becomes differentiated as masculine or feminine, psychologically, in the course of the many experiences of growing up.

To many, the possibility suggested by our work on the guinea pig may seem far-fetched. The two suggestions, however, that made by the Hampsons and that made here and originally by Phoenix *et al.* (1959), are not mutually exclusive. It has long been recognized that a complete or at least a partial emancipation from the influence of the gonadal hormones may have been a part of the evolution of man. If such an emancipation is complete during the embryonic and fetal periods in man, but not in the lower mammals, both conclusions could be correct. The job ahead, is to examine these concepts, a task which should not be difficult of accomplishment.

RULES OF HORMONAL ACTION ON THE NEURAL TISSUES MEDIATING MATING BEHAVIOR AND ON THE GENITAL TRACTS

An additional thought has been suggested by our work which has not, as far as we know, been expressed in the literature on animal behavior and psychology. Currently, endocrinologists are much interested in gaining an understanding of the mechanism of hormone action, and countless experiments have been directed toward this end. Physiologically minded psychologists and psychiatrists are asking the same questions. In their attempts to answer them, however, they could well be handicapped by the nature of their material, which, we assume, is nervous tissue. Unlike uterine tissue, tissues of the male accessory glands, and other genital tissues in which the study of isolated cells with well-known functions such as secretion, or motility is easily possible, the nervous tissues involved in the expression of mating behavior have not even been identified, to say nothing of being adapted to study by the methods of contemporary endocrinology. But the prediction will be made that if investigators who

are interested in behavior will also keep abreast of the efforts of the endocrinologists who are studying the mechanism of gonadal hormone action on the prostate, uterus, and other genital tissues, much will be found that can be taken over and will have applicability to the nervous tissues. The basis for this prediction is the now-abundant evidence that the rules of gonadal hormone action on uterine or vaginal tissue are similar to, if not identical with, those on the neural tissues mediating mating behavior in the female; and this may also be true for the corresponding tissues in the male.

It has long been known, for example, that in females of many species the full functioning of uterine epithelium and myometrium is dependent on the action of estrogen and progesterone in a synergistic relationship. Mating behavior in many species is also brought to expression by the same combination of hormones. In the ewe there is a reversal of the relationship seen in the guinea pig (Ford and Young, 1951) in that maximal vaginal responses are induced only when estradiol is preceded by injections of progesterone. Also in the ewe the maximal behavioral response is induced only when the hormones are injected in this order (Moore and Robinson, 1957). Old studies of young guinea pigs and rats have shown that tissues of the genital tracts (Price and Ortiz, 1944) and the tissues mediating mating behavior (Wilson and Young, 1941) are not responsive to exogenous estrogen when they are born, but that responsiveness is acquired as they grow, and—what is important in the present context—that the timetable of this change is the same for both types of tissue. Finally, among the analogies we will mention, are the effects of the prenatal morphogenic substances on genital tracts and neural tissues seen in the present study. We still

are not certain that androgens acting prenatally inhibit the development of the
Müllerian duct system while they are
suppressing the capacity of the tissues
mediating the feminine components of behavior, but it is clear that androgens
reaching the female embryo and fetus
stimulate Wolffian-duct development while
they are also giving direction to the organization of the neural tissues which
mediate the masculine behavior displayed
by the female.

The point to all this is that, although we
may be discouraged at the prospect of
learning much about the mechanism of
gonadal hormone action on neural tissues
from the study of neural tissues, we may
unwittingly be receiving valuable clues
from such work as Csapo's (1955, 1959a,
1959b) investigations of the site and mode
of action of estrogens and progesterone on
the myometrium, Kochakian's (1959)
studies of the mechanism of the action of
androgens on the genital tissues and
striated muscles of the male, Rosa's and
Velardo's (1959) studies of cyclic changes
in the oxidative enzyme activity in the
epithelial components of the uterine
mucosa, and many others. If the rules of
action of the gonadal hormones are the
same for such diverse tissues as uterine
epithelium, vaginal epithelium, myometrium, striated muscle, and prostate gland
epithelium on the one hand, and neural tissue, on the other—and they seem to be—is
it not likely that within a sex the mechanism
of action of these hormones on these tissues
may not also be similar? In our conceptualization of what is happening to the patterns
of behavior when female guinea pigs are
given androgens prenatally, we were helped
immeasurably by all that the experimental
embryologists had done before us. To those
of us who are interested in the mode of
action of gonadal hormones in bringing

mating behavior to expression, the work of
endocrinologists on entirely different tissues
may be equally helpful.

REFERENCES

BALL, J. 1937. Sex activity of castrated male
rats increased by estrin administration. *J.
Comp. Psychol. 24:* 135–144.

BEACH, F. A. 1958. Normal sexual behavior in
male rats isolated at fourteen days of age. *J.
Comp. & Physiol. Psychol. 51:* 37–38.

BLACK, J. A., and BENTLEY, J. F. R. 1959.
Effect on the foetus of androgens given
during pregnancy. *Lancet, 1*(7062): 21–24.

BURNS, R. K. 1942. Hormones and experimental modification of sex in the opposum.
Biol. Symposia. 9: 125–146.

BURNS, R. K. 1942. "Hormones and the Differentiation of Sex," in *Survey of Biological
Progress.* New York, Academic Press, Vol. 1,
pp. 233–266.

BURNS, R. K. 1961. "Role of Hormones in the
Differentiation of Sex," in *Sex and Internal
Secretions,* 3rd ed., ed. by YOUNG, W. C.
Baltimore, Williams & Wilkins.

CSAPO, A. 1955. "The Mechanism of Myome-
trial Function and Its Disorders," in *Modern
Trends in Obstetrics and Gynaecology,* 2nd
series, ed. by BOWES, K. London, Butterworth, pp. 20–49.

CSAPO, A. 1959a. Function and regulation of
the myometrium. *Ann. New York Acad. Sc.
75:* 790–808.

CSAPO, A. 1959b. "Regulation of the Myometrium," in *Cell, Organism, and Milieu,* ed. by
RUDNICK, D. New York, Ronald, pp. 107–
120.

DANTCHAKOFF, V. 1938a. Rôle des hormones
dans la manifestation des instincts sexuels.
Compt. Rend. Acad. Sc., Paris. 206: 945–
947.

DANTCHAKOFF, V. 1938b. Sur les effets de
l'hormone male dans une jeune cobaye
femelle traité depuis un stade embryonnaire
(inversions sexuelles). *Compt. Rend. Soc.
Biol. 127:* 1255–1258.

DANTCHAKOFF, V. 1938c. Sur les effets de
l'hormone male dans une jeune cobaye male
traité depuis un stade embryonnaire (production d'hypermales). *Compt. Rend. Soc.
Biol. 127:* 1259–1262.

ERIKSON, E. 1951. Sex differences in the play configuration of preadolescents. *Am. J. Orthopsychiat. 21:* 667–692.

FORD, D. H., and YOUNG, W. C. 1951. The role of progesterone in the production of cyclic vaginal changes in the female guinea pig. *Endocrinology. 49:* 795–804.

GOODALE, H. D. 1918. Feminized male birds. *Genetics. 3:* 276–299.

GOY, R. W., BRIDSON, W. E., and YOUNG, W. C. 1961. The maximally effective period for behavioral and genital modification of female guinea pigs treated prenatally with testosterone propionate. *Anat. Rec. 139:* 232. (*Abstract. Proc. Am. Assoc. Anat.*)

GOY, R. W., and YOUNG, W. C. 1957a. Strain differences in the behavioral responses of female guinea pigs to alpha-estradiol benzoate and progesterone. *Behaviour. 10:* 340–354.

GOY, R. W., and YOUNG, W. C. 1957b. Somatic basis of sexual behavior patterns in guinea pigs: factors involved in the determination of the character of the soma in the female. *Psychosom. Med. 19:* 144–151.

GREENE, R. R. 1942. Hormonal factors in sex inversion: the effects of sex hormones on embryonic sexual structures of the rat. *Biol. Symposia. 9:* 105–123.

GRUNT, J. A., and YOUNG, W. C. 1952. Differential reactivity of individuals and the response of the male guinea pig to testosterone propionate. *Endocrinology. 51:* 237–248.

HAMPSON, J. G. 1955. Hermaphroditic genital appearance, rearing and eroticism in hyperadrenocorticism. *Bull. Johns Hopkins Hosp. 96:* 265–273.

HAMPSON, J. G., and MONEY, J. 1955. Idiopathic sexual precocity in the female. *Psychosom. Med. 17:* 16–35.

HAMPSON, J. L., and HAMPSON, J. G. 1961. "The Ontogenesis of Sexual Behavior in Man," in *Sex and Internal Secretions*, 3rd ed., ed. by YOUNG, W. C. Baltimore, Williams & Wilkins.

HEBB, D. O. 1946. Behavioral differences between male and female chimpanzees. *Bull. Canad. Psychol. A. 6:* 56–58.

JOST, A. 1947. Recherches sur la différenciation sexuelle de l'embryo de lapin. I. Introduction et embryologie génitale normal. II. Action des androgènes de synthèse sur l'histogenese genitale III. Rôle des gonades foetales dans la différenciation sexuelle somatique. *Arch. Anat. Micro. Morph. Exp. 36:* 151, 242, 271.

JOST, A. 1953. Problems of fetal endocrinology: the gonadal and hypophyseal hormones. *Recent Progr. Hormone Res. 8:* 379–418.

JOST, A. 1957. "The Secretory Activities of Fetal Endocrine Glands and Their Effect upon Target Organs," in *Gestation, Tr. Third Conference*, ed. by VILLEE, C. A. New York, Josiah Macy, Jr., Foundation, pp. 129–171.

KAGAN, J., and BEACH, F. A. 1953. Effects of early experience on mating behavior in male rats. *J. Comp. & Physiol. Psychol. 46:* 204–208.

KOCHAKIAN, C. D. 1959. Mechanisms of androgen actions. *Lab. Invest. 8:* 538–556.

MONEY, J., and HAMPSON, J. G. 1955. Idiopathic sexual precocity in the male. *Psychosom. Med. 17:* 1–15.

MONEY, J., HAMPSON, J. G., and HAMPSON, J. L. 1955. An examination of some basic sexual concepts: the evidence of human hermaphroditism. *Bull. Johns Hopkins Hosp. 97:* 301–319.

MONEY, J., HAMPSON, J. G., and HAMPSON, J. L. 1956. Sexual incongruities and psychopathology: the evidence of human hermaphroditism. *Bull. Johns Hopkins Hosp. 98:* 43–57.

MOORE, N. W., and ROBINSON, T. J. 1957. The behavioral and vaginal response of the spayed ewe to oestrogen injected at various times relative to the injection of progesterone. *J. Endocrinol. 15:* 360–365.

PHOENIX, C. H., GOY, R. W., GERALL, A. A., and YOUNG, W. C. 1959. Organizing action of prenatally administered testosterone propionate on the tissues mediating mating behavior in the female guinea pig. *Endocrinology. 65:* 369–382.

PRICE, D., and ORTIZ, E. 1944. The relation of age to reactivity in the reproductive system of the rat. *Endocrinology. 34:* 215–239.

RISS, W., VALENSTEIN, E. S., SINKS, J., and YOUNG, W. C. 1955. Development of sexual behavior in male guinea pigs from genetically different stocks under controlled conditions of androgen treatment and caging. *Endocrinology. 57:* 139–146.

ROSA, C. G., and VELARDO, J. T. 1959. Histochemical observations of oxidative enzyme systems in the uterus and vagina of the rat. *Ann. New York Acad. Sc. 75:* 491–503.

TEDFORD, M. D., and YOUNG, W. C. 1960. Ovarian structure in guinea pigs made hermaphroditic by the administration of androgen prenatally, *Anat. Rec. 136:* 325. (Abstract, *Proc. Am. A. Anat.*)

TURNER, C. D. 1939. The modification of sexual differentiation in genetic female mice by the prenatal administration of testosterone propionate. *J. Morphol. 65:* 353–381.

VALENSTEIN, E. S., RISS, W., and YOUNG, W. C. 1954. Sex drive in genetically heterogeneous and highly inbred strains of male guinea pigs. *J. Comp. & Physiol. Psychol. 47:* 162–165.

VALENSTEIN, E. S., RISS, W., and YOUNG, W. C. 1955. Experimental and genetic factors in the organization of sexual behavior in male guinea pigs. *J. Comp. & Physiol. Psychol. 48:* 379–403.

VALENSTEIN, E. S., and YOUNG, W. C. 1955. An experimental factor influencing the effectiveness of testosterone propionate in eliciting sexual behavior in male guinea pigs. *Endocrinology. 56:* 173–177.

WELLS, L. J., CAVANAUGH, M. W., and MAXWELL, E. L. 1954. Genital abnormalities in castrated fetal rats and their prevention by means of testosterone propionate. *Anat. Rec. 118:* 109–133.

WELLS, L. J., and VAN WAGENEN, G. 1954. Androgen-induced female pseudohermaphroditism in the monkey (*Macaca mulatta*): anatomy of the reproductive organs.

Carnegie Institute of Washington Contributions to Embryol. 35: 93–106.

WILKINS, L., JONES, H. W., HOLMAN, G. H., and STEMPFEL, R. S. 1958. Masculinization of the female fetus associated with administration of oral and intramuscular progestins during gestation: non-adrenal female pseudohermaphrodism. *J. Clin. Endocrinol. 18:* 559–585.

WILSON, J. G., and YOUNG, W. C. 1941. Sensitivity to estrogen studied by means of experimentally induced mating responses in the female guinea pig and rat. *Endocrinology. 29:* 779–783.

WITSCHI, E., NELSON, W. O., and SEGAL, S. J. 1957. Genetic, developmental and hormonal aspects of gonadal dysgenesis and sex inversion in man. *J. Clin. Endocrinol. 17:* 737–753.

YERKES, R. M. 1943. *Chimpanzees. A Laboratory Colony.* New Haven, Conn. Yale University Press.

YOUNG, W. C. 1961. "The Hormonal Regulation of Mating Behavior," in *Sex and Internal Secretions*, 3rd ed., ed. by YOUNG, W. C. Baltimore, Williams & Wilkins.

YOUNG, W. C., DEMPSEY, E. W., MYERS, H. I., and HAGQUIST, C. W. 1938. The ovarian condition and sexual behavior in the female guinea pig. *Am. J. Anat. 63:* 457–487.

ZIMBARDO, P. G. 1958. The effects of early avoidance training and rearing conditions upon the sexual behavior of the male rat. *J. Comp. & Physiol. Psychol. 51:* 764–769.

8

ENVIRONMENTAL CONDITIONS AND THE APPEARANCE OF SEXUAL BEHAVIOR IN THE PLATYFISH

Evelyn Shaw

The striking influences and effects of early environment on the appearance of sexual behavior in such forms as mammals and birds has been extensively studied (review: Beach and Jaynes, 1954; mammals: Beach, 1958; Rosenblatt and Aronson, 1958; Valenstein, Riss, and Young, 1955; Valenstein and Goy, 1957; birds: Fisher and Hale, 1957; Schein and Hale, 1959; Wood-Gush, 1958). However, considerably less research on the effects of environment has been carried out on vertebrates belonging to lower phyletic levels—virtually none on reptiles and amphibians and a few incomplete experiments on fish (Seitz, 1940; Tinbergen, 1953).

In order partially to fill this gap, a series of interrelated experiments on fish were carried out in which environmental conditions were altered in seven different ways, in addition to the typical environmental conditions. In this way, it was possible to evaluate the influence, on sexual behavior, of isolation from species mates and from the general environment, per se, as modified by the age of the fish and the duration of isolation.

MATERIAL AND METHODS

Platyfish (*Xiphophorus maculatus*, Fig. 8-1), were obtained through the courtesy of the late Dr. Myron Gordon of the New York Zoological Society. They represented

FIG. 8-1. Platyfish, *Xiphophorus maculatus*—upper fish, a male; lower fish, a female. The arrow points to the gonopodium.

two strains of fish, one from the Rio Jamapa and the other from Rio Coatzacoalcos. The Rio Coatzacoalcos fish, Strain 163, were inbred for 20 generations and provided the parental males; Strain-30 fish from Rio

Jamapa were inbred for 7 generations and provided the parental females. More than 50 pairs of platyfish produced the offspring which were used in all experiments. Adults and young were kept in a temperature-controlled greenhouse under daylight and were fed live food consisting of *Daphnia* and microworms, a specially prepared formula of dried food, and prepared wet food.

RESUMÉ OF TYPICAL BEHAVIOR

A glossary and brief resumé of typical mating patterns are given. For greater detail, see Clark, Aronson, and Gordon (1954).

*Definition of Terms Describing
Sexual Behavior*

• SWINGING

The gonopodium is brought forward to either side, and is usually accompanied by

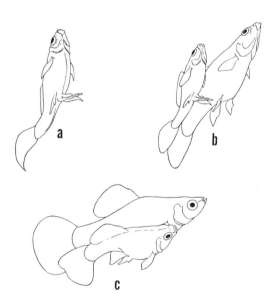

FIG. 8-2. Positions of fish when swinging (a), thrusting (b), and copulating, (c). (From Clark, Aronson, and Gordon, 1954)

the forward movement of the homolateral pelvic fin. Swinging is not necessarily

directed at the female; nor does it always occur in the vicinity of the female.

• SIDLING

The male moves alongside the female, bringing his mid-body region quite close to her body, and he passes from one side to the other, below the ventral or above the dorsal region of the female.

• THRUSTING

After sidling, the male usually thrusts his gonopodium by bringing it and the homo-lateral pelvic fin forward to one side and directing it toward the genital aperture of the female. Thrusts are quick movements.

• COPULATION

The tip of the gonopodium is juxtaposed to the female's genital aperture, and sperm transfer generally occurs. This is a long contact, often lasting several seconds, in contrast to the briefer thrusts. Immediately after copulation, the male characteristically whirls about the aquarium with quick dart-like movements. This behavior is seen only after copulation and not after thrusting.

• BACKING

The male approaches the female by backing toward her, tail first; he sometimes stops in front of the female or continues backing along her side.

• QUIVERING

The dorsal and caudal fins are folded, and the male's body vibrates rapidly. Quivering often occurs simultaneously with backing.

• S-CURVING

The male spreads his dorsal and caudal fins and curves his body into an s-curve with his head higher than his tail. During an s-curve he does not swim about the aquarium.

Soon after a female was placed into the male's tank, the male generally approached the female by *sidling;* and after several or many sidling passes, the male may have quickly thrust his gonopodium toward her genital region. *Thrusting* and sidling were frequently alternated. *Backing, quivering, swinging,* and *s-curving* were interspersed without specific sequential order although backing was often accompanied by a simultaneous quivering motion.

Copulation occurred infrequently. Successful copulation appeared to depend largely on female receptivity. It was noted that receptive females remained quiescent, swimming very slowly with their dorsal and anal fins folded against their bodies, whereas nonreceptive females kept their dorsal and anal fins expanded, swimming rapidly away from the male whenever he approached. Many of the females in these experiments were not receptive.

Behavior of Juvenile Fish (2 Weeks–2 Months Old)

• IN COMMUNITY TANKS

Of all the behavioral activities, s-curving occurred most frequently among young fish, while backing was seen occasionally, and quivering was not observed at all. A behavioral activity, which could have given rise to sidling, was noted: young fish approached caudally their brood mates, swam parallel to them and then past them. In two instances, the fish turned and repeated this swimming pattern, alternating from one side to the other.

No swinging, thrusting, or copulation was seen in community tanks as the fish were removed prior to complete gonopodial development.

• IN INDIVIDUAL TANKS (ISOLATION, ETC.)

Observations were made at least once a week. The only behavioral activity noted

was s-curving, which may have been a response to the disturbance created by the experimenter when the top cover was removed.

EXPERIMENTAL DESIGN

All young were removed from the female by Cesarean section 1–2 days prior to birth. Immediately upon removal they were placed into one of the experimental rearing conditions listed below where they remained until testing time.

• GROUP 1

Isolation, 27 males. Individual fish were placed into two-gallon aquaria. The sides were lined with ground glass and an air stone bubbled air through the water. These precautions were taken to insure visual isolation from species mates and from the greenhouse environment, and to prevent the fish from seeing their own reflections. Of the 300 fish treated in this manner, only 60, of which 27 were males, survived to sexual maturity. Many fish died during the first two weeks of isolation.

• GROUP 2

Individual, 12 males. Fish were reared individually from birth in clear-sided two-gallon aquaria. These fish were able to see the greenhouse environment, including other species of fish, but did not have visual or physical contact with their own species mates. There was no mortality, in sharp contrast to Group 1.

• GROUP 3

Controls, 15 males. Fish were reared together in 15-gallon community aquaria, containing both males and females, until the first signs of sexual maturity, namely, gonopodial differentiation. At the time, about 2½ months of age, each male was placed in a clear-sided two-gallon aquarium where he remained for several weeks during which gonopodial differentiation was completed.

• GROUP 4

Partial isolation, 13 males. Fish were reared as in Group 3. However, when they reached the first phases of sexual maturity they were placed into "isolation" aquaria.

• GROUP 5

Partial isolation, 10 males. Fish were reared for the first month of life in individual isolation aquaria, and then placed into community aquaria for one month to six weeks. When they began to differentiate sexually, individual males were placed into clear-sided two-gallon tanks.

• GROUP 6

Partial isolation, 13 males. Fish were reared in community aquaria for the first month and then placed into "isolation" aquaria, remaining there until testing time.

• GROUP 7

Partial isolation, 12 males. Two-gallon aquaria were divided into equal halves by a vertically placed glass plate. A fish was placed on each side of the plate. The sides of the aquaria were covered, and each fish was able to see only one other fish and was unable to see the surrounding greenhouse environment.

• GROUP 1R

Retested isolates, 15 males. After the first series of observations, Group-1 isolates were returned to their isolation aquaria. A virgin female was placed into each aquarium, remaining there for one month. The males were subsequently retested.

• GROUP 3R

Retested controls, 10 males. As in Group 1R, Group-3R fishes were permitted to remain with a female for one month, in a clear-sided aquarium. The males were subsequently retested.

The potential stimuli which may have been present in these experimental conditions are given in Table 8-11.

TESTING PROCEDURES FOR ALL GROUPS

Between three and four months after birth the males reached complete sexual maturity, as indicated by the appearance of hooks at the tip of the gonopodium. After full maturity was reached, each male was placed for at least 24 hours into the testing aquarium, a two-gallon aquarium lined on the interior with removable ground glass panels. It is important to note that, prior to the time of testing, *none of the fish in any of the groups had sexual experience with a female.*

At testing time five females were presented consecutively, each for a 10-minute duration, to the male. Since we were unable to control the state of female receptivity it was thought that opportunities with several females might give a better measure of the male's level of sexual activity. As mentioned earlier, nonreceptive females tended to inhibit sexual displays in the male because the females were constantly swimming away and, consequently, did not give the male many opportunities to display courtship behavior, such as thrusting, sidling and copulation.

Records of behavioral patterns, durations of patterns and sequences were taken on the Esterline-Angus recording machine, using the Aronson technique.

RESULTS

Comparison of Behavioral Activities in Groups Reared under Different Environmental Situations (Quantitative)

During observations of fish in the testing conditions the experimenter felt that those behavioral activities indicative of the highest level of sexual behavior, and indicative of specific response to the female, were thrusting and sidling. Each activity required orientation to the female, yet did not require, as in copulation, strong recep-

activities depended largely on the male and that the male may sidle up to a female and thrust his gonopodium even though she may be nonreceptive. Therefore, in the analysis of these results, the greatest weight as a clue to the level of sexual excitation in

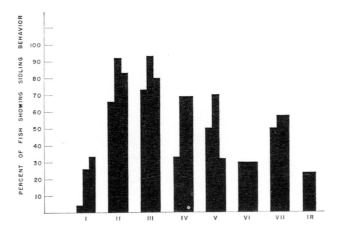

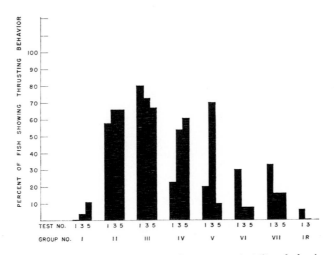

FIG. 8-3. Per cent of fish showing thrusting and sidling behavior.

tivity on the part of the female; and each took place with the female playing a minimal role. The other activities, such as swinging, s-curving and quivering can take place in isolation, in individual tanks, and do not necessarily require the presence of a female or another fish. Clark, Aronson, and Gordon (1954) also felt that these

each fish was placed on thrusting and sidling. Figures 8-3 and 8-4 present, respectively, the percentage of fish displaying thrusting and sidling and the frequency per tested fish. The illustrations clearly demonstrate that there are major differences among the groups reared under different environmental conditions.

• THRUSTING

The percentage showing thrusting among Group-1 fish was very low when compared with the control groups. (Table 8-1A gives the percentage of fish showing thrusting

trial. Had these fish become fatigued by this trial? They were most active during the earlier trials, while the others were not. Groups 4, 5, 6 and 7, when compared with Group 3, showed smaller numbers of performing fish.

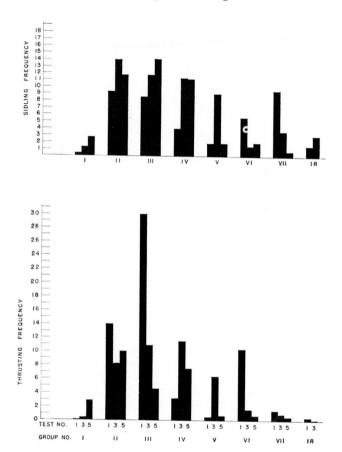

FIG. 8-4. Frequency of thrusting and sidling behavior per tested fish.

behavior, and Table 8-1B gives the frequency per tested fish). During the first test of Group 1, no thrusting behavior was displayed, but as the tests proceeded the number of thrusting fish steadily increased so that by the fifth test three fish thrust, each giving a high average frequency. Among Group-2 fish, the percentage of performing fish remained at equivalent levels during all the trials whereas Group-3 fish showed a slight decrease by the fifth

The number of times each fish thrust showed a wide range. During the fifth

TABLE 8-1A THRUSTING, PER CENT OF FISH
PERFORMING IN EACH GROUP

TEST	GROUP						
NO.	1	2	3	4	5	6	7
1	0	58	80	23	20	30	33
2	7	75	73	54	40	15	42
3	3.7	66	73	54	70	8	16
4	7	50	67	54	20	23	16
5	11	66	67	61	10	8	16

TABLE 8-1B   THRUSTING, FREQUENCY PER TESTED FISH

TEST NO.	GROUP						
	1	*2*	*3*	*4*	*5*	*6*	*7*
1	0	14.1*	29.9*	3.2*	0.5*	10.3*	1.4*
2	0.9	5.9*	17.4*	3.9*	0.5	3.0	4.2*
3	0.4	7.2*	10.8*	11.5*	6.2*	1.5	0.7
4	1.4	14.4*	5.3*	6.4*	0.2	0.8	0.4
5	2.7	10.0*	4.7*	7.4*	0.6	0.6	0.4

* Mann-Whitney U-test, p = <.01 when fishes of Group 1 were compared with each of the other groups.

trial, three Group-1 fish thrust, respectively, 51, 9, and 13 times. Among Group-2 fish, one fish thrust 71 times; another, 55 times during the first test; one fish thrust 75 times during the fourth test; another, 67 times during the fifth test. Among Group-3 fish, one fish thrust as many as 144 times; another, 99 times; and a third, 71 times during the first test. Group-4 fish showed maximum thrusting frequencies during the third trial; three fish thrust 39, 32, and 27 times respectively. A fourth fish thrust 44 times during the fourth test. Similarly, individuals of Group 5 showed high thrusting frequency during the third trial; four fish thrust, respectively, 31, 24, 18, and 11 times, but maximum thrusting frequency occurred in the fourth trial when one fish thrust 43 times. In contrast, three Group-6 fish thrust with high frequency during the first trial,

83, 31, and 16 times, and maximal thrusting among Group-7 fish occurred in the second test 56 times for one fish; the other thrusting frequencies were less than 12.

- SIDLING

The percentage of performing fish increased among Groups 2, 3, 4, 5, 6, and 7

TABLE 8-2A   SIDLING, PER CENT OF FISH PERFORMING IN EACH GROUP

TEST NO.	GROUP						
	1	*2*	*3*	*4*	*5*	*6*	*7*
1	3.7	66	73	31	50	30	50
2	14.8	75	73	54	50	38	50
3	26	92	93	69	70	30	58
4	26	92	93	69	40	30	42
5	33	83	80	69	30	30	58

TABLE 8-2B   SIDLING, FREQUENCY PER TESTED FISH

TEST NO.	GROUP						
	1	*2*	*3*	*4*	*5*	*6*	*7*
1	0.4	9.2*	8.5*	4.0*	1.9*	5.6*	7.6*
2	0.4	7.7*	9.7*	12.3*	2.1*	3.2	9.2*
3	1.2	14.0*	12.2*	11.3*	9.0*	1.5	4.2
4	2.4	16.6*	17.1*	12.9*	2.5	1.7	3.2
5	2.7	11.6*	14.1*	11.2*	1.9	1.9	1.2

* Mann-Whitney U-test, p = <.01.

TABLE 8-3A   COPULATIONS, PER CENT OF FISH PERFORMING IN EACH GROUP

TEST NO.	GROUP						
	1	2	3	4	5	6	7
1	0	8	40	0	10	8	0
2	7	16	27	0	0	8	8
3	3.7	8	33	23	0	8	0
4	11	8	20	0	0	16	0
5	11	16	6	7	0	0	0

TABLE 8-3B   COPULATIONS, FREQUENCY PER TESTED FISH

TEST NO.	GROUP						
	1	2	3	4	5	6	7
1	0	0.08	0.5*	0	0.1	0.08	0
2	0.1	0.25	0.5	0	0	0.08	0.08
3	0.07	0.08	0.3	0.2	0	0.08	0
4	0.2	0.08	0.3	0	0	0.16	0
5	0.1	0.5	0.2	0.07	0	0	0

* Mann-Whitney U-test, $p = <.01$.

to a high point during the third test, remaining at this level or becoming very slightly reduced during the subsequent tests (Table 8-2A). In contrast, the percentage in Group 1 was very low (one fish) during the first trial, but by the fifth trial had increased to the point where seven fish were showing sidling behavior.

The frequency of sidling per tested fish, in Group 1, also increased as the tests proceeded from 1 through 5 (Tables 8-2B). One fish sidled 21 times and the other 10 times during the fourth test; two fish sidled 24 times each during the fifth test. Among fish in Group 2, maximal sidling was seen during the third, fourth, and fifth tests, with the majority of fish sidling at least 25 times. Group-3 fish also showed a similar frequency with highest activity during the fourth trial when two fish sidled 39 and 41 times respectively. Among Group-4 fish, greatest activity occurred in the second test when one fish sidled 55 times; another sidled 21 times; and another, 10 times. Group 5 had the highest activity in the third test when four fish showed sidling 30, 23, 23, and 22 times. In contrast to Group 5, high sidling frequencies were found in the first test among three fish of Group 6; one sidled 49 times; another, 27 times; and the third, 15 times. Among Group-7 fish, high sidling activity was found in two fish in Test 1, two fish in Test 2, and two other

fish in Test 3. The highest score was 43, shown by a fish in Test 2. Two fish in Test 1 showed high sidling frequencies and scored 32 and 16 respectively. The above were the six active fish of the 12 in Group 7.

Groups 6 and 7 started with high-frequency levels and subsequently showed decline, while the percentage of performing fish remained at a fairly constant level.

• COPULATIONS

The numbers of copulating fish among all groups were low (Table 8-3A) when compared with the behavior shown by platyfish in the observations of Clark, Aronson, and Gordon (1954) and Kamrin and Aronson (1954). Of the isolates, Group 1, a total of four fish copulated at least once, and these were very active; one copulated

TABLE 8-4A   SWINGING, PER CENT OF FISH PERFORMING IN EACH GROUP

TEST NO.	GROUP						
	1	2	3	4	5	6	7
1	3.7	33	73	38	80	38	33
2	11	58	80	54	100	23	66
3	14.8	58	73	61	80	23	50
4	18.5	75	60	54	80	30	83
5	36.6	58	40	38	60	23	66

TABLE 8-4B SWINGING, FREQUENCY PER TESTED FISH

TEST NO.	GROUP						
	1	2	3	4	5	6	7
1	0.15	2.1*	4.6*	1.5*	4.2*	2.1*	1.5*
2	0.18	3.1*	4.9*	2.5*	5.5*	0.8	4.0*
3	1.0	2.1*	3.9*	2.3*	5.9*	0.6	2.6*
4	0.8	3.2*	3.1*	2.2*	3.2*	0.8	3.3*
5	1.5	3.2*	3.1	1.2	3.6	0.3	1.4

* Mann-Whitney U-test, p = <.01.

5 times during the fourth and fifth tests; another, 4 times during the second, third, and fifth tests; and the third, three times during the second and fourth tests. The fourth fish copulated only once during the fourth trial. Among Group-2 fish, six copulated; two copulated 3 times during the fifth test; three copulated once during Tests 1, 2, 3, and 4; one other fish copulated once during the second test. In Group 3, seven fish copulated; each of the seven copulated at least once during the first three trials, and two of these copulated during the fourth trial. Three fish in Group 4 copulated; three copulated during the third trial, and one of the three copulated once during the fifth trial. One fish in Group 5 copulated once during the first trial, and another fish copulated twice during the third trial. In Group 6, one fish was very active, copulating five times during the last three trials while another fish copulated once during the first trial. One fish copulated once during the second trial of Group-7 fishes. When the frequencies per tested fish are compared, the figures differ significantly in only one of the 35 tests (Table 8-3B).

• SWINGING

In Group 1, the number of fishes showing swinging increased as the tests proceeded from 1 through 5 (Table 8-4A). During the first trial one fish swung once; during the fifth trial, 10 fish showed swinging behavior with the average frequencies remaining equivalent. One fish displayed swinging 30 times in the last three tests, but did not show any other courtship behavior. By the fifth trial, Group 1 showed an activity level similar to the level found in the first trial of Group 2. The greatest number of fish displaying swinging was found in Group 5, a group that had spent their first month in isolation, the remaining time in community tanks. Their frequency was approximately five swings per fish. Among other groups the frequency per performing fish ranged between five and 10 times throughout the tests. When the groups are compared, per tested fish, Groups 1 and 6 do not differ from each other, but their scores are lower than the scores of other groups (Table 8-4B). It is important to note that Groups

TABLE 8-5A QUIVERING, PER CENT OF FISH PERFORMING IN EACH GROUP

TEST NO.	GROUP						
	1	2	3	4	5	6	7
1	15	66	73	54	80	46	58
2	30	66	73	61	90	38	50
3	37	83	93	77	80	61	58
4	26	66	93	46	100	46	66
5	37	58	73	61	100	38	42

TABLE 8-5B   QUIVERING, FREQUENCY PER TESTED FISH

TEST NO.	GROUP						
	1	*2*	*3*	*4*	*5*	*6*	*7*
1	0.7	3.5*	4.6*	2.2*	3.1*	2.2*	2.5*
2	0.9	3.4*	5.2*	4.5*	3.2*	1.7	1.6
3	1.2	4.7*	6.9*	3.9*	3.4*	1.2	2.2
4	0.9	2.9*	5.1*	4.9*	3.7*	1.9	2.1
5	1.1	2.1	6.9*	2.1*	2.4*	1.8	1.6

* Mann-Whitney U-test, p = <.01.

1 and 6 spent the longest period of time in isolation.

• QUIVERING

Among Group-1 fish, the percentage of participating fish showing quivering increased (Table 8-5A); four fish displayed quivering initially and 10 fish displayed it by the fifth trial. Among all the groups the frequency level per fish was equivalent. However, quivering is significantly higher, per tested fish (Table 8-5B), among fish that have had long periods of community experience.

• BACKING

The number of fish showing backing was highly variable in each of the groups (Table 8-6A). Backing, according to Clark, Aronson, and Gordon (1954), was not as

TABLE 8-6A   BACKING, PER CENT OF FISH PERFORMING IN EACH GROUP

TEST NO.	GROUP						
	1	*2*	*3*	*4*	*5*	*6*	*7*
1	15	33	53	15	40	38	8
2	22	25	13	31	60	15	25
3	30	50	11	15	50	31	42
4	37	42	53	31	70	15	50
5	37	33	67	15	50	15	33

TABLE 8-6B   BACKING, FREQUENCY PER TESTED FISH

TEST NO.	GROUP						
	1	*2*	*3*	*4*	*5*	*6*	*7*
1	0.2	0.7	2.5*	0.15	0.6	0.8	0.08
2	0.4	0.8	2.8*	0.6	1.0	0.3	0.2
3	0.5	1.0	2.4*	0.6	0.9	0.6	1.3
4	1.0	0.4	2.5	1.3	1.1	0.5	1.0
5	0.6	0.5	4.1*	0.5	1.1	0.3	0.7

* Mann-Whitney U-test, p = <.01.

obvious in the platies as in the swordtails. Group 5 was the only group which consistently showed a fairly high number of performing fish. The frequency of backing was low, except in some members of Groups 3 and 4, which had been reared in community tanks for the first two or three months of their lives. When the results are compared, per tested fish, only Group 3 shows significant differences in backing in the first three tests, when compared with Group 1 (Table 8-6B).

• S-CURVING

S-curving was displayed by only four groups: 1, 3, 4, and 7 (Table 8-7A). The disparity of rearing among these groups was great. For example, Group-1 fish were reared in isolation; Groups 3 and 4, under social conditions; and Group 7, in partial isolation.

<table>
<tr><td colspan="8">TABLE 8-7A   S-CURVING, PER CENT OF FISH
PERFORMING IN EACH GROUP</td></tr>
<tr><td rowspan="2">TEST NO.</td><td colspan="7">GROUP</td></tr>
<tr><td>1</td><td>2</td><td>3</td><td>4</td><td>5</td><td>6</td><td>7</td></tr>
<tr><td>1</td><td>30</td><td></td><td>33</td><td>23</td><td></td><td></td><td>25</td></tr>
<tr><td>2</td><td>18.5</td><td></td><td>26</td><td>7</td><td></td><td></td><td></td></tr>
<tr><td>3</td><td>22</td><td></td><td>26</td><td>7</td><td></td><td></td><td>17</td></tr>
<tr><td>4</td><td>26</td><td></td><td>26</td><td>0</td><td></td><td></td><td></td></tr>
<tr><td>5</td><td>18.5</td><td></td><td>26</td><td>0</td><td></td><td></td><td></td></tr>
</table>

<table>
<tr><td colspan="8">TABLE 8-7B   S-CURVING, FREQUENCY PER
PERFORMING FISH*</td></tr>
<tr><td rowspan="2">TEST NO.</td><td colspan="7">GROUP</td></tr>
<tr><td>1</td><td>2</td><td>3</td><td>4</td><td>5</td><td>6</td><td>7</td></tr>
<tr><td>1</td><td>2.0</td><td></td><td>1.4</td><td>8.0</td><td></td><td></td><td>3.6</td></tr>
<tr><td>2</td><td>4.8</td><td></td><td>2.0</td><td>1.0</td><td></td><td></td><td></td></tr>
<tr><td>3</td><td>6.0</td><td></td><td>2.7</td><td>1.0</td><td></td><td></td><td>1.0</td></tr>
<tr><td>4</td><td>4.6</td><td></td><td>5.0</td><td>0</td><td></td><td></td><td></td></tr>
<tr><td>5</td><td>3.8</td><td></td><td>3.7</td><td>0</td><td></td><td></td><td></td></tr>
</table>

* Not statistically analyzed per tested fish.

The frequency of s-curving was consistently high among Group-1 and Group-3 fish (Table 8-7B). One fish in group 1 s-curved once during the first test, and his s-curving increased to 34 by the fifth trial; another fish showed three s-curves during the first trial, and this increased to 28 by the third trial. The remaining fish showed between one to five s-curves during the five tests. Note that the peak of s-curving was reached by the third trial in Group 1, whereas in Group 3 the peak was reached during the latter trials—as the result of one fish s-curving 12 times during the fourth test and 10 times during the fifth. The

TABLE 8-8   GROUP 1R COMPARED WITH GROUP 1

	Test 1		Test 2		Test 3	
	GROUP 1	GROUP 1R	GROUP 1	GROUP 1R	GROUP 1	GROUP 1R
Quivering:						
Per Cent	15	60	30	27	37	27
Frequency	4.7	2.9	3.2	0.9	3.4	0.7
Thrusting:						
Per Cent	0	6	7	13	3.7	0
Frequency	0	0.2	13.0	1.9	1.0	0
Swinging:						
Per Cent	3.7	20	11	13	14.8	20
Frequency	4.0	0.5	1.4	0.2	7.0	0.9
S-Curving:						
Per Cent	30	33	18.5	26	22	20
Frequency	2.0	4.7	4.8	2.5	6.0	1.5
Sidling:						
Per Cent	3.7	33	14.8	33	26	33
Frequency	1.0	1.5	2.8	3.9	4.7	3.0
Backing:						
Per Cent	15	20	22	20	30	13
Frequency	1.5	0.3	1.8	0.3	1.7	1.2
Copulating:						
Per Cent	0	6	7	6	3.7	13
Frequency	0	.06	1.5	.06	2.0	0.13

Frequency = frequency per performing fish.

TABLE 8-9   LATENCY AND BEHAVIORAL APPROACHES

	GROUP						
	1	*2*	*3*	*4*	*5*	*6*	*7*
				Test 1			
Latency of first approach mean*	5'5"	3'47"	2'37"	4 20"	2'9"	3'0"	5'18"
Latency of first approach range†	28"–544"	58"–484"	22"–464"	29"–570"	38"–364"	30"–498"	46"–470"
First two behavioral acts	S-Curving Backing	Quivering Sidling	Sidling Thrusting	Quivering Thrusting	Quivering Sidling	Quivering Sidling	No clear-cut trend
				Test 3			
Latency of first approach mean*	3'4"	2'4"	1'34"	2'15"	2'7"	4'7"	3'43"
Latency of first approach range†	20' –540"	18"–420"	12"–301"	12"–433"	54"–330"	62"–526"	12"–580"
First two behavioral acts	S-Curving Sidling Quivering Swinging	Sidling Thrusting	Sidling Quivering	Sidling Quivering	Quivering Sidling Swinging	Quivering Sidling	Quivering Sidling
				Test 5			
Latency of first approach mean*	1'47"	1'35"	1'40"	2'2"	2'3"	2'22"	2'3"
Latency of first approach range†	1"–380"	31"–186"	42"–240"	44"–274"	44"–491"	33"–241"	9"–483"
First two behavioral acts	S-Curving Quivering Sidling Backing	Sidling Quivering	Sidling Backing	Sidling Quivering	Quivering Sidling	Sidling Quivering	Sidling Quivering

* In minutes and seconds.
† In seconds.

remaining fish showed no more than two s-curves each during the tests. Group-4 fish showed high s-curving during the first trial; one fish s-curved 14 times; another, 8 times. In Group 7, one fish s-curved eight times, second test, and 10 times, fourth test. The other performing Group-7 fish each s-curved a maximum of two times during any test.

Behavioral Activity after One Month's Experience with Females

Fifteen isolates (Group 1R) and 10 controls (Group 3R), which had been placed with virgin females in individual aquaria for one month, were retested under conditions similar to the original testing tech-

TABLE 8-10 LATENCY OF RESPONSE AND INITIAL BEHAVIORAL ACTIVITY AMONG RETESTED GROUPS

	TEST *1*		TEST *3*	
	*1*R	*3*R	*1*R	*3*R
Latency mean*	4′30″	2′50″	2′3″	2′
Latency range†	35″–570″	2″–436″	24″–370″	31″–270″
First two behavioral	S-Curving	Sidling	S-Curving	Sidling
activities	Quivering	S-Curving	Backing	Thrusting

* In minutes and seconds.
† In seconds.

nique (three consecutive trials, however, instead of five). Table 8-8 compares Group 1R with Group 1 and summarizes the percentage of performing fish and the frequency per tested fish. Among Group-1R fishes, the numbers of participating fish did not increase significantly; nor did their frequency levels, even though seven of the female partners dropped broods. Three of these males showed no response in the test conditions, and two showed a high frequency of s-curving. A large number showed quivering during the first test; but the numbers decreased during the successive tests, and the numbers of fish showing sidling remained the same but with increased frequency. S-curving was displayed as in earlier trials, but the frequency per fish increased.

Among the controls, seven of the 10 female partners dropped broods; the controls showed a slight reduction in their frequencies of thrusting and sidling.

Latency of Approach and First Behavioral Approaches

Tables 8-9 and 8-10 give the approach time and the first two behavioral acts directed at the female during Tests 1, 3, and 5 (Test 5 was not taken in Group 1R and 3R). The average, latency high among all groups during the first test, decreased during the third test and fifth test.

The first approach displayed by Group-1 fish was consistently s-curving. The second approach was more variable—either sidling, quivering, or backing—not in definitive, sequential order. A first approach of sidling behavior was consistently shown among Group-3 fish; the second approach was more variable. Among the other groups quivering and sidling alternated as first and second approaches. No single approach was dominant in Group 7 during the first trial, but during the third and fifth trials, sidling and quivering alternated as the first or second approach. Comparing Groups 1 and 1R, we see that latency was not reduced among Group-1R fish and that the first behavioral approach remained an s-curve.

Qualitative Observations

• GROUP 1

The initial sidling displays of seven fish were slightly above or slightly below the female's positions. After 5–10 sidling passes the motor aspects of sidling became typical, resembling the community-reared controls and their patterns. One other fish showed sidling, throughout all observations, with his dorsal fin fully erected (usually it is folded) even though his positional orientation was accurate.

Among the fish which thrust, the first thrusts were accomplished without the homolateral pelvic fin brought forward. Three fish thrust 3–5 times and a fourth fish thrust 20 times without the accompanying pelvic fin. All subsequent thrusting, however, followed the typical motor patterns, as shown by the controls.

• GROUP 2

During the first displays of sidling behavior, four fish oriented either slightly above or slightly below the female. Five fish (including three of the above) did not thrust directly at the female's genital opening; the gonopodium was either anterior or posterior to the opening during, at the most, the first five thrusts. In one instance, a fish thrust towards the female when his gonopodium was ½ inch away; he ejaculated visible spermatophores into the water, and broke into the characteristic postcopulatory whirl. No further positional disorientation was observed after these thrusts.

• GROUPS 3, 4, 5, AND 6

Typical behavioral patterns were displayed.

• GROUP 7

In the sidling approach the male normally swims from the rear toward the caudal fin of the female, comes up behind her and then parallels her laterally. However, among four of these fish, the first 3–5 sidling approaches were made at right angles to the female's lateral body wall without sidling. (This right-angle approach may have resulted from the male's orientation to his partner fish through the glass partition. The partition restricted his movements and his approaches may have been made at right angles to the partition.) One fish thrust 1 inch away from the female and soon afterwards broke into the typical postcopulatory whirl.

A comparison of behavioral activity was made among fish that were reared opposite males in contrast to fish reared opposite females. The highest sidling scores in Trials 1 and 2 were given by five males reared opposite females and by one male reared opposite a male. Three males reared opposite females and three males reared opposite males gave low scores.

• GROUP 1R

There were no behavioral differences in motor pattern among Group-1R fish when compared with the controls.

Gross examination and smears of the gonads did not reveal any anatomical differences between control and experimental fish.

DISCUSSION

Evaluation of Rearing Conditions

Few fish (Group 1), reared in an environment where they *did not have physical or visual contact with species mates, or with the surrounding environment,* showed sexual behavior. In contrast, many fish (Group 2), also reared without physical or visual contact with species mates, showed sexual behavior; they, however, *did have visual contact with the surrounding environment.* Intermediate numbers of fish (Groups 4, 5, 6, and 7) which had experience with the general environment and/or with species mates displayed sexual behavior.

Although the rearing conditions were different in the seven groups there are similarities among several so that they can be classified into five categories. In the first category, the fish from birth was removed from the general environment and from species mates and was restricted to the limited environment of his tank, the water in the tank, his food, and any sensations he

TABLE 8-11   POTENTIAL STIMULI IN ENVIRONMENTAL CONDITIONS, GROUPS 1–7, 1R, 3R

	1	2	3	4	5	6	7	1R	3R
Visual									
Species mates	−	−	+	+	+	+	+	+	+
Food	+	+	+	+	+	+	+	+	+
General environment	−	+	+	+	+	+−	−	−	+
Self-reflection	−	+	+	+	+	+	+	+	+
Auditory	+	+	+	+	+	+	+	+	+
Olfactory									
Species mates	−	−	+	+	+	+−	−	+	+
Food	+	+	+	+	+	+	+	+	+
Self	+	+	+	+	+	+	+	+	+
Gustatory									
Species mates	−	−	+	+	+	+−	−	+	+
Food	+	+	+	+	+	+	+	+	+
Self	+	+	+	+	+	+	+	+	+
Tactile									
Species mates	−	−	+	+	+	+−	−	+	+
Self	+	+	+	+	+	+	+	+	+
Physical stimuli									
S-Curving	+	+	+	+	+	+	+	+	+
Swinging	+	+	+	+	+	+	+	+	+
Thrusting	−	−	+	+	+	−	−	+	+
Sidling	−	−	+	+	+	−	+	+	+
Backing	+	+	+	+	+	+	+	+	+
Quivering	+	+	+	+	+	+	+	+	+
Following	−	−	+	+	+	+−	+	+	+
General orientation to species mates	−	−	+	+	+	+−	+	+	+

+ = present in environment.
− = absent from environment.
+− = present during one phase of experiment. Absent during another.

may have gained from his own body (Group 1). In another category, the fish were treated as above but had visual access to the surrounding greenhouse environment (Group 2). In the third main condition the fish had physical and visual contact with species mates and the surrounding environment, but they also experienced the restricted environment of isolation tanks (Groups 4, 5, and 6). The main differences among the three groups in this category were the length of time spent in isolation and the period of life during which they were isolated. In the fourth category, the fish had visual contact only with a species mate, but did not have visual access to

the greenhouse environment (Group 7). The fifth category represented the controls which had social contact with species mates (Group 3).

The potential stimuli, present in each of these main categories and in each group, are shown in Table 8-11. For example, stimuli in Groups 3, 4, and 5 were identical. Yet, the number of fish showing sexual behavior was larger in Group 3 than in Groups 4 and 5. Fish of Group 4 spent one month in isolation while they developed sexually, whereas fish of Group 5 spent their initial month of life in isolation. However, when the latter groups were compared, the numbers of performing fish were not significantly different. To analyze this, it was important to compare Group-6 fish with those of Groups 4 and 5. A significant point emerged: the number of fish showing sexual behavior was higher in Groups 4 and 5 than in 6. (Group 6 was so low that it did not have many more participants than Group 1.) We knew that Group-6 fish had community experience during their first month, physical and visual contact with species mates, and access to the surrounding environment and that the stimuli present during the first month were similar to stimuli found in Groups 4 and 5. But the main difference between Groups 4 and 5 and 6 was the length of time spent in isolation. Groups 4 and 5 spent about one month in isolation and Group 6, two to three months. Evidently these early experiences with species mates and general environmental conditions were not sufficient to overcome the dampening effects of long-term isolation.

Continuing with the comparison of rearing conditions, stimuli among Groups 1, 2, and 7 were alike except at two points—general environment and species mates. Group 1 could not see the environment or other fish; Group 2 could see the environment but not species mates; and Group 7 could see species mates but not the general environment. Group 1 showed the lowest scores, Group 2 showed high activity, in numbers of performing fish, and in frequencies, and Group 7 showed low levels of activity. These differences suggested that visual experiences with species mates were not as critical as thought by Tinbergen (1951), but that, visual experiences with a broad environment were extremely important. It is Schneirla's hypothesis (1957) that the organism takes more from the environment than merely the energy essential for nutrition and that there are many stimulating effects of the species

milieu which subtly contribute to the organism's experiences. Hebb (1949) stated that the richer the experiences of a group (rats) during development, the better able they were to profit by new experiences at maturity. This has been confirmed in several other species, and a similar phenomenon may be present at the lowest phyletic level of vertebrates, the fishes, where a wide range of experiences during development may lead to a greater ability to adjust to new situations.

Motor Patterns

Tinbergen (1953) "raised a three-spined stickleback from the egg stage on in isolation" and reported that it showed the typical chain of courtship activities after reaching sexual maturity, without any deviations of the motor patterns. Several platyfish, raised in isolation in these experiments, also showed characteristic courtship patterns after reaching sexual maturity. At first, however, the patterns, per se, were not precise. For example, initial thrusting was accomplished without the simultaneous forward movement of the homolateral pelvic fin; only after a number of thrusts was the fin incorporated. Clark, Aronson, and Gordon (1954) found that the pelvic fin was important in the transfer of sperm to the female. They postulated that the fin may be a supplementary part of the ejaculatory mechanism. The fact that the pelvic fin was brought forward, not by sexually mature, but by inexperienced males suggested that the gonopodium and the pelvic fin did not function on a synchronized reflex system. The fish may have found that bringing the pelvic fin forward was more "comfortable" during the forward motion of the gonopodium and, once experiencing this, continued to thrust in this fashion. This difference in motor pattern however, is not clearly understood, and further work is prerequisite to understanding its significance.

Positional orientation among isolates and semi-isolates was also disrupted, particularly orientation in sidling. A number of males, initially, did not swim into the proper position along the female's lateral flank. Positional orientation may require several practice trials which, once achieved, can be maintained. Fish with some community experience during their first month never showed any orientative difficulties upon reaching sexual maturity, indicating that those processes giving rise to positional orientation may have been made early in life probably rapidly, and were retained though not reinforced by subsequent experiences.

Response to Females

The typical sexually excited male platyfish, when presented with a female, approached the female by sidling, thrusting, and, if she was receptive, copulation. Other activities which appeared intermittently included quivering, backing, s-curving, and swinging; these were considered to be indicative of lower levels of excitation, and, in the case of s-curving, considered to be aggression and/or fear. Clark, Aronson, and Gordon (1954) divided these various behavioral acts into three stages of activity, placing sidling and thrusting in the second stage of sexual activity, with backing and quivering as concomitant activities. Backing and quivering, in these experiments, were not considered reliable indications of sexual arousal. Backing occurred infrequently in platyfish and quivering often occurred in alternation with s-curving. However, if we assumed that sidling, as the first approach, and thrusting, as the second approach, were indicative of high levels of excitation (copulation was excluded, since its occurrence was dependent upon the fe-

male) and that the other activities were indicative of lower levels, the initial responses became useful as measures of sexual arousal. The controls, during the first test, showed sidling and thrusting in sequential order. This sequential pattern was not seen in any other groups, although one of these two activities appeared either as a first or second approach in other few groups; they did not appear in the long-term isolates, and in another group of fish visually isolated from the environment but not from species mates. As the tests proceeded from 1 through 5 the isolates continued to show s-curving, but fish in five of the other groups began to display sidling. This change of initial approaches, from Tests 1 through 5, with a simultaneous reduction in latency time, suggested that if Groups 3 to 7 were tested sufficiently long, all would ultimately display typical patterns of sexual behavior to the females.

Isolates Given Subsequent Experience with Females

Isolates, retested after one month's experience with females in their isolation aquaria, did not show a significant increase in frequency of courtship activities or in the number of fish displaying these activities. It seemed paradoxical that 7 of the 15 females dropped broods. Evidently copulation occurred but did not stimulate and increase the general level of sexual excitation. Moreover, experiences with a female were inadequate in bringing the latency levels close to those of Groups 2 and 3. It appeared that long-term isolation strongly inhibited the appearance of sexual behavior. Similar results were reported by Valenstein and Goy (1957) who found that certain strains of guinea pigs which were reared in isolation from the time of weaning, tested, subsequently placed with females for long periods, then retested, still gave low measures of sexual behavior. Experience with females did not enhance the return to a more typical state of sexual display. In fish, as in guinea pigs, the age at which sexual experience was gained may be critical. These platyfish, when retested, were approximately 5 months old. Typically, platyfish come into sexual maturity at 2-3 months. It was conceivable that patterns of sexual behavior could not be organized effectively at 5 months even if adequate stimuli were present, and that the inhibition, produced through isolation, was an irreversible process among many of these isolated fish.

CONCLUSIONS AND SUMMARY

1. The appearance of sexual behavior in platyfish, reared under various interrelated environmental conditions, was affected by conditions of rearing. Fish reared in isolation, without visual access to species mates and the general environment showed the greatest inhibition; fish reared without visual access to species mates but with access to general environment did not show inhibition; and fish reared with visual access to species mates but not to the environment showed a moderate degree of inhibition.

2. The technique of isolating an animal from species mates had been employed primarily as a method for evaluating the role of physiological determinants, without major consideration of the environmental conditions, on the appearance of sexual behavior. However, the current experiments dealt with environmental situations as the experimental variables and used the technique of isolation as one of several variables. The importance of isolation became considerably lessened when it was shown that other environmental alterations (not necessarily complete isolation) also inhibited the appearance of sexual behavior.

Moreover, the two conditions of isolation from species mates gave different results. In one, sexual behavior was inhibited; in the other, sexual behavior appeared in its full complement.

3. It appeared that visual access to species mates was not as important to the appearance of sexual behavior as visual access to the general surrounding environment.

4. Sexual behavior, once inhibited in long-term isolates, could not be elicited, even after the isolates had experiences with females.

5. It was important to define clearly the conditions of rearing since even small changes in (1) length of time of isolation, (2) period of life at which isolation occurred, and (3) general environmental conditions subtly affected sexual behavior in the platyfish.

REFERENCES

BEACH, F. A. 1958. Normal sexual behaviour in male rats isolated at fourteen days of age. *J. Comp. & Physiol. Psychol.* 51: 37–38.

BEACH, F. A., and JAYNES, J. 1954. Effects of early experience upon the behavior of animals. *Psychol. Bull.* 51: 239–263.

CLARK, E., ARONSON, L. R., and GORDON, M. 1954. Mating behavior patterns in two sympatric species of xiphophorin fishes; their inheritance and significance in sexual isolation. *Bull. Am. Mus. Natural Hist.* 103(Art. 2): 139–225.

FISHER, A. E., and HALE, E. B. 1957. Stimulus determinants of sexual and aggressive behavior in male domestic fowl. *Behaviour.* 10: 309–323.

HEBB, D. O. 1949. *The Organization of Behavior. A Neuropsychological Theory.* New York, Wiley, pp. vii–xii, 1–335.

KAMRIN, R. P., and ARONSON, L. R. 1954. The effects of forebrain lesion on mating behavior in the male platyfish, *Xiphophorus maculatus. Zoologica.* 39: 133–140.

ROSENBLATT, J. S., and ARONSON, L. R. 1958. The decline of sexual behavior in male cats after castration with special reference to the role of prior sexual experience. *Behaviour.* *12*: 285–338.

SCHEIN, M. W., and HALE, E. B. 1959. The effect of early social experience on male sexual behaviour of androgen-injected turkeys. *Animal Behav.* *7*(3–4): 189–200.

SCHNEIRLA, T. C. 1956. "Interrelationships of the 'Innate' and the 'Acquired' in Instinctive Behavior," in *L'Instinct dans le Comportement des Animaux et de L'Homme,* ed. by GRASSÉ, P.-P. Paris, Masson & Cie, pp. 387–452.

SCHNEIRLA, T. C. 1957. "The Concept of Development in Comparative Psychology," in *The Concept of Development,* ed. by HARRIS, D. B. Minneapolis, University of Minnesota Press, pp. 78–108.

SEITZ, A. 1940. Die Paarbildung bei einigen Cichliden I. Die Paarbilgung bei Astato

tilapia strigigena Pfeffer. *ztschr. f. Tierpsychol.* *4:* 40–84.

TINBERGEN, N. 1951. *The study of instinct.* London, Oxford University Press.

TINBERGEN, N. 1953. *Social Behavior in Animals.* London, Methuen.

VALENSTEIN, E. S., and GOY, R. W. 1957. Further studies of the organization and display of sexual behavior in male guinea pigs. *J. Comp. & Physiol. Psychol. 50:* (2): 115–119.

VALENSTEIN, E. S., RISS, W., and YOUNG, W. C. 1955. Experimental and genetic factors in the organization of sexual behavior in male guinea pigs. *J. Comp. & Physiol. Psychol.* *48*(5): 397–403.

WOOD-GUSH, D. G. M. 1958. The effect of experience on the mating behavior of the domestic cock. *Animal Behav.* *6*(1 and 2): 68–71.

9

INTERACTION OF HORMONAL AND EXPERIENTIAL INFLUENCES ON DEVELOPMENT OF BEHAVIOR

Daniel S. Lehrman

Beach (1947), in his now-classic review of sexual behavior in mammals, pointed out that the mating patterns of various animals were influenced, in their development and expression, both by the effects of gonadal hormones and by the effects of individual experience. Further, different species and the two sexes within the same species might differ with respect to the relative degree of dependence of their sexual behavior upon the presence of various hormones and upon various situational and experiential factors.

Recent research makes it increasingly clear that the animal's individual experience plays a role in the development of many behavior patterns which are demonstrably hormone-induced and, conversely, that the effects of hormones play a role in many behavior patterns which are dependent upon the animal's previous experience (Lehrman, 1956; Schneirla, 1956). It is the purpose of this chapter to review and discuss a number of instances of such interactive relationships between the effects of hormones and of individual experience.

* Work from the author's laboratory, reported in this paper, has been supported by Grant No. M2771 from the National Institute of Mental Health, U.S. Public Health Service, for which grateful acknowledgment is made.

HORMONE-EXPERIENCE INTERACTIONS

Sexual Behavior in the Guinea Pig

W. C. Young and his collaborators (Young, 1957) have carried out a many-sided analysis of the origin of individual differences in the sexual behavior of the guinea pig. Both male (Young and Grunt, 1951) and female (Goy and Young, 1957) guinea pigs show considerable individual variability in various quantitative measures of sex behavior, and these differences are persistent, so that they reflect stable differences among individuals, rather than fortuitous variations in the behavior of individuals. That these individual differences may be based in part upon genetic factors is indicated by the fact that consistent differences in the pattern and in the intensity of sexual behavior can be noted between animals of different inbred strains, and between inbred and heterogeneous strains, both in the male (Valenstein, Riss, and Young, 1954) and in the female (Goy and Young, 1957).

Grunt and Young (1952, 1953), investigating the nature of these genetic differences, divided groups of male guinea pigs into those showing high, medium, and low "sex drive," as measured by a score reflecting several different aspects of the sexual behavior pattern. When these animals were castrated, their sexual behavior scores all fell to the same minimal level. Some 16 weeks after castration, replacement therapy was instituted consisting of daily injections of testosterone propionate. This treatment resulted in the reinstatement of sex behavior. Further, when they were all injected with the same amount of male sex hormone, the animals tended to show the same relative amount of sex behavior as they had previously shown under the influence of endogenous androgen. A fourfold increase in the level of administered androgen, beyond that required for reinstatement of the pattern, had no further effect upon the sex behavior scores, and did not alter the relative standing of the different groups. Similar results have been obtained with females (Goy and Young, 1957). This indicates that the differences in the sex behavior of the various strains of guinea pigs are the result, not of differences in the amount of circulating sex hormones, but rather of differences in the responsiveness to sex hormones of the tissues mediating sex behavior.

The experiments cited so far make it clear that the sex hormones play an important role in establishing and maintaining sexual behavior in the guinea pig, and that this role varies, depending upon differences in the genetic constitution of the animals. A further group of experiments demonstrates the contribution of individual experience to the effectiveness of the hormonal induction of sex behavior, and the interaction of this contribution with that of genetic differences.

Valenstein, Riss, and Young (1955) reared different groups of male guinea pigs, of several different strains, under conditions of social isolation or of association with other animals of the same age. All animals were weaned from their mothers when they were 25 days old. The "isolated" males were raised in isolation after weaning, while the "social" males were kept with 3–5 females of the same age, until the age of 73 days. The animals were tested for sexual behavior, starting at 77 days of age.

In males of two inbred strains, the "social" animals showed significantly higher scores on a variety of measures of sexual behavior than did the isolated animals. In the group of genetically heterogeneous animals, no such differences appeared. The authors suggested that this might be because the genetically heterogeneous males grow much more rapidly than do those of either of the two inbred strains, and thus might reach, within 25 days, a stage of development at which they could acquire the experience which contributes to the differences between isolated and social animals. They therefore repeated the experiment with genetically heterogeneous males, weaning them at 10 days of age instead of 25. Under these conditions, the social males had significantly higher scores than did the isolated ones.

It is thus apparent that experience during early life (i.e., before sexual maturity) contributes, in this species, to the development of the normal pattern of sexual behavior. In a further experiment, Valenstein, Riss, and Young (1955) found that caging with other males was just as effective as caging with females for the development of the normal sexual pattern. Since both intact males and estrous females may initiate mounting behavior, while spayed females do not, Valenstein and Goy (1957) next reared "social" animals by caging them with *spayed* females. This procedure resulted in a markedly lower level of sexual behavior than did rearing with either intact males or intact females. The experience involved in these experiments occurs before sexual maturity and is effective even in animals castrated at birth, indicating that the activity of the gonads is not necessary for the occurrence or effectiveness of the experience (Riss *et al.*, 1955). Essentially similar results, in all respects, are found when these experiments are repeated on females (Goy and Young, 1957).

These experiments, which only partially reflect the tenacity with which this group of investigators has explored this problem,

the "isolated" males were kept in isolation until the same age. From the age of 73 days, all the animals were kept under the same (isolated) conditions. They were given weekly tests of sexual behavior from 11 to 17 weeks of age, the results of which can be seen in the left-hand field of Figure 9-1. The social animals had, clearly and consistently, higher sexual behavior scores than the isolated ones. At the age of 17 weeks, some of the animals of each group

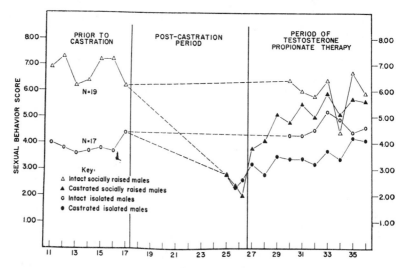

FIG. 9-1. Sexual behavior scores of socially raised and isolated male guinea pigs before castration (left), after castration (center), and during androgen replacement therapy (right). (From Valenstein and Young, 1955)

demonstrate clearly that hormonal, genetic, and experiential influences all play substantial measurable roles in the development and expression of sexual behavior in this species. A final experiment by Valenstein and Young (1955) provides a direct demonstration of the interaction between the effects of both experience and hormones. This experiment is illustrated in Figure 9-1. Two groups of male guinea pigs were weaned from their mothers at the age of 25 days. Each animal of the "social" group was then caged with five females of the same size until the age of 73 days, and

were castrated, while the rest were left intact. The animals were then kept in isolation until they were 27 weeks old, without further sexual experience, except that the castrated animals were tested starting at 25 weeks, to make sure that their sexual behavior had regressed to the level characteristic of castrated animals. It will be seen that the sexual behavior of both the isolated-reared and the social-reared animals had, by eight weeks after castration, regressed to the same minimal level. Starting at 27 weeks of age, all the castrated animals received replacement therapy consisting of daily injections of testosterone propionate, the dosage level being the same for the isolated-reared as for the social-reared animals. During the period of hormone therapy, the castrates and the noncastrated controls were given weekly tests for sexual behavior. The results of these tests are shown on the right-hand field of Figure 9-1, where it will be seen that, under the same hormone dosage, the sexual behavior of the social-reared castrates rose to a higher level than did that of the isolated-reared castrates, the level of sexual behavior eventually reached by each group approximating that maintained by the uncastrated animals which had been reared in the same manner.

Sexual Behavior in Cats

Using a somewhat different technique, Rosenblatt and Aronson (1958*a*, 1958*b*) have investigated the relationship between the effects of both sexual experience and hormones upon sexual behavior in male domestic cats. These investigators allowed different groups of cats to have different amounts of sexual experience, then castrated them and studied the decline in sexual behavior after castration as a function of the amount of sexual experience before castration.

Two groups of animals were used: a group of maximally experienced animals which were allowed many opportunities to associate with sexually receptive females, so that each animal achieved from 32 to 81 copulations; and a group of minimally experienced males which were allowed no opportunity to copulate with females, some of the males merely being tested with females to determine the age at which sexual behavior matures, but being allowed no more than a single preliminary mounting of a female. After the maximally experienced animals had

achieved the requisite amount of experience, and after an equivalent age had been reached in the minimally experienced ones, all the animals were castrated. They were then tested weekly with sexually receptive females. Rosenblatt and Aronson developed a "sex behavior score" which combined into a single quantitative measure various aspects of the frequency and latency of different parts of the mating pattern. The way in which this sex behavior score declined after castration, in the two groups of cats, is shown by the two light lines in Figure 9-2 (we may ignore the heavier lines for the moment). The upper curve (triangles) shows the change in sexual behavior score after castration, week by week, for the maximally experienced males, while the lower curve (circles) shows similar measurements for the minimally experienced males. It will be seen that sexual behavior in the experienced animals declined slowly and that 15 weeks after castration it was still at a higher level than that shown by the inexperienced animals.

Male cats castrated before puberty do not develop sex behavior (Rosenblatt and Aronson, 1958*a*) and the persistence of sex behavior in experienced animals after castration contrasts with the failure of inexperienced animals to develop sex behavior after (postpuberal) castration. This indicates that, while the presence of male hormone is essential for the development of the behavior, the sexual experience acquired under the influence of this hormone leads to changes in the animal which persist after the hormone is withdrawn, and which make possible the maintenance of sex behavior in its absence.

In a further experiment, Rosenblatt and Aronson (1958*a*) castrated a number of male cats before puberty (at 4 months of age). At the age of 11 months (comparable to the normal age of sexual maturity), these animals were tested for sexual behavior with sexually receptive females, with negative results. After 10 such tests, staged about two weeks apart, androgen replacement therapy was begun. One group of animals (maximally experienced) was permitted to have access to sexually receptive females during the period of androgen administration. Four of the six animals of this group developed normal sexual behavior, achieving between 30 and 134 copulations. The animals of the second

persist after the hormone is withdrawn as does sexual behavior occurring under the influence of endogenous hormone in intact, normal animals.

The effects of the hormone on the animal during prepuberal and early pubertal periods—and, indeed, during postpuberal periods before the actual occurrence of sexual experience—appear from these experiments not to be important as influences on the development of sexual behavior. On the other hand, regressive long-term changes following castration appear to

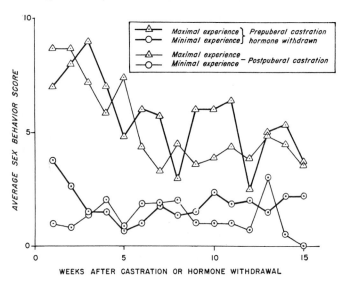

FIG. 9-2. Average sex behavior scores for 15 weeks following hormone withdrawal by castration or by cessation of androgen treatment, in male cats with and without sexual experience. (From Rosenblatt and Aronson, 1958a)

group were not permitted access to receptive females during the period of androgen therapy. Hormone treatment was then discontinued, for both groups of animals, and all animals were then subjected to weekly tests for sex behavior. The results of these tests are shown by the heavy lines in Figure 9-2. It will be seen that the occurrence of sex behavior in prepuberally castrated animals, injected with androgen after the age of normal puberty, is similar to that of intact animals, and that sexual experience acquired under the influence of this injected hormone has the same effect in organizing sexual behavior so that it can

make the expression of sexual behavior much more difficult, since long-term observations (lasting several years) after castration show that sexual behavior even in maximally experienced animals declines to a low level. When such animals are later injected with sex hormone for a period of several months, and then the hormone is withdrawn, subsequent weekly tests show that the sex behavior has risen to a level comparable to that shown just after the original castration, and that it declines at about the rate shown after the original castration by maximally experienced animals, *whether or not any additional sexual experience was allowed during the second period of hormone administration* (unpublished observations by Cooper, referred to by Rosenblatt and Aronson, 1958a). This indicates that the experience of sexual behavior, which can become organized and can develop only under the influence of male sex hormone, leads to long-persisting changes in organization, the effects of which are, in later life, interactive with the concurrent effects of sex hormones.

Parental Behavior in Ring Doves

Male and female ring doves (*Streptopelia risoria*) both share in the care of the eggs and young. The young are at first fed on "crop-milk," a substance produced by the walls of the parents' crops and regurgitated by them to the young (Craig, 1909). The dove's crop produces crop-milk under the influence of prolactin secreted by the bird's pituitary gland (Riddle, 1937). The pituitary, in turn, is stimulated to produce this hormone by stimuli arising from participation in the act of incubating the eggs (Patel, 1936). I have studied the effect of prolactin upon this parental regurgitation-feeding behavior, and the interaction between the effect of prolactin and that of previous parental experience (Lehrman, 1955).

Ring doves were injected with prolactin in sufficient quantity to cause complete development of the crop, and suppression of sexual behavior (Bates, Riddle, and Lahr, 1937). At the end of the seven-day injection period, the doves were placed singly in cages each containing a hungry young dove, 7 days of age. Equal numbers of male adults and female adults were used as experimental animals. Half of the subjects had had previous breeding experience consisting of the successful completion of two breeding cycles during which young were reared; the other half, of the same age as the experienced birds, had been kept in isolation since just before sexual maturity and had thus never had breeding experience. Control birds, both experienced and inexperienced, were tested without previous prolactin treatment.

No untreated birds, whether experienced or inexperienced, made any attempt to feed the young. Among the birds injected with prolactin, there was a striking difference between the behavior of the birds with, and those without, breeding experience. None of the inexperienced birds fed the young during a 24-hour test period. Among the experienced birds, 10 (out of 12) fed the squabs by regurgitating crop-milk to them, the average latency until the first regurgitation being about 60 minutes after the birds were introduced into the cage.

Although the inexperienced birds failed to feed the young in response to prolactin injection, their behavior was nevertheless quite different from that of inexperienced birds which had not been injected with prolactin. They showed no sexual behavior, were quieter, and exhibited various signs of tension, such as repeated swallowing, pecking at food without eating, etc. Under the prolactin treatment, the crops of the inexperienced birds developed just as much as did those of the experienced birds.

This experiment showed that, although prolactin induces various physiological changes in doves regardless of their previous experience, these changes lead to the performance of parental feeding behavior only in animals which have had previous breeding experience. A further experiment throws some light upon the mechanism of this relationship between the effects of prolactin and of the animal's earlier experience. Two groups of experienced doves were injected with prolactin, in the same manner as just described. One day before they were due to be tested with young doves, the birds were injected intradermally with a long-acting local anesthetic. Half of the birds were anesthetized by small injections distributed through the skin over the crop and into the wall of the crop. The other half of the birds were injected with the same amount of the local anesthetic distributed in small injections in the skin of the back (a control for possible systemic effects). Local anesthesia of the crop prevented the appearance of regurgitation-feeding responses, *or of parental approaches to the young*, in 8 of the 12 birds so treated; the same anesthetic injected into the back failed to inhibit parental feeding responses in 10 of the 12 birds.

Since local anesthesia of the crop prevents the appearance of parental feeding responses after prolactin injection, it seems likely that afferent inflow from the crop, engorged by the effects of prolactin, is at least a part of the basis for the ability of prolactin to induce parental regurgitation behavior.

Riddle and Burns (1931) found that regurgitation responses of ring doves, originally occurring as a response to the forcible introduction of a drug tablet into the crop, readily became conditioned (after 3–13 trials) to the sound of the experimenter opening the door of the cage. The regurgitation response is thus apparently quite easily conditioned, and this may be a part of the basis for the difference in behavior between experienced and inexperienced birds injected with prolactin. Regurgitation responses originally elicited by tactual stimulation by the young, upon which the parents are sitting, may become conditioned to visual and auditory stimuli from the young; the parents may thus *approach* the young when their crops are engorged only after such conditioning, while before conditioning they respond only to tactual contact with the young which they are brooding. This view is supported by observations of experienced and inexperienced birds feeding newly hatched young for the first time.

Mrs. R. Wortis and I, in an unpublished experiment, have obtained somewhat similar data in relation to the elicitation of incubation behavior by progesterone. This hormone, injected into experienced ring doves, reliably induces the birds to sit on eggs (Riddle and Lahr, 1944; Lehrman, 1958a). We have subjected 10 pairs of birds with previous breeding experience and 10 pairs, of the same age, without breeding experience to a seven-day course of progesterone injections. At the end of the hormone treatment, the birds were introduced, in pairs, into standard breeding cages supplied with a nest and eggs. Doves that have not been injected with progesterone, placed in a similar situation, do not sit on the eggs until after several days,

TABLE 9-1   LATENCY OF INCUBATION RESPONSE OF PAIRS OF PROGESTERONE-INJECTED RING DOVES WITH AND WITHOUT PREVIOUS INCUBATION EXPERIENCE*

	EXPERIENCED		INEXPERIENCED	
	MEDIAN	RANGE	MEDIAN	RANGE
Time to first standing on nest	<1 min.	<1 min.–3 min.	60.5 min.	<1 min.–>2 hr.
Time until incubation is established	21.5 min.	6 min.–3 hr.	24.5 hr.	82 min.–no response

* Measured from time birds are introduced into a cage containing nest and eggs.

during which they first build a nest (Lehrman, 1958*b*, 1959).

A striking difference was observed in the response of the experienced and of the inexperienced birds to the progesterone injection. These differences are summarized in Table 9-1. The experienced birds obviously approach and sit on the eggs more quickly and more often than do inexperienced birds subjected to the same hormone injection.

DISCUSSION

Hormone-Experience Interactions

The groups of experiments described above do not by any means exhaust the possible types of interactions between hormonal and experiential effects. A number of other types could be cited. So-called "social-dominance" hierarchies, which depend upon relations among animals which recognize each other individually (Guhl and Ortman, 1953) can often be altered by the administration of sex hormones. For example, exogenous androgens have been reported to cause an increase in the "social status" of ring doves (Bennett, 1940), domestic hens (Allee, Collias, and Lutherman, 1939; Allee and Foreman, 1955), and chimpanzees (Clark and Birch, 1945), while estrogenic hormones tend to lower the standing of the animal, both in domestic hens (Allee and Collias, 1940) and male chimpanzees (Clark and Birch, 1946). Experience of stress stimulation in infancy affects the development of the pituitary-adrenal relationship in rats, which in turn influences the animals' reactions when adult (Levine, 1960; Levine, Alpert, and Lewis, 1957). Other examples could be given.

It is obviously not possible to account for all of the effects described here by assuming a single type of interaction between the effects of experience and of hormones. Experiential influences upon behavioral responses to sex hormones in guinea pigs, as analyzed by Young and his co-workers, depend at least partly upon the animals' experience before they are sexually mature, while the experiential effects demonstrated in cats by Rosenblatt and Aronson clearly depend upon postpuberal sexual experience. In most of the work we have done on ring doves so far, it is apparent that animals with similar histories before sexual maturity may respond to exogenous hormones quite differently, depending upon differences in their reproductive experience when mature. The data on the effects of sex hormones upon social rank demonstrate still another possibility: here a continuing relationship, dependent upon the animals' experience with each other, is altered by the intrusion of the effects of sex hormones into the existing situation.

The implication of these studies is therefore not that any particular kind of relationship consistently or necessarily obtains between the effects of hormones and those of experience, but rather that a full understanding of the organization and causation of behavior patterns, even in those cases in which we have a good deal of knowledge of the physiological mechanisms, can only be achieved by analysis of the ontogeny. In all the cases considered, and in many others, analysis of the ontogenetic processes contributing to the development of the behavior enormously expands and deepens our understanding of the nature of the behavioral organization, and this is true regardless of what conclusions are eventually reached, in any particular case, about the extent to which experiential factors do or do not play a role in the ontogeny.

Species Differences and Phylogenetic Problems

The differences between guinea pigs and cats, just cited, imply that the relationships between experiential and hormonal determinants of behavior vary from species to species, and there is abundant evidence that such interspecific variability is no less striking with respect to the phenomena which we are discussing than with respect to any other biological processes. For example, socially reared rats and individually reared rats do not differ in their sexual behavior, in sharp contrast to the situation in guinea pigs (Beach, 1942, 1958).

Beach (1947) suggested, for mammals, that there is a regular phylogenetic progression in the physiological mechanisms underlying sexual behavior, with lower mammals being more dependent on the immediate presence of the relevant hormones, and relatively independent of influences from the cerebral cortex, while in higher mammals the increasing development of the cerebral cortex is associated with increasing modifiability of sexual behavior and increasing independence of such behavior from immediate control by gonadal hormones.

Beach's summary of the data available in 1947 demonstrated the existence of such trends among mammals. More recent discussions, however, suggest certain modifications of the details of these generalizations. For example, Rosenblatt and Aronson (1958a) point out that *prepuberally* castrated rats, hamsters, and guinea pigs may actually show somewhat more sexual behavior when tested as adults than do similarly treated cats or chimpanzees. In contrast, when experienced animals are castrated postpuberally, sexual behavior persists much longer in cats and primates than in the rodents. Formulations of the relative "importance" of hormonal and of cerebral influences must therefore depend, to some extent, upon the extent to which experience has contributed to the development of the behavior pattern in question.

Aronson (1959) points out that data from fishes, amphibians, reptiles, and birds, while they support the general picture of vertebrate sexual behavior as being related to gonadal activity, do not suggest that such behavior is more dependent upon gonadal hormones in these forms (which lack a cerebral cortex) than in mammals. Further, Aronson points out that different aspects of the mechanisms underlying sexual behavior, such as distance perception of the female, tactual sensitivity to the female, erection capacity, etc., may be differentially affected by hormones (Soulairac, 1952), and that individuals and species may differ from each other with respect to (1) the relative dominance of the various components in the sex behavior pattern and (2) the degree to which the various aspects of the pattern are affected by castration and by gonad hormone replacement therapy. It follows from this that, although phylogenetic trends from lower to higher vertebrates are by no means obvious when we use generalized notions of "sex drive" or "sexual arousal" for our definition of sexual activity, detailed analysis of the part-processes involved in sexual behavior, and of their integration, will provide much better insight into evolutionary trends than we now have.

Some Remarks on Terminology

I have avoided the use of the term "learning," preferring the less restrictive expression "experiential influences." As Schneirla (1956, 1957) has pointed out, the concept of "experience" may be taken to connote "*all* stimulative influences upon the organism through its life history." Such stimulative influences begin to work before birth and include a wide variety of *kinds* of effect, from pervasive developmental influences of the chemical environment to the most specific kinds of learning as we know it in adult animals (Hebb, 1953). The term "learning" inevitably brings to mind the principal parameters of the type of experiment ordinarily associated with "learning theory": performance improves as a regular function of practice on successive trials; performance tends to deteriorate as a regular function of periods of nonpractice; there are regular relationships between the rate of improvement of performance and such variables as the distribution of practice, various aspects of "reward," etc. "Learning" in this restricted sense undoubtedly does occur in connection with, and participates in the development of, various types of "species-specific" (Beach, 1960) or "instinctive" (Schneirla, 1956) behavior. However, it must be remembered that the concepts of "learning" which are derived from traditional learning experiments may be misleading when applied to the kinds of behavior which we are discussing here, for several reasons.

- "LEARNING" AND "EXPERIENTIAL INFLUENCES"

First, learning theory is almost entirely derived from experiments on adult mammals. Many of the experiential effects relevant to the development of the types of behavior considered in this paper occur at early developmental stages and have effects which are much more widely generalized among many aspects of the animal's behavior than is the case with the learning of specific responses, or specific associations, by adult animals. Carmichael (1936) has suggested that the effects of stimulation in very early developmental stages may be in part to alter growth patterns, including

those of the nervous system, so that the effects of "maturation" in such cases may not be conceptually distinguishable from those of "learning" (Kuo, 1932). Hebb (1949) has similarly pointed out that distinctions between the effects of learning and of growth processes do not have the same significance in adult stages as in the more labile earlier stages of development. Indeed, different groups of laboratory rats reared under different living conditions may, when adult, perform quite differently in "standard" learning situations (Christie, 1951, 1952).

In general, while the concept of "experiential influences" certainly includes those ordinarily associated with the term "learning," it also includes so many other kinds of processes that it seems preferable, when trying to define the basic problems of the ontogenetic relationships out of which behavioral organizations emerge, to use the more inclusive term, reserving finer distinctions, when useful, for those specific cases in which the actual mechanisms have been analyzed.

- MOTIVATION AND "EXPERIENCE"

There is a second reason for caution in the application of the paradigms of learning theory to the analysis of the ontogeny of species-specific behavior: such behavior often develops in association with physiological conditions which form the basis for strong motive states, and which limit the range of stimulation to which the animal can be effectively sensitive. For example, Aronson (1959) suggests that sex hormones cause cutaneous changes, changes in olfactory thresholds, and changes in the composition and strength of various muscles, and that these effects must be regarded as possibly relevant to the ways in which the hormones change sexual behavior. Similarly, the changes in bodily tensions associated with parturition appear to influence the behavior of the parturient mammalian mother toward her young (Schneirla, 1956), and the tension of milk in the mammary glands later plays a role in her nursing behavior (Cross, 1952). These effects imply changes in sensitivity, no doubt compounded by central effects of the hormones, which may add additional effects on sensitivity to various types of stimulation (Morgan, 1959). This suggests that in the study of the ontogeny of species-specific behavior, the analysis of the participation of experiential influences requires much closer attention to the effects of physiological and motivational conditions upon the effectiveness of "experience" than has traditionally been characteristic of learning experiments.

Locus of Experiential Effects in Behavior Sequences

The traditional test of the presence of "learning"—that performance should improve on successive repetitions of the behavior—is not always helpful in analyzing the participation of experiential influences in the development of hormone-induced instinctive behavior patterns.[*] For example, although experienced ring doves feed their young somewhat sooner after the eggs hatch than do inexperienced ones of the same age (Lehrman, 1955), these differences are quantitatively not large; and the fact remains that ring doves, like most other animals, can carry out the normal behavior patterns associated with the reproductive cycle on the first occasion when such a cycle occurs.

[*] Although various investigators have reported that maternal behavior is more efficient in multiparous than in primiparous mammals (Hediger, 1950; Ross *et al.*, 1956; Seitz, 1958), it is by no means clear whether this is the result of learning or of growth changes, since controls for age are usually absent in these reports (Dieterlen, 1959; Lehrman, 1960).

How can we reconcile the fact that animals can perform various behavior patterns adequately during the first reproductive cycle with the fact that, in many cases, experienced and inexperienced animals differ so strikingly in their behavioral response to injected hormones?

At least a partial solution to this problem may be found in the fact that experience during the early stages of a reproductive cycle may have important effects, not on behavior during the same stages of the next cycle, but upon behavior during subsequent stages of the same cycle. The attachment of the ring dove to its nest, which develops during the time when the nest is being built, may serve both to localize the laying of eggs in the nest and to ensure that, after the eggs are laid, the birds are bound to come into contact with the eggs in such a way as to lead to the stimulation of incubation behavior. Similarly, the fact that the birds are sitting on the eggs when they hatch makes possible the development of relationships between parents and young, even though the birds show no tendency to approach the young until after such relationships have been established. In this case, the experience that the birds have during early parts of the cycle has the effect of moulding a pattern of behavior toward the nest (and eggs) which, when it persists into the changed physiological condition of the next stage, contributes to the probability that the behavior appropriate to this next stage will occur. This is clearly an effect of experience, although it does not necessarily result in the behavior being more efficient during the second reproductive cycle than during the first, since the experience with the nest during the first cycle may help ensure adequate reactions to the eggs during that same cycle. However, we may take birds who are *not* now tied to the nest (e.g., reproductively inactive birds), and inject them with hormones which duplicate in them the physiological conditions characteristic of one of the later stages, such as the incubation period. We can then see a striking difference between the behavior of birds with previous breeding experience and that of birds without such experience. The latter, even though they are now in such a physiological condition that they would sit on eggs if they were (because of their experience during the immediately preceding stage) spending most of their time on the nests, do not, in a high percentage of the cases, approach the eggs. On the other hand, the birds with previous experience, subjected to the same hormone treatment, are induced to approach the eggs. What the previous breeding experience appears to have done is to make it possible for the birds to react in ways which they have previously found satisfying within the same physiological (i.e., motivational) condition. Because birds which *normally*, in the course of an ordinary breeding cycle, come into such physiological condition are at the time closely attached to the nest, they will inevitably come into contact with the eggs, which induce incubation behavior enabling them to learn to approach the eggs later on the basis of distance perception of them.

Thus we are able to account for the apparently contradictory facts that the birds sit adequately on their eggs during their *first* breeding experience, and that they will not sit on eggs offered by the experimenter, after hormone injection, unless they have had previous breeding experience.

Similarly, the behavior of the parturient mother cat toward her young, which consists of alternate vigorous licking (an extension of self-licking) and quiet lying in proximity to the neonates, facilitates the onset of suckling. This interaction between mother and young, based in part upon the physiological condition of the mother at parturition, has as a consequence the development of the somewhat different relationships which can be seen later.

This is clearly seen in sheep and goats, in which removal of the neonate from the mother for a short period after birth, or interference with the parturient mother's licking of the neonate, may seriously disturb the development of mother-young relationships (Blauvelt, 1955; Collias, 1956). The effects of short periods of separation (one-half to one hour) at birth may still be apparent two or three months later, in the form of weakened bonds between mother and young (Hersher, Moore, and Richmond, 1958).

The experience of the mother early during the parturient and postparturient periods, based in part upon her hormone-induced physiological condition, clearly contributes to the behavior which develops later, although this does not at all necessarily mean that the normal behavior of a primiparous mother and that of a multiparous one will be different (Schneirla, 1956). A further consideration is the fact that experience which takes place later in the reproductive cycle cannot be expected to be transferred intact into the earlier stages of the next reproductive cycles when the animal is in a quite different physiological condition.

CONCLUSION

It will be seen from these remarks, as well as from all of the descriptions of hormone-experience interactions described earlier in this paper, that analysis of the contribution of experiential influences to the development of hormone-induced behavior requires a formulation much broader and more subtle than would be suggested by simple questions implying (1) that "learning" is demonstrated only when the behavior improves on successive repetitions of the reproductive cycle or (2) that "learning" requires previous opportunity to observe another animal performing the activity.

REFERENCES

ALLEE, W. C., and COLLIAS, N. 1940. The influence of estradiol on the social organization of flocks of hens. *Endocrinology. 27:* 87–94.

ALLEE, W. C., COLLIAS, N. E., and LUTHERMAN, C. Z. 1939. Modification of the social order in flocks of hens by the injection of testosterone propionate. *Physiol. Zoöl. 12:* 412–440.

ALLEE, W. C., and FOREMAN, D. 1955. Effects of an androgen on dominance and subordinance in six common breeds of *Gallus gallus. Physiol. Zoöl. 28:* 89–115.

ARONSON, L. R. 1959. Hormones and reproductive behavior: some phylogenetic considerations, in *Comparative Endocrinology,* ed. by GORBMAN, A. New York, Wiley, pp. 98–120.

BATES, R. W., RIDDLE, O., and LAHR, E. L. 1937. The mechanism of the anti-gonad action of prolactin. *Am. J. Physiol. 119:* 610–614.

BEACH, F. A. 1942. Comparison of copulatory behavior in male rats raised in isolation, cohabitation and segregation. *J. Genet. Psychol. 60:* 121–136.

BEACH, F. A. 1947. A review of physiological and psychological studies of sexual behavior in mammals. *Physiol. Rev. 27:* 240–307.

BEACH, F. A. 1958. Normal sexual behavior in male rats isolated at fourteen days of age. *J. Comp. & Physiol. Psychol. 51:* 37–38.

BEACH, F. A. 1960. Experimental investigations of species-specific behavior. *Am. Psychologist. 15:* 1–18.

BENNETT, M. A. 1940. The social hierarchy in ring doves. II. The effect of treatment with testosterone propionate. *Ecology. 21:* 148–165.

BLAUVELT, H. 1955. "Dynamics of the Mother-Newborn Relationship in Goats," in *Group Processes, Tr. First Conference,* ed. by SCHAFFNER, B. New York, Josiah Macy, Jr., Foundation, pp. 221–258.

CARMICHAEL, L. 1936. A re-evaluation of the concepts of maturation and learning as applied to the early development of behavior. *Psychol. Rev. 43:* 450–470.

CHRISTIE, R. 1951. Experimental naïveté and experiential naïveté. *Psychol. Bull. 48:* 327–339.

CHRISTIE, R. 1952. The effect of some early experiences in the latent learning of rats. *J. Exper. Psychol. 43:* 381–388.

CLARK, G., and BIRCH, H. G. 1945. Hormonal modifications of social behavior. I. The effect of sex-hormone administration on the social status of a male-castrate chimpanzee. *Psychosom. Med. 7:* 321–329.

CLARK, G., and BIRCH, H. G. 1946. Hormonal modifications of social behavior. III. The effects of stilbestrol therapy on social dominance in the female-castrate chimpanzee. *Bull. Canad. Psychol. A. 6:* 1–3.

COLLIAS, N. E. 1956. The analysis of socialization in sheep and goats. *Ecology. 37:* 228–239.

CRAIG, W. 1909. The expression of emotion in the pigeons. I. The blond ring dove. *J. Comp. Neurol. 19:* 29–80.

CROSS, B. A. 1952. Nursing behaviour and the milk ejection reflex in rabbits. *J. Endocrinol. 8:* xiii–xiv.

DIETERLEN, F. 1959. Das Verhalten des syrischen Goldhamsters (*Mesocricetus auratus* Waterhouse); Untersuchungen zur Frage seiner Entwicklung und seiner angeborenen Anteile durch geruchsisolierte Aufzuchten. *Ztschr. f. Tierpsychol. 16:* 47–103.

GOY, R. W., and YOUNG, W. C. 1957. Somatic basis of sexual behavior patterns in guinea pigs. *Psychosom. Med. 19:* 144–151.

GRUNT, J. A., and YOUNG, W. C. 1952. Differential reactivity of individuals and the response of the male guinea pig to testosterone propionate. *Endocrinology. 51:* 237–248.

GRUNT, J. A., and YOUNG, W. C. 1953. Consistency of sexual behavior patterns in individual male guinea pigs following castration and androgen therapy. *J. Comp. & Physiol. Psychol. 46:* 138–144.

GUHL, A. M., and ORTMAN, L. L. 1953. Visual patterns in the recognition of individuals among chickens. *Condor. 55:* 287–298.

HEBB, D. O. 1949. *The Organization of Behavior: A Neuropsychological Theory.* New York, Wiley.

HEBB, D. O. 1953. Heredity and environment in mammalian behavior. *Brit. J. Animal Behav.* 1: 43–47.

HEDIGER, H. 1950. *Wild Animals in Captivity.* London, Butterworth.

HERSHER, L., MOORE, A. U., and RICHMOND, J. B. 1958. Effect of postpartum separation of mother and kid on maternal care in the domestic goat. *Science.* 128: 1342–1343.

KUO, Z. Y. 1932. Ontogeny of embryonic behavior in Aves. III. The structure and environmental factors in embryonic behavior. *J. Comp. Psychol.* 13: 245–272.

LEHRMAN, D. S. 1955. The physiological basis of parental feeding behavior in the ring dove (*Streptopelia risoria*). *Behaviour.* 7: 241–286.

LEHRMAN, D. S. 1956. "On the Organization of Maternal Behavior and the Problem of Instinct," in *L'Instinct dans le Comportement des Animaux et de l'Homme,* ed. by GRASSÉ, P.-P. Paris, Masson & Cie, pp. 475–520.

LEHRMAN, D. S. 1958a. Effect of female sex hormones on incubation behavior in the ring dove (*Streptopelia risoria*). *J. Comp. & Physiol. Psychol.* 51: 142–145.

LEHRMAN, D. S. 1958b. Induction of broodiness by participation in courtship and nestbuilding in the ring dove (*Streptopelia risoria*). *J. Comp. & Physiol. Psychol.* 51: 32–36.

LEHRMAN, D. S. 1959. On the origin of the reproductive behavior cycle in doves. *Tr. New York Acad. Sc.* 21: 682–688.

LEHRMAN, D. S. 1961. "Hormonal Regulation of Parental Behavior in Birds and Infrahuman Mammals," in *Allen's Sex and Internal Secretions,* ed. by YOUNG, W. C., Baltimore, Williams & Wilkins.

LEVINE, S. 1960. Stimulation in infancy. *Scient. Am.* 201(5): 81–86.

LEVINE, S., ALPERT, M., and LEWIS, G. W. 1957. Infantile experience and the maturation of the pituitary-adrenal axis. *Science.* 127: 1347.

MORGAN, C. T. 1959. "Physiological Theory of Drive," in *Psychology: A Study of a Science,* ed. by KOCH, S. New York, McGraw-Hill, Vol. 1, pp. 644–671.

PATEL, M. D. 1936. The physiology of the formation of the pigeon's milk. *Physiol. Zoöl.* 9: 129–152.

RIDDLE, O. 1937. Physiological responses to prolactin. *Symposia Quant. Biol.* (Cold Spring Harbor, N.Y.). 5: 218–228.

RIDDLE, O., and BURNS, F. H. 1931. A conditioned emetic reflex in the pigeon. *Proc. Soc. Exper. Biol.,* New York. 28: 979–981.

RIDDLE, O., and LAHR, E. L. 1944. On broodiness of ring doves following implants of certain steroid hormones. *Endocrinology.* 35: 255–260.

RISS, W., VALENSTEIN, E. S., SINKS, J., and YOUNG, W. C. 1955. Development of sexual behavior in male guinea pigs from genetically different stocks under controlled conditions of androgen treatment and aging. *Endocrinology.* 57: 139–146.

ROSENBLATT, J. S., and ARONSON, L. R. 1958a. The decline of sexual behavior in male cats after castration with special reference to the role of prior sexual experience. *Behaviour.* 12: 285–338.

ROSENBLATT, J. S., and ARONSON, L. R. 1958b. The influence of experience on the behavioural effects of androgen in prepuberally castrated male cats. *Animal Behav.* 6: 171–182.

ROSS, S., DENENBERG, V. H., SAWIN, P. B., and MEYER, P. 1956. Changes in nestbuilding behaviour in multiparous rabbits. *Brit. J. Animal Behav.* 4: 69–74.

SCHNEIRLA, T. C. 1956. "Interrelationships of the Innate and the Acquired in Instinctive Behavior," in *L'Instinct dans le Comportement des Animaux et de l'Homme,* ed. by GRASSÉ, P.-P. Paris, Masson & Cie, pp. 387–452.

SCHNEIRLA, T. C. 1957. "The Concept of Development in Comparative Psychology," in *The Concept of Development,* ed. by HARRIS, D. B., Minneapolis, University of Minnesota Press, pp. 78–108.

SEITZ, P. F. D. 1958. The maternal instinct in animal subjects: I. *Psychosom. Med.* 20: 215–226.

SOULAIRAC, A. 1952. Analyse expérimentale des actions hormonales sur le comportement sexuel du rat mâle normal. *J. Physiol. Path. Gén.* 44: 327–330.

VALENSTEIN, E. S., and GOY, R. W. 1957. Further studies of the organization and display of sexual behavior in male guinea pigs. *J. Comp. & Physiol. Psychol.* 50: 115–119.

VALENSTEIN, E. S., RISS, W., and YOUNG, W. C. 1954. Sex drive in genetically heterogeneous and highly inbred strains of male guinea pigs. *J. Comp. & Physiol. Psychol.* 47: 162–165.

VALENSTEIN, E. S., RISS, W., and YOUNG, W. C. 1955. Experiential and genetic factors in the organization of sexual behavior in male guinea pigs. *J. Comp. & Physiol. Psychol.* 48: 397–403.

VALENSTEIN, E. S., and YOUNG, W. C. 1955. An experiential factor influencing the effectiveness of testosterone propionate in eliciting sexual behavior in male guinea pigs. *Endocrinology.* 56: 173–177.

YOUNG, W. C. 1957. "Genetic and Psychological Determinants of Sexual Behavior Patterns," in *Hormones, Brain Function, and Behavior,* ed. by HOAGLAND, H. New York, Academic Press, pp. 75–98.

YOUNG, W. C., and GRUNT, J. A. 1951. The pattern and measurement of sexual behavior in the male guinea pig. *J. Comp. & Physiol. Psychol.* 44: 492–500.

10

DEVELOPMENT OF AFFECTION IN PRIMATES

Harry F. Harlow

There are no broad categories of human behavior which have been less thoroughly explored than those relating to affection. This is no accident, for it is intrinsically difficult to analyze the basic variables underlying each and all of the affectional patterns, if human subjects are used. Affectional patterns are both subtle and complex; they evolve relatively late in the individual's life history; and their fundamental nature is hidden or obscured by superimposed cultural patterns.

SEQUENCE OF AFFECTIONAL PATTERNS

However, no one will question that a sequence of affectional patterns does unfold within all cultures, in spite of any and all variations that arise and persist. The initial affectional pattern is that of the neonatal and infantile attachment to the mother, which is in turn followed by the affectional pattern of infant for infant and child for child. These patterns persist, develop, and differentiate; and finally after trials and tribulations, latency periods, *Sturm und Drang*, and adolescence, culminate in the heterosexual affectional pattern.

These researchers were supported by Grants Nos. M772 and RG4587 from the National Institutes of Health, a grant from the Ford Foundation, and by funds from the Graduate School of the University of Wisconsin.

The inevitable consequence of the heterosexual affectional pattern is known as the population explosion. Each small burst arouses the maternal affectional pattern which, interacting with the infant-to-mother pattern, reinstates the cycle, affectional, not vicious.

STUDY OF AFFECTIONAL PATTERNS

Guided by either faith or folly, we are convinced that the fundamental variables underlying each and all of these basic affectional patterns may be determined and quantified through experimentation, using rhesus monkeys as subjects. We are under no illusion that we will ever learn all there is to know about human affectional patterns by studying and observing monkeys, but we are convinced that such a program will discover a great many facts that are true and uncover a great many theories that are false. The little that we have learned to date leaves us unimpressed with the present theories concerning human affectional patterns. Within the complex fields of love and affection it would appear that a million years of acculturation have led man to love too much and learn too little.

Our initial efforts to unravel the affectional variables have been largely limited to the analysis of the behavioral patterns demonstrated by infants for mothers, and even here we have made only a bare beginning—but in the field of affection that is the way beginnings are made. We hazard the guess that there are not only multiple separable affectional patterns, infant to mother, infant to infant, male to female, and mother to infant, but that all of these pass through progressive and relatively separate stages. Each of the affectional response patterns is constantly changing and can only be described and understood in terms of the life cycle. Variables of significant importance at an early developmental stage may later become unimportant, and conversely, variables of little or no importance in the immature animal may attain great subsequent importance.

DEVELOPMENTAL STAGES OF THE INFANT-MOTHER AFFECTIONAL SYSTEM

As a working hypothesis, we think of the normal infant-mother affectional patterns as progressing through four semiseparable stages—reflex, attachment, security, and independence.

Reflex Stage

The reflex stage is characterized by those mechanisms which act to unite the infant to the mother physically, specifically the contactual and nursing systems. Contact responding is so automatic that it meets the definition of a thygmotropism or a postural reflex. It is as predictable as the grasp reflex and more predictable than the Babinski or Moro. If the newborn monkey is placed on its back, it rights itself and assumes normal prone posture, even though locomotion is limited or absent. However, if the newborn monkey is put on its back and a cloth pad is placed on its belly, it will clasp the cloth and make no attempt to right itself. Actually, if the neonatal monkey

is put on its back and happens to clasp two limbs together during the act of turning, the righting reflex will be inhibited, and the monkey will not assume prone posture.

Nursing reflexes also may be demonstrated during the first day of life. If the human attendant touches his finger to the upper lip of the newborn rhesus monkey, this contact will elicit reflex head turning to the contacted side and subsequent oral clasping. A more dramatic reflex can be obtained by touching a cloth pad to the face of a neonatal monkey and then gradually withdrawing the pad. The monkey, possessing only minimal locomotor capability and heretofore apparently inert, often follows the pad with surprising speed and facility; indeed, it may scurry across a 3-foot table and even be drawn over the edge. This response is possibly homologous to the human rooting reflex, an involuntary behavior pattern designed to insure contact with the breast and subsequent reflex contact with the nipple.

The contact and nursing reflexes are the basic variables operating to insure intimate bodily responsiveness between the infant and its mother. Such attachments are doubtless essential for the survival of a helpless baby monkey raised in a feral environment, but it is obvious that they must be replaced or superseded if an infant is ever to come into full monkeyhood or childhood. If this were not true, the mother would shortly come to resemble the central figure of an extended Laocoön group. On the basis of observation rather than experimentation, we suggest that the automatic contactual and nursing reflexes drop out at a fairly early age. If these reflexes operate through central mechanisms similar to the Babinski, it is entirely possible that the reflex phase of infant-mother affection could be prolonged or indefinitely extended by appropriate cortical lesions.

Attachment Stage

The specific affectional reflexes are gradually replaced by the more complex and variable voluntary responses which characterize and define the attachment phase of affectional development. Before we describe these reponses and the test situations in which they are elicited, it is necessary to discuss the appearance and nature of two sets of nonaffectional responses.

• NONAFFECTIONAL RESPONSES

Fear responsiveness. If the neonatal monkey is removed from his mother or his nest, he whimpers and cries in such a manner as to suggest distress but gives no indication of specific fears of specific objects. Indeed, the neonatal monkey, as soon as he can locomote, will exhibit positive exploratory responses to most external stimuli, including mechanical "monsters" that leave an older animal in a state of abject terror. Actually, there is some indication that the more potentially terrifying the monster is, the stronger are the early exploratory and investigatory responses. Although it is hard to specify exact dates, it is a matter of only a short time before many external objects, particularly large, mobile, illuminated objects evoke strong adversive responses. The maturation and development of fear responses occur during the attachment phase of affectional development, and fearful stimuli are one of the primary variables we use for the measurement of infant-mother attachments. These fear responses constitute a third response system that tends to bind the infant to the mother. One of the most interesting observations concerning fear is that the selfsame stimuli which elicit approach at one maturational stage elicit avoidance at a subsequent stage.

Curiosity-manipulatory responses. Transi-
tion from a reflex affectional stage to an attachment phase is concurrent with the development of a second set of nonaffectional responses, the curiosity-manipulatory responses which we will describe in more detail in a later section. The curiosity-manipulatory responses have a dual role in relation to infant-mother interaction. Curiosity about external stimuli becomes a powerful separating mechanism, whereas curiosity about and manipulation of the mother's body serves apparently as an infant-mother binding device.

• AFFECTIONAL RESPONSES

Returning to the affectional responses characterizing the attachment phase, we find that the previous tight reflex or tropistic clinging response is usually released in a short period of time and that the infant subsequently moves about on the mother's body and manipulates it.

Affectional attachment is characterized by signs of comfort and relaxation in the mother's presence and by disturbance in her absence. Our experiments demonstrate that affectional attachments cannot be formed to a wire surrogate and are invariably formed to a cloth mother. This statement is supported by the results of the open-field test conducted in a room $6 \times 6 \times 6$ feet in which was placed a number of objects, including a small artificial tree, a crumpled piece of paper, a folded gauze diaper, a wooden block, and a doorknob. In this situation, monkeys raised from birth onward on a single nursing wire mother seldom made any attempt to attach themselves to her and obtained no emotional comfort from her presence. Sometimes they ran wildly about the room, bumping into objects but playing with none; or they ran to some wall or corner of the room, clasped their heads and bodies, and rocked convulsively back and forth. Such activities closely resemble the autistic behavior seen frequently among neglected children in and out of institutions (Fig. 10-1).

Contrariwise, monkey infants raised on any cloth mother, nursing or nonnursing, rushed violently to her in the open-field tests, climbed upon her, rubbed against her, and clung tightly to her. Then, after they rubbed in enough "affectional attachment," their fears seemed to vanish and they relaxed (Fig. 10-2). However, in the absence of the mother, these same cloth-raised babies were extremely disturbed. They frequently rushed across the room, threw themselves on their faces, clutched their

FIG. 10-1. Infant monkey showing disturbed behavior in open-field situation.

heads and bodies, and screamed in distress. Disturbance indices, measured by frequency of crying, rocking, and jerking, were doubled or tripled; but these quantitative measures give an incomplete picture of the degree and nature of the infant's disturbance.

Although we speak of stages, we think of these not as being sharp and discrete, ushered in and out by precise critical periods, but rather as intervals characterized by some striking event or events. Automatic, involuntary responses characterize the reflex stage; the importance of the mother's or surrogate's presence to the

infant's happiness characterizes the attachment stage. The concept of stages is not meant to imply that single variables are not operating during successive stages; nor is it meant to imply that the importance of particular variables is never altered within a single stage.

Responsiveness to contact and nursing reflexes characterizes the earliest reflex

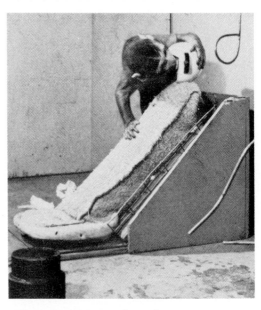

FIG. 10-2. Infant monkey playing on surrogate mother in open-field situation.

neonatal behavior, but these variables also operate in the subsequent attachment phase, although in different form. Coexistence in no way implies equal importance at any or all developmental stages of the infant-mother affectional system.

To test the absolute and relative importance of contactual and nursing variables during the attachment stage, the author placed eight newborn rhesus monkeys in individual cages, each with equal access to a welded-wire mother surrogate and a cloth mother surrogate with a terry cloth robe over its welded-wire frame. Four of the infants received their milk from the wire mother and four from the cloth mother, the milk being furnished in either case by a nursing bottle with its nipple protruding through the body wall. The test situation is illustrated in Figure 10-3, and the time spent on the two surrogates is

FIG. 10-3. Cloth and wire mother surrogates.

presented in Figure 10-4. It is apparent that the infant monkeys spent far more time on the cloth mother than the wire mother regardless of nursing condition, and that the infants securing nourishment from the wire mother showed no tendency to

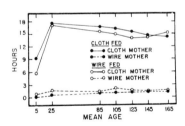

FIG. 10-4. Time on cloth and wire surrogate mothers.

spend increasing amounts of time on her body. These data fail to demonstrate that nursing is a variable of any importance in the formation and maintenance of infant-mother bonds and present strong evidence that affection is not a response dependent on learned or derived drives associated with the reduction of hunger or thirst.

In a more definitive study, however, four infant monkeys were tested under the same conditions except for the fact that both surrogates were cloth mothers, differing only in the fact that one was covered with brown and the other with green terry cloth. Color and nursing conditions were arranged in a balanced experimental design, and the data are given in Figure 10-5. The results are notable in that there rapidly developed a significant preference for the nursing cloth mother, but this preference decreased with time and became nonexistent after 110 days of age. This is a dramatic illustration

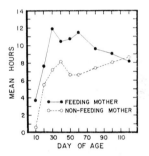

FIG. 10-5. Time on differentially colored surrogate mothers.

of the fact that a variable may be of importance at one time in the development of an affectional system and of no importance subsequently. Certainly nursing and activities associated with the breast are not variables underlying the persistent, relatively inextinguishable affectional bonds of the infant for the mother.

There are apparently other variables which are of importance during early development and of little subsequent importance. One of these is rocking motion which was measured by comparing the preference of rhesus infants for rocking as opposed to nonrocking cloth surrogates, and for rocking as contrasted to stationary planes. The planes were slightly inclined flat surfaces with the same terry cloth covering used on the cloth mothers. As can be seen in Figures 10-6 and 10-7, a preference developed by 40 days of age for the rocking mother vs. the stationary mother and for the rocking plane vs. the stationary plane. This preference increased to a peak and then disappeared by 180 days. Rocking motion may be physiologically beneficial to the relatively immobile infant but of no importance to the older, more active animal. It

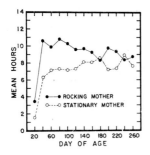

FIG. 10-6. Time on rocking and stationary surrogate mothers.

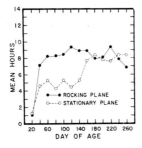

FIG. 10-7. Time on rocking and stationary planes.

may provide pleasure to the young infant and none to the more mature animal, probably because the amount of activity normal for the older infant affords adequate proprioceptive stimulation.

The inclined-plane environment provided the infant monkey with completely adequate contact but denied it any capability of intimate clinging, thus making possible an analysis of the importance of clinging as contrasted to contact. A group of

four infants was raised with inclined planes in the cubicles adjoining the living cage, and another group was raised with cloth surrogates in the cubicles. Both groups were subsequently tested in the open-field test, first in the presence of an inclined plane and later with a cloth surrogate present. As is shown in Figure 10-8, the groups raised on planes actually preferred the surrogates, even though their over-all responsiveness to both planes and surrogates was low. The behavior of the group raised on cloth surrogates was more complex. Their over-all responsiveness to both surrogates and planes was high for

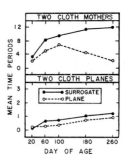

FIG. 10-8. Responsiveness to cloth planes and cloth surrogate mothers.

approximately 100 days and then continued very high for the cloth surrogates while dropping for the planes. These data demonstrate clearly that clinging as well as contact is a variable of importance, whether it acts independently or as a factor augmenting and supporting contact. Also, these data suggest, even though they do not prove, that clinging is important for the baby monkey.

We believe that visual responsiveness, particularly to the face, is an important affectional variable, but it is fairly late in maturing and difficult to explore experimentally. Interest in and manipulation of the surrogate's face became progressively frequent from 45 days onward, and since the mother was defenseless, many faces were chewed apart and many eyes plucked out like the proverbial raisins in the face of a gingerbread man. One of our infants was raised on a cloth mother whose face was a smooth round ball. At 90 days of age he was placed on two cloth mothers with ornamental faces, and he quickly developed the habit of rotating their faces 180 degrees so that he saw only the smooth round portion. Subsequently, he learned to remove both heads from the bodies, roll them into the living cage, and ignore them.

We raised one monkey from birth onward in a cage from which he could constantly observe a cloth mother but never contact her. No indication of affectional responsiveness was obtained when open-field tests were made at 60 days of age, but the data from this single exploratory experiment was in no way definitive. The assumption that vision is a late-maturing affectional variable, independent of its function as a conditioned affectional stimulus, is reasonable since the human infant shows strong visual interest in the human face beginning at 2.5 to 3 months of age and, in turn, commences social smiling, a response outside the baby monkey's repertoire.

Contact, nursing, and fear are the response systems binding the baby to the mother, and we believe that curiosity represents the primary system releasing the baby from the mother. Laboratory tests demonstrate that strong exploratory motives have developed in the infant monkey long before temporary or permanent separation between infant and mother transpires. The 3-day-old baby monkey may operate the window of a Butler visual exploration box hundreds of times for the privilege of exploring the world outside. Figure 10-9 shows a baby looking at a cloth mother, and although this is the best possible stimulus, we know that seeing, just seeing,

is in and of itself a powerful incentive. Manual and oral exploration have been observed under laboratory test conditions in infant rhesus under 10 days of age, and compulsive and persistent manipulation and solution of mechanical puzzles ordinarily develop between 20 and 30 days of age. However, before the infant will leave the mother, the curiosity responses must become strong enough to override the fear

FIG. 10-9. Infant monkey responding in Butler box.

response, and the mother must not block the infant's exploratory efforts, or, on the positive side, the real mother may encourage them.

Security Stage

Our criterion for the transition from the stage of affection attachment to that of affectional security is that of consistent, active, exploratory responsiveness to a new environment under the presence or aegis of the surrogate or real mother, or attempted exploratory responsiveness under conditions of maternal restraint. It is obvious that many factors influence the time of transition from attachment to security in terms of our suggested criterion. Monkey babies raised on wire surrogates will attain affectional security later than monkeys raised on cloth surrogates. We believe that monkey infants raised on cloth surrogates will attain affectional security later than babies raised on real monkey mothers, but

FIG. 10-10. Exploration and play around mother surrogate.

this is the kind of speculation to be settled by experiment. Situational as well as personal variables would greatly influence the time of appearance of our criterion of affectional security, since security itself would be influenced by the degree to which any test environments are new, strange, or terrifying.

The behavior pattern of affectional security appears to develop gradually. In the home-cage fear tests the frightened baby rushed to the mother. After repeated tests and with increasing age, the monkey re-

laxed more quickly, and quietly observed and visually explored the monster more thoroughly. After extended testing, the infant left the mother and even manually and orally explored the previously frightening object. The development of the same behaviors was observed in the open-field testing and finally expressed itself in terms of free play oriented about the cloth mother surrogate, as illustrated in Figure 10-10.

A variant of the open-field test, the open-field-fear test, provided very striking data. In this experiment a cloth mother surrogate was placed on the side of the test room opposite a plastic start-box. The direct path to the cloth mother was blocked by a Plexiglass screen, and the infant had to bypass a fearful monster to attain the cloth mother. The situation induced severe trauma in the infants, but in almost all cases they circled the monster to contact the mother. After a number of trials, many infants would go to the mother and after absorbing quantities of contact comfort and security by rubbing against her body would go out and explore, manipulate, and—in three cases—attack and destroy the frightening beast. Thus, even though affectional security develops gradually, it becomes a behavioral item of great importance, and its appearance in the presence of a surrogate mother can be highly dramatic.

Independence Stage

Naturalistic accounts of the behavior of monkeys make it perfectly obvious that there is a final stage in the development of infant-mother affectional patterns characterized by independence of the infant. This stage is complete when all physical contact between infant and mother ceases. Observations in the wild suggest that even after all physical contacts do cease, often upon the appearance of a sibling, the infant may still spend considerable time near and around the mother; and if monkey infants could only talk, we might study subhuman jealousy. We have had neither the time nor adequate physical facilities to study the phase of affectional independence, and it is possible that the affectional bond between monkey infant and cloth mother surrogate is so strong that affectional independence will never occur. We have studied monkeys that had been completely separated from their mother surrogates for 6 months and had rarely seen them during the preceding year. Placed in the open-field-fear situation, they rushed and embraced their cloth mother surrogates, even though they were now considerably larger than their mothers. A number of them developed the technique of picking up their mothers and carrying them about the room, and this we regard as the zenith of the security phase of affectional development. It clearly disproves the old maxim that "You can't take it with you." If you can't, the monkey does not know it, and wearing mother around its neck gives the monkey a sense of security.

INFANT-FOR-INFANT AFFECTIONAL SYSTEM

The independence phase of the pattern of infantile affection for the mother should result in the gradual formation of affectional patterns between infant and infant, the second of the major developmental affectional systems. We have at the present time limited data on the nature, the development, and the factors which influence the infant-for-infant affectional patterns. We tentatively hypothesize that visual and manipulatory incentives are the basic variables behind the formation of infant-infant affection. These mechanisms, supported by the security which the presence or near-presence of the mother gives the infant, lead it to explore the physical environment about its family group, and other infants

are an essential part of the feral physical environment. At an appropriate maturational stage these other infants become more rewarding exploratory-manipulatory incentives than sticks and stones, and a series of infant-for-infant affection patterns are consequently released.

The effect of previous maternal or surrogate-maternal affectional experience upon infant-infant affection is an open question.

FIG. 10-11. The together-together raised monkeys.

We have one pair of infants that were raised together from Day 90 onward, and we call them our together-together monkeys (Fig. 10-11). These monkeys appear to be fixated at a pre-Freudian level of complete fixation. In other words they are our fixated-fixated animals, and they show little or no sign of developing normal infant-infant affectional patterns either to each other or to other infants. We have eight rhesus infants raised in our social-surrogate situation: each has a cloth surrogate mother but can make limited physical contacts with the other through the bars of a grill (Fig. 10-12). These monkeys show strong, perhaps unduly strong attachments to their mothers, but at least their infant-infant affectional development

FIG. 10-12. The social-surrogate situation.

is far more normal than is that of the together-together monkeys. We have observed two monkeys that were raised under conditions of complete social isolation for two years. Their initial social responsiveness was passive catatonia even when hauled and bitten by playmates only half

their size, and two years of continuous subsequent social contact have done more to heal the physical than the social scars. The isolated monkeys are now no longer entirely passive in a social situation, but they are still behavioral deviants. We have two monkeys in whom both prefrontal lobes were removed at six days of age. These animals show no intellectual loss of any type whatsoever, not even on delayed-response tests, but appear to exhibit a certain social unawareness for, or interest in, other infant monkeys. Such data are too good to be true and they undoubtedly are not true! Time will tell. We have two infants with chemically induced phenylpyruvic oligophrenia, and there is some indication that they are both academic and social morons.

However, when I first found myself talking about three different groups of two experimental monkeys each I began to feel ill at ease—I knew there was something wrong—I had to do something. What I did was go and read the *Journal of the Experimental Analysis of Behavior,* and there was the answer—I should have reduced the number of monkeys in each group from two to one.

11

HOSTILITY AND AGGRESSION IN ANIMALS

John P. Scott

When an inexperienced male mouse is attacked by a trained fighter his first reaction is to fight back, kicking and biting. The two mice roll over and over in a furry ball. If the inexperienced mouse is hurt, as usually happens, he starts to run away with the victorious animal in hot pursuit. If confined to a small cage, he cannot escape and soon begins to adopt a defensive posture, standing on the hind legs with the paws outstretched. If the other mouse continues to attack, he may eventually lie flat, becoming perfectly passive except to squeak when touched. This is the sort of behavioral raw material with which we shall deal in this paper.

Several patterns of behavior are involved: fighting, escape, defensive posture, and passivity. Together they may be called agonistic behavior.

To take an entirely different sort of animal, the tiny sticklebacks studied by Tinbergen (1953) and his associates, we find that these small fish live in schools most of the year. They may occasionally struggle over bits of food, but there is no serious fighting. During the breeding season the school breaks up, and each male guards a particular locality as a territory. When a strange male comes near he swims rapidly toward it as if to bite. If the stranger does not retreat, the resident stands on his head in the sand in a posture of threat. The final stage is an actual attack with the teeth.

In these two examples we can see that agonistic behavior consists of a group of several alternate behavior patterns which appear when one animal comes into physical conflict with another. We also see that agonistic behavior is organized into a behavioral system having the function of adaptation and adjustment to conflict. The nature of such a system and its organization depend upon the species involved.

What have hostility and aggression to do with agonistic behavior? These are concepts which have been used to describe aspects of human behavior and as such are involved in value judgments and codes of ethics. By human standards, hostility and aggression are bad things. They are also bad, or at least poor, as scientific concepts, because they are almost impossible to define in any objective way. In this paper I am therefore going to talk primarily about agonistic behavior, using hostility and aggression only as terms which help connect animal phenomena with the problems of human behavior.

RESULTS OF PREVIOUS WORK

In Collias' (1944) classic review, *Aggressive Behavior Among Vertebrate Animals,* he came to three principal conclusions:

First, a great deal of fighting in vertebrates is connected with the phenomenon of territoriality. Second, fighting in animal groups tends to become organized into social-dominance hierarchies which have the net effect of greatly reducing the amount of fighting. Finally, one of the major physiological factors connected with fighting in vertebrates is the male sex hormone.

In a recent volume (Scott, 1958) I reviewed the evidence regarding the causes of fighting in animals and the possible application of these findings to human behavior. In the first place, fighting is strongly affected by learning. Success in fighting is a powerful reinforcing agent, so that successful experienced animals are much more highly motivated to fight than inexperienced ones. Animals also form strong habits of not fighting, either as a result of lack of success and the resulting punishment, or, more importantly, by simply not fighting. This last mechanism is one of our most effective and satisfactory methods of social control of fighting.

A great deal of human fighting and aggressive behavior is maladaptive, and much of it can be explained as the result of frustration. However, the animal experiments indicate that the maximum amount of fighting is produced not by frustration but by success in fighting. Furthermore, habit formation controls aggression even where frustration exists, and the frustrated animal only attacks those individuals which he is in the habit of attacking.

The comparative physiology of fighting behavior in animals yields the extremely important conclusion that the primary stimulation for fighting behavior is external; that is, there is no spontaneous internal stimulation which makes it necessary for an individual to fight irrespective of the outside environment. The physiological and emotional factors involved in the agonistic behavioral system are thus quite different from those involved in sexual and ingestive behavior. This leads to the hopeful conclusion that effective control of agonistic behavior is theoretically possible. In any practical situation this may be quite difficult because a vertebrate animal has a behavioral system organized to produce fighting behavior in response to certain kinds of external stimulation, and the complete elimination of such stimulation may be impossible.

Experiments with heredity and agonistic behavior show that important individual differences do exist within the same species, both in the ease with which fighting can be stimulated and in the capacity to fight or escape successfully. Besides this, there are important sex differences in vertebrates, the males with few exceptions being more aggressive and better adapted for fighting than the females. In mammals there is more to this difference than the presence and absence of the male sex hormone. The available data indicate that the female nervous system is unresponsive to the male hormone in respect to modifying fighting behavior.

Finally, there are three major ways in which social fighting is controlled among animal societies. One of these is the organization of social-dominance hierarchies mentioned above. The agonistic behavior between two individuals becomes organized by learning and habit formation into a regular relationship of threat and avoidance. Many variations of the dominance relationship exist; but in its most typical form the dominant animal threatens, and the subordinate animal submits or avoids.

A second method of social control arises in connection with the process of primary socialization. In many species the young do not fight in early life and tend to form a habit of peaceful behavior which remains in adult existence, or fighting may first arise in a playful form and a dominance relationship be formed without serious fighting taking place. Older animals may establish dominance over younger ones simply by threats or carrying them around.

A third method related to the other two is a system of territoriality, which keeps strange animals apart and usually limits fighting to threats between neighboring animals at the boundaries.

These general methods are highly effective in controlling destructive fighting in well-organized animal societies. This means that under natural conditions hostility and aggression, in the sense of destructive and maladaptive agonistic behavior, are hard to find in animal societies.

With this background, we can now turn our attention to some of the newer significant research on agonistic behavior in mammals.

AGGRESSION IN MAMMALIAN SOCIETIES

Rodents

Calhoun (1950) established an experimental colony of wild Norway rats and studied their behavior for two years. There was always an abundant supply of food on hand, but this was always placed in one spot in the center of the area. The only essential difference from wild conditions was that the movements of the rats were limited by a fence rather than by physical or social barriers. Under these restricted conditions, numbers in the colony never rose above 200. However, this control in population was not achieved by bloody fighting. The rats close to the food supply established themselves in holes and were avoided by rats from outlying points. This meant that the outlying rats never got as much food as those in the more favored positions and were consequently in poorer

physical condition. Their reproductive rate was low.

The dominance relationships of the rats were produced not by violent fighting but by a process which Calhoun called "psychological drubbing." When a young rat wandered into the area occupied by an adult, the latter would seize it, shake it, and chase it away without biting it or doing any actual harm. Thus the young rats learned to avoid the established adults.

At the same time the rat colony showed a form of unconscious cooperation. Rats near the food pile would carry it away and store it in various outlying areas. These food supplies were not guarded, and the outlying rats would come and take them away without having to run the gantlet into the central supply. This trait of food scattering in wild rats thus has value for the survival of the social group.

This was a well-organized animal society, albeit living under somewhat strenuous conditions, in that the marginal members of the colony had no opportunity to migrate. As such it was quite similar to the natural rat colonies existing in city blocks in a neighboring community. Calhoun (1948) studied such a population for several months by trapping and marking. It had about the same population as the artificial colony and appeared to be stable and well organized. Then Calhoun released 112 alien rats into the area. The result was a very high death rate in the population, partly because of conflict between the strangers and the home rats, and partly because of exposure to predators. The death rate among the alien rats was three times as large as that in the home group, and the net result was a smaller population than the original one. As we shall see, this is a typical effect in disorganized animal societies.

It is a common observation among scientists who work with house mice in the laboratory that if a group of strange adult males are put together they begin to fight and frequently kill each other. On the other hand, if a litter of males grows up together and forms a naturally organized group they rarely fight even as adults. The same thing is true of deer mice in the laboratory, although these animals are much closer to their wild ancestors and have been subject to less artificial selection. Terman (1959) has recently made a highly significant observation on the behavior of these animals under natural conditions. When strange deer mice come together in a large field they do not fight but show the behavior of mutual avoidance. If one animal is fastened by a tether, the free animal moves away. Even if a deer mouse comes to his accustomed nest and finds a stranger tethered there, he will avoid him. Apparently these rodents fight only when two conditions are present. One is a disorganized population when strangers are forcibly brought together. Even so, the mice do not fight unless a second condition is present: that no escape is possible. Agonistic behavior is so organized in these animals that fighting is not the first, but the last, resort.

Still another picture of the control of aggression in a rodent society is presented in King's (1955) study of the black-tailed prairie dog. These are probably the most highly social of any species of rodent, and much of their behavior takes place in the daytime, so that it can be accurately observed. Unlike the nocturnal rodents, they divide their land into territories with definite boundaries. Each territory is occupied by one or two males and several females which have a common burrow system below ground. In the spring, during the breeding season, each female occupies a definite burrow and drives off others which attempt

to enter. Eventually, young begin to appear above ground and make contacts with other animals. When any animal crosses a boundary it is met by one of the home animals. Both go through a display of threats, after which the intruder retreats. There is little actual fighting, and King observed only one serious injury, which occurred after experimental interference with the social organization. As the young grow up, the territory becomes crowded, and the adults move out, leaving the burrow system for the young and inexperienced animals. The older ones move out to the edge of the colony where they set up a new territory and start building new burrows. Thus the colony has an orderly system of expansion which gives the maximum protection to the young and inexperienced animals and exposes the older ones to the maximum danger. Furthermore, the prairie dogs warn each other of predators by calling. Here again it is the more experienced animals on the edge of the colony who are likely to react first and protect the others.

Ungulates

In species like the red deer of Scotland (Darling, 1937) or the mountain sheep of North America (Scott, 1945), agonistic behavior is highly regulated by heredity and physiology. During most of the year there is almost no fighting or conflict. Serious fighting between the males appears in the rutting season in the autumn. The red deer, which are quite similar in their behavior to the elk or wapiti in North America, indulge in pushing contests whenever they come together, and each male attempts to round up a herd of females, mating with each as they become receptive. All this activity is highly exhausting, and a male is able to maintain his dominance for only a few days or weeks after which he becomes tired out and gives way to a challenging male. The beaten animal, however, is rarely injured in any serious way, although occasionally deaths from starvation occur if two males happen to lock their antlers.

In the rutting season of mountain sheep a pair of males will back off and run at each other, meeting head on with a considerable clash. An occasional animal will suffer a fractured skull, or, more usually, the beaten animal retires from the scene.

The most interesting fact about the fighting of these ruminants is that fighting always occurs in pairs. It is always a fair fight between two individuals, and deer or sheep never gang up on one another. This appears to be a hereditary characteristic for the control and regulation of fighting. The same animals are highly allelomimetic in their escape from predators.

Carnivores—Wolves and Dogs

Wolves have had a popular reputation for ferocity over a period of centuries. These observations were largely made by farmers who only saw wolves as they attacked livestock and had no opportunity to see wolves at home. Murie (1944, pp. 30–31), who made an intensive study of a wolf pack under natural conditions in Alaska, says:

"The strongest impression remaining with me after watching the wolves on numerous occasions was their friendliness. The adults were friendly toward each other and were amiable toward the pups, at least as late as October. This innate good feeling has been strongly marked in the three captive wolves which I have known. Undoubtedly, however, wolves sometimes have their quarrels."

The wolves hunted together and brought back food which they cached near the den or fed to the young pups. The only fighting observed by Murie occurred when a strange wolf approached the den. It was attacked by the entire group and driven off in spite of adopting a submissive posture.

Again, the entire wolf pack combined to attack grizzly bears which came near the den and robbed them of their stored food. The wolves were unable to damage the grizzlies, but worried them until they left.

Since 1945 we have maintained a large colony of dogs at the Roscoe B. Jackson Memorial Laboratory. One of the standard procedures is to raise a litter of pups and keep them together until they become adults. Playful fighting appears quite early in development, and on this basis the litter forms a dominance order in which all fighting is reduced to occasional threats and growls (Pawlowski and Scott, 1956). For example, one litter of Shetland sheep dogs was kept in a pen some 20 $\times$ 40 feet in size. The most dominant animals could range throughout the pen, while the subordinate ones were confined to the vicinity of the house and food supply. Whenever an observer came near, the attention of the dominant animals was distracted, and the subordinate ones left their accustomed places to come and see what was going on. The dominant animals then threatened the subordinate ones and chased them back to their places without, however, ever inflicting any actual wounds. This is a typical case; serious fighting almost never breaks out except when strange animals are placed together.

Litters in breeds of cocker spaniels and beagles rarely show any sign of serious agonistic behavior. On the other hand, the fox terrier breed shows undue aggressiveness at a very young age. Puppies of any breed begin to show a tendency to gang up on each other about 7 weeks of age, but in most this is momentary and playful. In the fox terriers this type of fighting is serious and persistent and may result in death if the animal attacked is not removed. We found that we were never able to raise animals in litters larger than three, as one fox terrior can withstand the attack of two, but not three, opponents. This means that the terrier breed has been selected for unusual aggressiveness and, in fact, appears to be more aggressive than wolves. This applies even where they are raised in larger spaces. This hereditary trait limits their capacity for living in groups.

On the other hand, some of the breeds have been selected in the opposite direction for an unusual capacity for group living. Among beagles, which are used for hunting in packs, it is often possible to place strange adult males together without any actual fighting breaking out. If fighting does occur, it can easily be suppressed by human intervention. Among these breeds, fighting is not likely to occur even under conditions of social disorganization.

Unlike the ungulates described above, these carnivores exhibit the capacity for combined group attacks, and aggression is limited in different ways. At the same time, they also have the capacity for developing remarkably peaceable and cooperative social groups. Our evidence indicates that social disorganization is a primary cause of fighting. Confinement may aggravate the effects but is not itself a primary cause. Heredity can either increase or decrease the capacity to respond to social disorganization.

Primates

Carpenter (1934, 1940) has studied two species of primates which also seem to show different hereditary capacities for expressing aggression. The howling monkeys form groups of adult males and females which stay constantly together. When these groups come into contact they make vocal signals and continue to stay apart. There is no fighting between males, and receptive females move freely from one male to another.

At another extreme are the gibbons, which are so aggressive that males always attack other adult males, and females attack other females. The result is that the largest social group of gibbons is a male and female pair with their immature offspring. Clashes occur as the pairs come into contact at the edges of their usual territories.

Until recently our picture of baboon behavior was based on Zuckerman's (1932) study of Monkey Island in the London Zoo. This was a large colony of strange wild baboons confined in an area 100 feet long and 60 feet wide, large by zoo standards but extremely small in comparison to the natural range. The baboons began to fight and continued to do so over a period of three years. Sometimes the males literally pulled the smaller females to pieces. We now realize that this was a disorganized population composed of strange adults forced into close proximity in a very unequal sex ratio. Matters were not helped by the later introduction of other strangers.

Washburn's (1958) recent studies of baboon societies under natural conditions in South Africa present an entirely different picture. Adult males have a strong dominance organization, maintain their distance from each other, and almost never come into conflict. An immature male may come close to an adult and be chased and chastised, but never physically injured. Washburn described a case in which an old male pursued a young one out to the tip of a branch in a tree, shook it vigorously until the young male almost lost his hold, and then stopped. This looks as if the adults become dominant over the immature animals without inflicting physical injury. At the same time the adult males will attack any predator as a group and are almost never bothered by them. In fact, almost the only opportunity for a predator to approach is at night when the colony is sleeping.

Conclusions

On the basis of the above data it is apparent that each species has certain genetically determined behavior traits which under normal and natural conditions allow the development of social organization which exerts effective control over harmful fighting. Serious fighting between members of a natural social group is the exception rather than the rule. Far from showing violent competition between individuals, animal societies are generally highly cooperative and mutually protective. We can also draw the conclusion that one of the major causes of destructive fighting in animal societies is social disorganization.

HUMAN APPLICATIONS

Perspective

We can observe a human society in much the same way as we watch animals, but with the limitation that the observer frequently has to be a participant. When we do this, we find that the vast majority of human behavior is peaceful and well controlled. For example, I recently spent three months in Chicago, a community where violence is supposed to be relatively frequent. Yet I never once saw a case of overt fighting or aggression in that time. I read about it, and I could have found it, had I made a special effort; but the vast majority of observed behavior in this community was peaceable and cooperative. There is no more evidence of "fang and claw" behavior in the ordinary human society than in a well-organized animal society.

We tend to evaluate human behavior against an absolute standard of perfection required by our own moral codes rather than against animal societies, or even against the statistical evidence of what has been achieved by a human society under optimum conditions. Judging by biological standards, human beings have much the same capacities for social control of aggression as other primates.

At the same time, there is no reason for being complacent and satisfied about our behavior. Our biological heritage also includes capacities for developing harmful and destructive behavior under conditions of social disorganization (Leighton, 1955). The social control of behavior must be developed anew in each generation; it cannot be created for all time. We have every indication that social disorganization does exist in our own as well as many other human societies (Faris, 1955), and the psychiatrists and clinical psychologists among the audience may well be asking, "What about the concealed hostility and aggression which we see every day in our patients?" The vast need for psychological and psychiatric services is evidence that our society is far from perfect.

Family Disorganization

All of our present data indicate that fighting behavior among the higher mammals, including man, originates in external stimulation and that there is no evidence of spontaneous internal stimulation. Emotional and physiological processes prolong and magnify the effects of stimulation, but do not originate it. This means that in any practical instance the first place to look for causes is in the individual's social environment—as, for example, in the case of a schoolboy who continually attacks his fellow pupils and rebels against the teachers. There may be internal causes that aggravate his behavior, resulting from previous experience or inherited temperament, but there is always some real external stimulation. Someone (and more often several people) may be teasing, abusing, or physically attacking the boy. Investigation usually reveals some kind of family disturbance. There may be a background of divorce, illegitimacy, neglect, desertion, adultery, or any of the other ills which indicate a disorganized family (Glueck and Glueck, 1950).

Cultural Disorganization

More than this, there appear to be certain focal areas where many individuals are involved in violence (McNeil, 1959). In American cities, these are frequently sections in which there are large proportions of recent immigrants. Many of these are men without families. In the past we have sometimes blamed this or that nationality for the results. I would like to suggest that the disorder has a more general cause.

In any animal population, throwing a large number of strange individuals together and confining them in a small area creates a condition of maximum social disorganization, in which fighting escapes from social control. The severity of fighting is increased by a high proportion of males. There is every reason to expect that crowding a large number of strange people together in a tenement will also result in social disorganization, and that the disorder will be more serious if complicated by differences in culture and language. This supports Faris' (1955) conclusion that crimes of violence are largely the result of social disorganization.

The remedy is, of course, to help immigrants to organize themselves as rapidly as possible. After all, we had the same problem on the American frontier—an initial period of crime and lawlessness which ended when the new settlers organized themselves to maintain order.

The Development of Social Disorganization

It is a well-recognized fact that the majority of crimes of violence in our society are committed by persons under the age of 25. In a recent year nearly half of them were committed by persons under 18. This suggests that we might examine the problem of social disorganization from a developmental viewpoint.

Young children are normally closely controlled by their families and parents, and under these conditions, fighting of any serious sort is repressed or reduced to teasing and similar milder forms. It is not until adolescence that a child begins to be released from family control, and he will not come under similar control again until he marries and forms new family relationships. It is precisely in this transition from one family to another that we observe the maximum expression of dangerous fighting behavior. In short, this is the period in which family social organization is the weakest.

The risk that any particular child will exhibit harmful aggressive behavior during this period is largely determined by the nature and organization of his primary family, as indicated above. This is, of course, a relative matter. Our statistics on crime represent the number of people who are caught, but one can guess that very nearly 100 per cent of male children will exhibit some instance of destructive and hostile behavior during this period. We also observe that the rates are anywhere from two to five times as great for males as females, depending on age and type of crime; boys are likely to exhibit delinquency in agonistic behavior while delinquent girls are usually involved in sexual behavior. This partly reflects biological differences between males and females, particularly the effect of the male hormone on aggressiveness, but also reflects the social tradition of longer family control over girls.

During this period the developing young adult is not completely free of social control, and he normally passes into the social organization of groups other than the family, particularly those associated with the school. For some individuals this is an easy transition, and they usually are reasonably well behaved. For others it is not an easy process, particularly for those coming from disorganized families, and they may join a noninstitutional group, the boy's gang.

Now, sociologists point out that this is not social disorganization, although its roots may lie in disorganization. The reason why a juvenile gang makes trouble is that it is *well* organized for violence and crime. In the mores of its subculture, aggression is justifiable and laudable (Cohen, 1955). Here we have a paradox—albeit a perfectly reasonable one—that one major cause of destructive fighting and hostile behavior is social disorganization and that another is social organization itself: a group organized for fighting. This brings us to another aspect of the agonistic behavior of people: war.

WAR

The concepts of social disorganization and organization as major factors producing fighting can also be applied to war. However, war is a phenomenon different from individual agonistic behavior and even from group fighting within a society. This point cannot be made too often, for our first reaction is to generalize from what we know about individual behavior and assume that we can solve the problem of war on the same basis. War, however, is a conflict between human societies and as such has aspects which are unknown among individuals.

To take an example, one would never have predicted from the behavior of individual Norwegians in 1938 that they would shortly begin to fight. Yet they were soon involved in a war, being attacked by another human society. While warfare involves all the individual human activities included under the definition of agonistic behavior, it is agonistic behavior organized on a different level—that of societies rather than of individuals or of small groups—and as such has peculiar properties of its own. One of these is the almost axiomatic fact that in any conflict, other things being equal, the society which is most highly organized for fighting is likely to be the winner. This means that social organization itself is one of the major causes of war. A society which professes war as a cultural ideal and has a superior military organization is (judging from history) highly likely to attack its neighbors. However, while such societies are well organized within themselves, they are disorganized with respect to each other.

It is fascinating to pursue this idea of social disorganization as a cause for human conflict. In every human society the change from agricultural and feudal organization to industrial and economic organization has been accompanied by a great deal of individual and group violence, sometimes erupting into civil war. The transition from one type of organization to another automatically produces social disorganization and violence. However, it is hopeful that the newer type of organization appears to be a better method of social control than the old. No real statistical comparisons are possible, but we have every reason to believe that modern society controls aggression much more effectively than did the corresponding societies of the Middle Ages.

To return to the problem of war, there is nothing like human warfare among animal societies. We can recognize the capacity for group fighting among the wild primates, and hence for the eventual development of war, but nothing like real war actually exists. The organization of animal societies keeps contacts between separate societies to a minimum and hence seldom produces disorganization between societies. Furthermore, without verbal communication there is no way of producing the type of organization directed toward war. In fact, there was probably nothing like war in preverbal man, judging from the examples of the most primitive societies persisting in recent historical time. True warfare did not exist among the Australian desert aborigines or the Eskimos, although either might band together to hunt down an individual (Spencer and Gillen, 1927; Swanton, 1943). In such hunting and food-gathering societies it would be almost impossible to carry on a group expedition for more than a few hours or days. The group would simply have to stop to hunt and get something to eat. Warfare seems to be in part a product of technology. Until men began to domesticate animals and plants they could neither store enough food to conduct a large-scale war nor accumulate enough goods to be worth stealing.

The effect of the development of human language and culture was to produce a new type of social organization within groups. It did not at the same time automatically create organization between these groups. In warfare we are dealing primarily not with social disorganization within a society, for the well-organized society is likely to be successful in war, but rather disorganization on a larger scale between societies themselves. To draw an analogy, the development of new means of communication and transportation has had the effect of throwing a large number of strange human societies in close proximity, with little or no organization between them. The effect has been very much the same as throwing a strange group of individual rats or monkeys together: a great deal of useless and destructive fighting between the groups.

In many cases the outcome of a war has been that both sides have lost.

Understanding this large-scale phenomenon is a difficult matter, and one for which we do not yet have completely appropriate concepts. Biologists agree that once language and communication arose in human societies, a new type of organization was possible which to a large extent escaped the mechanism of biological evolution. We are here dealing with a different sort of evolution, whose basic mechanisms are symbolic thinking, knowledge, and communication rather than the genes, and which proceeds at a far more rapid rate than biological evolution.

Thinking in these terms, we can reach a somewhat hopeful conclusion. Animal societies have evolved successful methods for the control of destructive and hostile behavior within themselves through the mechanisms of territoriality, socialization, and dominance. We have every reason to expect that human societies will eventually evolve methods for controlling warfare *between* themselves (Swanton, 1943). This, of course, is a statement of faith rather than science, and it may seem to be of little value amid immediate and pressing dangers.

We need to remember that the evolution of human societies is no longer a result of inevitable biological change, but rather the effect of continuous conscious effort. One of our basic common tasks is to work out methods of world organization which will be acceptable and workable to all. To be effective these must be based on a deep understanding of man's basic biological nature and capacity for social organization.

What I have said indicates that we are making such progress, discouragingly slow at times, but nevertheless moving ahead. In the future this should be one of the primary tasks of biological and social scientists. We need to put less effort into such superficial psychological problems as why people prefer one T.V. program to another and more on the major aspects of animal and human behavior.

SUMMARY

1. Many animal species have the capacity for agonistic behavior and hence for destructive fighting.

2. Animal societies have evolved several basic methods for the social control of aggressive and hostile behavior, including territoriality, the dominance order, and the process of socialization.

3. Essentially the same methods (often not recognized or called by different names) are effectively used for the control of aggression in human societies.

4. Well-organized animal societies exhibit little overt fighting; one of the basic causes of destructive fighting is social disorganization.

5. At the same time, successful fighting is based on good organization, even at the individual level. The animal which has its behavior well organized for fighting by training and experience is likely to be successful, and social organization itself is one of the major causes of fighting.

6. The conclusions from animal observations and experiments have their most direct application to human behavior at the level of individuals or small groups.

7. One of the major causes of aggression in human societies appears to be family disorganization.

8. In our society, individual development goes through a phase of social disorganization in the adolescent and young-adult period.

9. Cultural disorganization results from movements of large numbers of strange individuals into a new area, as in the case of immigration into large cities.

10. The problem of warfare involves organization at another level, that between societies. Disorganization between societies is one of the major causes of war and may itself result from good organization at a lower level—the society well organized for war.

REFERENCES

CALHOUN, J. B. 1948. Mortality and movement of brown rats (*Rattus norvegicus*) in artificially supersaturated populations. *J. Wildlife Management. 12:* 167–172.

CALHOUN, J. B. 1950. The study of wild animals under controlled conditions. *Ann. New York Acad. Sc. 51:* 1113–1122.

CARPENTER, C. R. 1934. A field study of the behavior and social relations of howling monkeys. *Comp. Psychol. Monographs. 10*(2): 1–168.

CARPENTER, C. R. 1940. A field study of the behavior and social relations of the gibbon (*Hylobates lar*). *Comp. Psychol. Monographs. 16*(5): 1–212.

COHEN, A. K. 1955. *Delinquent Boys: The Culture of the Gang.* Glencoe, Ill., Free Press.

COLLIAS, N. 1944. Aggressive behavior among vertebrate animals. *Physiol. Zool. 17:* 83–123.

DARLING, F. F. 1937. *A Herd of Red Deer.* London, Oxford University Press.

FARIS, R. E. L. 1955. *Social Disorganization*, 2nd ed. New York, Ronald.

GLUECK, S., and GLUECK, E. 1950. *Unraveling Juvenile Delinquency.* Cambridge, Mass., Harvard University Press, for Commonwealth Fund.

KING, J. A. 1955. *Social Behavior, Social Organization, and Population Dynamics in a Black-tailed Prairie Dog Town in the Black Hills of South Dakota.* Ann Arbor, Mich., University of Michigan Press.

LEIGHTON, A. H. 1955. Psychiatric disorder and social environment. *Psychiatry. 18:* 367–

McNEIL, E. B., 1959. Psychology and aggression. *J. Conflict Resolution. 3:* 195–293.

MURIE, A. 1944. *The Wolves of Mt. McKinley.* Washington, D.C. U.S. Government Printing Office.

PAWLOWSKI, A. A., and SCOTT, J. P. 1956.

Hereditary differences in the development of dominance in litters of puppies. *J. Comp. & Physiol. Psychol. 49:* 353–358.

SCOTT, J. P. 1945. Social behavior, organization, and leadership in a small flock of domestic sheep. *Comp. Psychol. Monographs. 18*(4): 1–29.

SCOTT, J. P. 1958. *Aggression.* Chicago, University of Chicago Press.

SPENCER, B., and GILLEN, F. J. 1927. *The Arunta.* London, Macmillan.

SWANTON, J. R. 1943. *Are Wars Inevitable?* Washington, D.C., Smithsonian Institution.

TERMAN, C. R. 1959. Social factors influencing spatial distribution in populations of prairie deer mice. Doctoral dissertation, Michigan State University.

TINBERGEN, N. 1953. *Social Behaviour in Animals.* London, Methuen.

WASHBURN, S. L. 1958. Naturalistic observations of wild primates. Paper delivered at Am. Anthropol. A. Ann. Meeting.

ZUCKERMAN, S. 1932. *The Social Life of Monkeys and Apes.* New York, Harcourt, Brace.

12

EXPERIMENTAL STUDIES OF THE BEHAVIOR OF AN AGGRESSIVE, PREDATORY MOUSE,

Onychomys leucogaster

Lincoln D. Clark

In the preceding chapter and at greater length in his book (1958), Scott has summarized most of the literature concerned with hostility and aggression in animals. He has emphasized a number of principles which characterize agonistic behavior in vertebrate animals. These can be summarized as follows:

1. Fighting is strongly influenced by learning. The experience of success in fighting acts as a potent re-enforcement to aggressive behavior, while absence of fighting or recurrent defeat decreases motivation to fight.

2. The social structure of animal groups is such as to limit destructive levels of aggression. During infancy, the animal passes through a period of not fighting or of repeated defeat by more mature members of the group. This phase of "primary socialization" is followed in adulthood by various forms of dominance hierarchies. These result in an over-all decrease in fighting. After the initial conflicts, which are practically never lethal, required to establish the dominance order, the relationships between individuals stabilize on peaceful terms. Occasional threats by more domi-

nant animals are reacted to with submission or avoidance by those lower in the hierarchy.

3. The phenomenon of territoriality, the system whereby animals distribute living space and food supplies and stabilize the level of stimulus contacts with other animals, is also of crucial importance in reducing agonistic behavior. On the other hand, violation of habitual territoriality can precipitate aggression.

4. A group of animals disorganized in terms of either social or geographic factors is liable to develop a higher incidence of destructive, agonistic behavior.

5. Fighting behavior represents patterns of response to certain kinds of external stimulation. In contrast to sexual or ingestive behavior, there appears to be no internal need to fight irrespective of environmental conditions.

Onychomys leucogaster PHYSICAL CHARACTERISTICS AND BEHAVIOR IN NATURAL HABITAT

The subject of the experiments to be reported is the Northern Grasshopper Mouse, *Onychomys leucogaster*. The interesting

179

behavior of this small rodent was noted in field observations by Bailey (1931) in southern Utah in 1888. Its ecology and reproduction have recently been studied by Ergoscue (1960). Several groups of these animals, along with other species of wild rodents, were obtained for laboratory study in a search for animal behaviors which might serve as screening tests for the psychopharmacological effects of drugs. In the course of this survey, the unique value of this mouse for experimental study of agonistic behavior was incidentally found.

Onychomys leucogaster is a cricetid rodent of stocky build with a short tapering tail. Adult mice weigh 25–40 gm. and are 5–6 inches from the tip of tail to nose. Their pelage is bicolored. The underparts of the body are white; the upper portion, gray in juveniles, brownish to pinkish cinnamon or buff in adults, and again gray in old age (Hall and Kelson, 1959). The subspecies studied was *utahensis,* originally trapped in semiarid, sagebrush-covered terrain about 50 miles west of Salt Lake City, Utah. They had been in captivity for several generations when first studied from a behavioral standpoint.

Onychomys are unusual mice in that they are carnivorous and predatory in habit. Despite their small size, they trail, stalk, seize, and kill other mice quickly by gnawing into the brain stem at the base of the skull. They commonly prey upon voles, pocket mice, deer mice, and small kangaroo rats. Insects, particularly grasshoppers and scorpions, are also eaten. Seeds are ingested when animal food is not available. In the laboratory, they subsist well on commercial mouse pellets. Like true carnivores, they eat relatively large meals. As predators, they are reported to range over a wider area than other mice, pre-empting the burrows of other small animals as they move from one locale to another. During attacks they emit a high-pitched squeaking sound. At other times, they lift their heads, close their eyes, and produce a whistling call which is difficult to localize because of its ventriloquistic quality. While some naturalists have fancifully compared this call with the howling of the predatory wolf, its real purpose is not known. In terms of their aggressiveness and method of killing, *Onychomys* have many similarities to weasels and, to a lesser extent, to shrews, whose limited vision and olfactory sense make them less effective predators.

Onychomys are also remarkable for their adrenal weight, which runs as high as 2000 mg./kg. body weight. This is the largest adrenal gland proportional to body weight found in any animal reported in a recent extensive comparative study by Zundel and Woodbury (unpublished). The histological structure of the *Onychomys'* adrenal and its steroid metabolism are being studied, but the results are not available at this date. It is likely that this finding is comparable in significance to the large adrenals of other aggressive animals such as the wild Norwegian rat or the breed of terrier dogs.

ADVANTAGES OF *Onychomys* AS AN EXPERIMENTAL ANIMAL FOR THE STUDY OF AGONISTIC BEHAVIOR

These mice have a variety of features which should encourage investigators to use them as experimental subjects for studying aggression. First, they are small, easily handled, and inexpensive to maintain in the laboratory. Secondly, because they are naturally predatory, their agonistic behavior is easily elicited, continues with minimum re-enforcement, and persists in stable patterns for long periods of time. Thirdly, episodes of fighting can be readily quantified since this behavioral pattern is highly predictable under a given set of conditions and offers easily recorded end-points. In most of the studies in this paper the measure of aggressive level was the time elapsing between the introduction of the victim and his death. This was supplemented by a simple rating scale to indicate frequency and persistence of attacks. Finally, it was found that experiments could be devised to study the effects of prior experience and social interaction upon the agonistic behavior of *Onychomys*.

EXPERIMENTAL STUDIES

The mice were raised in colony cages (18×18 inches) in groups of five. Under these conditions no fighting occurs. Such animals are designated as "novice" since they have had no fighting experience. Litters of young born into the colony have a high survival rate; no cannibalism has been seen. In fact, other colony members share the same nest with the mother and litter. When the nesting area is threatened by approach of a strange object, all members cluster together and join in a concerted attack as if protecting the young.

If care is used to avoid the stimulus conditions which precipitate fighting, mice of other species can be introduced into colonies of novice mice. Furthermore, novice mice may be placed in separate cages and paired with alien mice. For descriptive purposes, these are called respectively, "colony coexistent" and "paired co-existent" groups. An interesting sequence occurs when the strange mouse is first introduced. *Onychomys* immediately approaches and, after sniffing the body of the strange mouse for a few moments, "acts out" the method of attack characteristic of his species. He approaches from the rear, grasps the stranger with front and rear legs, and places his mouth at the base of the skull, even taking a few playful nips. After two or three repe-

titions of this performance within the first few minutes after the stranger's arrival, the behavior disappears; coexistence ensues, and different species share the same nesting area. Mice which have coexisted with *Onychomys* include the Prairie Deer Mouse (*Peromyscus maniculatus bairdii*), the Piñon Mouse (*Peromyscus truei*), the Woodland Deer Mouse (*P.m. gracilis, P.m. sonoriensis*), and albino laboratory mice (Carworth Farms No. 1-CF #1). This phenomenon of the coexistence of a predatory. mouse and his prey has been described in the short-tail shrew by Rood (1958).

An early goal was to determine conditions which precipitated aggression, reenforced it, or conversely inhibited it. We first placed an *Onychomys* and a potential victim together under a 1-liter beaker inverted on an electrified grid. A few mild shocks induced immediate attacks. It was soon found that shocks were not necessary and that confinement in the beaker for five minutes once a day led to lethal attacks on the first to the eighth trial. The mean for 13 animals was 3.6 trials. Nonlethal attacks invariably appeared during the first trial. The tendency in early trials was for *Onychomys* to spend part of his time exploring and seeking to escape from the beaker. Exploratory activity soon disappeared, however, and *Onychomys* would concentrate on attacking his companion. It is likely that habituation to the beaker environment before introduction of the victim would result in even earlier lethal attacks.

Any environmental change which excites *Onychomys* will increase his aggression. The more active the victim, the more he will stimulate *Onychomys* to attack. The survival value to the potential victim of catatonic immobility or "playing possum" is dramatically evident in these experiments. Artificially reducing the excitability of the victim by tranquilizing him with chlorpromazine will prolong his survival time. The effects of electric shocks have already been described. Tweaking *Onychomys'* tail with forceps or rattling the beaker similarly agitate the animal and heighten aggression.

The method of attack is quite constant. He pursues the victim, repeatedly pouncing upon him, until he obtains a secure hold. If the victim assumes the usual defensive posture of facing the antagonist in an erect, sparring position, *Onychomys* will nip at his tail or rear legs to compel him to turn, thus exposing his back. He seizes the victim from the rear with both front and rear feet and anchors his teeth at the base of the skull. Once in this position, he almost invariably kills the victim within 10 seconds.

The majority of animals used in these studies were male. However, females are highly aggressive and effective killers. A systematic study to determine whether or not there are quantitative differences in aggression between the sexes has not yet been carried out.

In summary, the aggressive behavior of *Onychomys* is a response to stimulus conditions which heighten the excitability of the animal. These include painful stimuli, sudden changes in the environment, vigorous activity on the part of the victim, and confinement in a small space.

The nature of the "emotional" state induced by these conditions can, of course, only be inferred. However, it is reasonable to assume that the experience of pain and unfamiliar environmental changes producing fear are the most likely. The technique of confinement probably acts through the latter mechanism. This is suggested by research which indicates that crowding of CF #1 mice into a small cage, as is done in the amphetamine aggregation test, increases central nervous system excitability as meas-

ured by reduction of threshold to pentylenetetrazol-induced seizures. It is likely that the cause of this excitability is a sudden disruption of the customary territoriality of the animal. With repeated exposure to aggregation, CF #1 mice apparently adapt to the new territoriality since pentylenetetrazol threshold returns to normal and the enhanced toxicity of amphetamine due to aggregation no longer occurs. A variety of experimental operations designed to induce fear, such as immobilization of CF #1 mice in plastic tubes and aversive conditioning, also produce significant reduction of pentylenetetrazol threshold (Swinyard *et al.*).

Attack behavior can also be precipitated in *Onychomys* by conditioned fear. This was accomplished by exposing the animals to buzzer and shock trials in a grid-floored plastic box. In conditioned animals, the buzzer or environment alone will induce attacks upon the companion mouse with which they have previously lived in peaceful, paired coexistence. Unfortunately, the absence of accessible veins for intravenous injection in *Onychomys* has prevented us from measuring the pentylenetetrazol threshold associated with this conditioned response.

The effectiveness of starvation as a means of initiating aggression in novice *Onychomys* in paired coexistence with CF #1 mice and *P.m. bairdii* was studied. These animals were observed regularly during daylight hours; no aggressive behavior was seen. The companion mouse was found dead and partially eaten in two trials after 48 hours of total starvation, in 6 trials after 72 hours, in 10 trials after 96 hours, and in 4 trials after 120 hours. Although it is possible that *Onychomys* killed his companion, it is more likely that he died of starvation and was then eaten. The longer survival periods occurred after repeated trials during which adaptation to starvation presumably had occurred. *Onychomys* apparently tolerates long periods of food deprivation. On only one occasion, after 144 hours, were both mice found dead. It can be concluded that starvation, even in this predatory animal, has little or no stimulus value for initiating aggressive behavior. If it does, the degree of deprivation must be severe.

On the assumption that fear as a factor precipitating aggression would be associated with sympathetic discharge, an effort was made to simulate the humoral aspects of this response by administration of epinephrine in various doses to *Onychomys* in paired coexistence with other mice. However, no signs of aggressive behavior were produced by treatment with this drug. This negative finding is again consistent with the general principle that internal, physiological changes are insufficient stimuli for the fighting response.

During early fighting experiences, if the victim is too large, vigorous, or aggressive in response to attack and *Onychomys* is unsuccessful in his efforts to effect a kill, he will soon stop attacking. If the victim survives for 12–24 hours, peaceful coexistence ensues. If the victim mouse defends himself too vigorously or jumps about wildly in the confined space and accidentally knocks *Onychomys* about, *Onychomys* assumes the upright defensive posture and if the trauma continues will temporarily fall into a catatonic state. Such encounters can be produced by using the large vigorous Piñon mouse as a victim. As an alternative to continued aggression, *Onychomys* may therefore cease attacking, go on the defensive, or withdraw into catatonic immobility. Even after the aggressive pattern is well established, it can be suppressed by repeated failures or systematic defeat. However, it is otherwise quite per-

manent. Animals which have had no fighting experience for over six months will attack and kill victims placed with them, though not with the efficiency of mice regularly given opportunities to fight.

As one would expect, *Onychomys'* fighting is strongly re-enforced by success. Therefore, a series of easy victories increases aggressiveness and rapidity of kills. The weight of the victims may then be gradually increased until *Onychomys* can readily kill mice which weigh twice his own body weight. The time elapsing between introduction of the victim and the kill may be as brief as 20 seconds. When fighting trials are carried out at regular intervals, at the same time of day, with victims of the same species and of approximately equal body weight, the time for the kill becomes sufficiently constant to be used as a base line for studying the influence of various factors upon aggressive behavior.

So far, only preliminary studies in a small number of animals have been carried out on factors which might influence stabilized levels of aggression. However, the results are sufficiently interesting to deserve mention at this time. In line with the principles of agonistic behavior outlined in the introduction of this paper, total starvation for 24- and 72-hour periods did not increase aggressiveness. The effects of chlorpromazine given orally in doses of 16, 30, 32, 37.5, and 45 mg./kg. were studied. *Onychomys* is remarkably resistant to chlorpromazine. Although slight sedation appeared with dose levels of 16, 30, and 32 mg./kg., there was no evidence of behavioral toxicity, and the level of aggression and speed of kill were not significantly altered. However, 37.5 mg./kg. produced evident ptosis and slight-to-moderate ataxia. At 45 mg./kg., motor impairment was severe. While these animals did attack the victim, they did so less frequently and with less persistence and failed to kill during the five-minute trial. It would appear that chlorpromazine alters fighting behavior in *Onychomys* only in doses which produce gross toxicity and that motor impairment is a major factor in their failure to kill the victim.

An even more interesting observation, however, was made when the fighting behavior of the animals was studied the day after a single fighting trial on chlorpromazine. To our surprise, in all of the eight animals which received 16, 30, and 32 mg./kg. doses, the level of aggression was much increased and time for the kill markedly reduced the next day. This effect was most striking after trials at 16 mg./kg., but was also clearly evident after 30- and 32-mg. doses. All of these animals had remained aggressive and made kills on their chlorpromazine trials. In contrast, all of the eight animals which received 37.5- or 45-mg. doses were less aggressive the day following chlorpromazine, and killing times were appreciably longer than predrug levels or did not occur at all during the five-minute trial. There was no evidence of a drug hangover in the form of motor impairment to account for this effect. Apparently the experience of a successful fight, during which *Onychomys* is medicated with chlorpromazine in doses which do not impair his capacity to kill, powerfully re-enforces aggressive behavior on the next opportunity to fight. By the second day after medication, killing times return to predrug levels. If animals fail to achieve fighting success because of chlorpromazine, the experience has an inhibiting effect upon aggression in the next trial, as would failure from any cause. These findings suggest an interesting hypothesis, i.e., the affective state of an animal at the time he performs an aggressive act modifies the re-enforcing value of the experience for future behavior

of a similar kind. It is possible that anxiety reduction from chlorpromazine during the aggressive act accounts for its enhanced re-enforcing value. The converse, the effects of chlorpromazine upon the experience of defeat, remains to be systematically studied. However, the finding in animals which received 37.5 and 45 mg./kg. doses suggests that chlorpromazine does not reduce the inhibiting effects of failure.

The aggressive behavior of groups of 3–4 *Onychomys* has been studied in two types of colonies which differ in terms of the experience of the animals during the period when the fighting response was acquired. Both groups were trained to fight in a series of eight trials under a 1-liter beaker over a two-week period. However, the members of one colony were returned to their home cage between fighting trials, while members of the other were housed separately during this period and then rejoined to form a colony. Because of the marked behavioral differences which appeared in these two types of groups, the first has been termed a "cooperative" and the second a "socially disorganized" colony.

The "cooperative" group lived together without internecine conflict as they had during the training period. Victims introduced to the colony in its 18×18 inch cage were promptly killed. The victim was hotly pursued by all members of the colony; several mice would share in the killing and would eat the carcass. While particular mice in the group were more aggressive than others and more often participated in the kill, all participated at times; and no mouse was actively excluded. In contrast, when mice which had lived separately during fighting training were first returned together, a good deal of fighting occurred between members of the group. This reached destructive proportions. They suffered loss of ears and tails; three members of one colony were killed; and most lost weight. When a victim was introduced, members of the colony fought bitterly over which would make the kill. The dominant mouse was obliged to hold his competitors at bay or drive them into the nesting area before he could seize and kill the victim. Rapid kills occurred only when there was a markedly dominant mouse capable of achieving this feat. However, this dominant role could be maintained for only short periods and shifted from one mouse to another. After a kill had occurred, a period of 10 or 15 minutes of excited behavior would follow during which the *Onychomys* would attack one another. Accordingly, frequent introduction of victims intensified self-destructive aggression within the group.

At times when no clear-cut dominance was present, killing effectiveness was much impaired as the members expended their efforts sparring with one another. Under these conditions, some of the "victims" survived and established separate nesting areas where they coexisted, precariously, for many months. Other mice could be added to such coexisting colonies and might or might not be killed, depending upon the dominance situation at the time. Although the new arrival might be killed, previous survivors to whom colony members had become habituated would not be fatally attacked. It should be emphasized, however, that this type of coexistence is considerably different than that which can be established with individual or group *Onychomys* which have had no killing experience. Under these conditions, the alien mice establish *separate* nesting areas and spend much of their time in hiding since they are subject to abortive attacks when they go too close to the *Onychomys*.

The above characteristics of the cooperative and socially disorganized colonies per-

sisted without change for six months. The former remained a highly effective killing group even when victims were offered at intervals as long as two weeks. In contrast, disorganization and internecine conflict of the latter were perpetuated by periodic introduction of victims. It has already been pointed out that this procedure can lead to destruction of the colonies if repeated frequently.

An alternative form of the disorganized colony is one in which precarious coexistence with some victims is admixed with destruction of others and reactivation of conflict among the *Onychomys*. It is interesting that the survivors of self-destructive colonies are the less aggressive animals. It is true that these animals may have been subjected to repeated defeat in colony life. However, subsequent studies of their fighting in individual trials under conditions which should re-enforce this behavior indicate that like the meek who will inherit the earth they owe their survival to being less aggressive and thereby avoiding fatal encounters.

SUMMARY

A series of studies which illustrate the value of *Onychomys leucogaster* as a laboratory animal for study of aggression has been reviewed. The aggressive behavior of this animal follows a highly predictable pattern and can be readily quantified. Experimental conditions can be devised whereby it is possible to study factors which influence the first expression of this genetically determined behavioral trait as well as factors which re-enforce or inhibit it once it has become established as a response. In general, fighting in *Onychomys* conforms to the principles which characterize the aggressive behavior of other vertebrate animals. It is markedly affected by learning and aroused by external factors which abruptly alter the animal's interaction with the environment.

Chlorpromazine was found to have an interesting effect upon the aggressive behavior of *Onychomys*. Medication with this drug in dosage ranges which did not impair fighting ability because of motor toxicity markedly increased the re-enforcing value of a fighting experience. A possible interpretation is that the affective state of an animal at the time of a behavioral response, in this instance an aggressive one, alters the effectiveness of the behavior in terms of re-enforcement. Chlorpromazine presumably reduces the level of "anxiety" or fear associated with aggression. In any event, this phenomenon has potential value as a novel screening procedure for psychopharmacologic agents.

Onychomys may also be conveniently employed to study aggressive behavior in social groups. Methods have been described whereby novice, nonfighting colonies of mice may be selectively converted into groups which coexist peacefully with other species, which cooperatively direct aggression toward aliens, or which become socially disorganized and suffer from internecine conflict that results in the death of colony members as well as an impaired effectiveness in destroying alien animals.

REFERENCES

BAILEY, V. 1931. Mammals of New Mexico. *North American Fauna*, No. 53. Washington, D.C., U.S. Department of Agriculture.

ERGOSCUE, H. J. 1960. Laboratory and field studies of the Northern Grasshopper Mouse, *J. Mammal.* 41: 99–110.

HALL, E. R., and KELSON, K. R. 1959. *The Mammals of North America.* New York, Ronald, Vol. II.

ROOD, J. P. 1958. Habits of the short-tailed shrew in captivity, *J. Mammal.* 39: 499–507.

SCOTT, J. P. 1958. *Aggression.* Chicago, University of Chicago Press.

SWINYARD, E., CLARK, L. D., MIYAHARA, J., and WOLF, H. 1961. *J. Pharm. and Exp. Ther.* 132: 97–102.

13

MATERNAL BEHAVIOR AND ITS ENDOCRINE BASIS IN THE RABBIT

M. X. Zarrow

Paul B. Sawin

Sherman Ross

Victor H. Denenberg

Maternal behavior is one of the significant elements in the reproductive complex of the mammal. Some of the more commonly observed behavioral patterns in different species include nest building, nursing, aggressive protection, and retrieving of the young.

It is obvious that a disturbance in the physiological balance, especially endocrine, of the mother during gestation or an irregularity in the normal pattern of maternal behavior can induce failure in the delivery or proper care of the young. As such, both elements must be maintained optimally for successful reproductive performance; and fundamental to either physiological or experiential factors is the contribution of the gene. With modern advances in the biochemistry, neurophysiology, and pharmacology of the reproductive-endocrine complex,

the time now seems ripe for exploration of maternal behavior as it is related to all these fields.

The investigations of maternal behavior to be described herein originated from studies involving reduced growth, vitality, vigor, and reproductive index attendant to inbreeding of the domestic rabbit. This work is still under way and has been extended through the collaborative efforts of investigators in the areas of physiology and psychology. The importance of the rabbit for biological research of all types is well known. From a behavioral point of view, the rabbit has not been studied extensively by the psychologist. This is unfortunate since the rabbit provides a system in which accurate timing of embryos and of fetal development can be accomplished, perhaps with greater precision than in other mammals. In addition, this animal provides a system in which there are obvious behavioral characteristics which may be correlated with physiological mechanisms. The phenomenon of nest building and of pull-

This investigation was supported, in part, by Research Grants Nos. RG5228, RG5229, and RG-6263 from the Division of Research Grants and MY1604 from the National Institute of Mental Health, National Institutes of Health, U.S. Public Health Service.

ing hair to line the nest are perhaps major markers of endocrine changes during gestation.

PROBLEM OF MATERNAL BEHAVIOR

Maternal behavior in mammals involves an important set of interrelationships between the mother and young in which a high degree of variability exists both among mothers of different species and among mothers of the same species. This variability is related in various ways to the supply and demand for the common requirements of warmth, food, and protection against the elements and predatory species. Each species appears to have its own pattern of solving the problem of advancing its young from a rather specific, limited, biologically controlled environment to one in which the external stimuli become of greater and greater importance. Grossly, the possible environments may be classified into three different kinds, "natural," "domestic-breeding," and "laboratory." In the first, the mother and young are entirely dependent upon their own resources, surrounded by a relatively unlimited variety and supply of materials and food. In the last two, the supply of food may be controlled, but the protection and richness of the environment usually becomes relatively fixed, particularly under the usual laboratory circumstances. It can be expected that important differences are almost certain to appear as a function of rearing in these different environments, and that some aspects of maternal behavior of any species can only be adequately studied under a completely natural environment. Recently, Richter (1959) has developed this thesis from his comparative studies on the wild and the domestic rat.

In the work to be reported here from the Jackson Memorial Laboratory, we believe that the environment is closest to that of the domestic breeding colony in that the cage size and nesting facilities, though limited and artificial, are more nearly adequate to demonstrate most aspects of normal reproduction and particularly the maternal behavior pattern of the species. In the continuation and extension of this program, both at Purdue University and at the Jackson Laboratory, we hope to attack experimentally and to analyze most of the behavioral processes in a controlled laboratory environment. Although we realize that such an environment can be criticized because it is artificial, nevertheless only under controlled conditions can the many factors involved be isolated and critically tested.

The objectives of this research program have been to study the role of three major influences: the genetic, the endocrine, and the experiential factors affecting maternal behavior. Fundamental to an understanding of the role of the physiologic and experiential factors in maternal behavior is the contribution of the gene. Variations in the ultimate behavior of the organism are controlled by the gene as expressed through physiological and psychological mechanisms. Postnatal interactions between the mother and young are of major importance, and the generally unexplored, prior experiences of the doe may also be of great importance. Some of these events are probably interrelated by way of the endocrine systems, such as the prolactin control of lactation, the estrogen-progesterone-pituitary interaction, and the role of the placenta, fetus, and even the physical distention of the uterus in reproductive behavior. However, the story is far from complete. For example, we know little about the relation of the environmental and individual-experience factors with the endocrine or other physiological mechanisms. The following results represent some of our findings to date and indicate our multiple approach to the problem.

EXPERIMENTAL RESULTS

Genetic Aspects of Maternal Behavior

The first studies by Sawin and Curran (1952) called attention to significant racial differences with respect to time of nest building and nest lining, location of nest, quantity of hair plucked, and aggressive protection of the young. Later, Sawin and Crary (1953) analyzed the differences and associations of these racial elements in three closely bred races and one mixed population. Time of nest building and time of plucking of hair with which to line the nest were found to be most closely associated. In Race X, these events occur from 2–4 days prepartum and in the others, at or shortly after birth.

Later extension of the statistical analysis by Ross and Denenberg, based on additional data and including additional characters, has confirmed the original observations and revealed new information. An orderly progression of nest building from four days prepartum through the day of parturtition

has been found with different races (Fig. 13-1 and Table 13-1). It should be noted that all nests are built on the day of or prior to delivery. In addition, Race IIIc shows the highest percentage of no nest

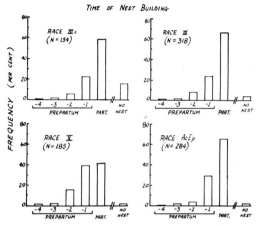

FIG. 13-1. Histogram of time of nest building in four races of rabbits.

building. Since it has also been established that Race IIIc is characterized by having significantly more scattering and cannibalism of their young than the other races, this suggests a possible relationship between lack of nest building and the above (Denenberg *et al.*, 1959).

TABLE 13-1   FREQUENCY DISTRIBUTION OF TIME OF OCCURRENCE OF NEST BUILDING FOR RABBITS OF DIFFERENT RACES FOR 1953 THROUGH JUNE, 1959

					RACE			
	IIIC		III		X		ACEp	
	NO.	PER CENT	NO.	PER CENT	NO.	PER CENT	NO.	PER CENT
No nest	22	14.3	11	3.5	3	1.6	4	1.4
Partum nest	90	58.4	209	65.7	76	41.7	187	65.9
Prepartum 1 day	33	21.4	72	22.6	71	38.4	83	29.2
Prepartum 2 days	7	4.6	22	6.9	29	15.7	8	2.8
Prepartum 3 days	2	1.3	3	0.9	3	1.6	2	0.7
Prepartum 4 days	0		1	0.3	3	1.6	0	
Total	154	100.0	318	100.0	185	100.0	284	100.0

No. = number of rabbits; per cent = per cent rabbits.

It should be emphasized that the racial characteristics of prepartum nest building for Race X and the relatively high frequency of no nest building for Race IIIc have remained constant for a period of more than seven years, thus emphasizing the importance and stability of genetic factors.

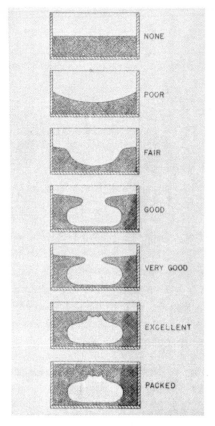

FIG. 13-2. Illustration of a graded series of maternal nests built by the pregnant rabbit. The various types of nest observed grade from no nest at all to a hollowed-out and closed-over nest well packed with hair plucked from the body and nesting material. (From Sawin and Crary, 1953)

Experiential Aspects of Maternal Behavior

The building of a maternal nest by the rabbit is not an all-or-none phenomenon.

Sawin and Crary in 1953 reported a graded series of nests in the pregnant rabbit which varied from no nest at all to a hollowed out and covered nest, well packed with hair from the body and intermingled with nesting material (Fig. 13-2). From this, a scale has been established with values of 0 (no nest) to 6 (packed). Recent observation has led us to conclude that in most instances the animal first collects the nesting material, brings it into the box, and hollows out a nest. This is then followed by hair plucking which is also brought into the box and used to line and cover the nest. This sequence of events and the maternal nest box used at Purdue University are illustrated in Fig. 13-3.

In order to investigate the effects of experience on nest building, the data collected by Sawin were analyzed for nest quality using the Sawin scale (Fig. 13-2). The study included only the first four successive parturitions of mothers who had four or more successful deliveries. The quality of the nest was found to increase significantly in a linear manner through the first three successive litters (Fig. 13-4). The slight drop with the fourth litter was not significant.

Although the findings in this experiment are clear, the interpretation is quite another problem. The most likely interpretation would indicate that the improved quality is due to prior experience in nest building. However, changes in endocrine balance and other physiological phenomena cannot be disregarded. The information on the effects of repeated litters on endocrine interactions or on triggering mechanism is not available.

The importance of individual experience on the part of the doe has not yet been well assessed. In other species such as the rat, the now-classic work of Wiesner and Sheard (1933, p. viii) indicates that " . . .

maternal behavior can arise, and can be evolved artificially, in the complete absence of the somatic conditions which are usually and normally associated with maternity." The work of Riess (1954) is also of interest here. Riess reported that female rats reared study Beach and Jaynes (1956) report that experience in giving birth, nest building, and retrieving during one pregnancy and lactation period has no effect upon maternal performance in a second reproductive episode in the rat.

FIG. 13-3. Maternal nest box used at Purdue University and sequence of nest building. A, the nest box with straw inside; B, hollowed-out straw nest; C, same nest as B now completely covered with hair; D, same nest with hair removed to expose the young.

in cages with no objects which could be picked up or transported do not build nests at parturition, even though the appropriate material is provided at that time. The role of these "experience" factors appears to be of importance, even though in a recent Other important work on maternal behavior in the rat has been carried out by Seitz. In two studies (1954, 1958) he has demonstrated a negative relationship between litter size and maternal behavior, with mothers of small litters behaving significantly more "maternally" than females with large litters. Seitz has also shown that the adult behavior patterns of rats reared in litters of six were quite different from those of rats reared in litters of twelve.

Further attempts at an analysis of the maternal behavior complex were carried out by Denenberg *et al.* (1958). No significant differences were found for interest in the young or for preparturient aggression

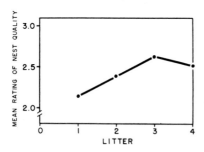

FIG. 13-4. Mean nest-quality score for the first four litters of 84 females. (From Ross et al., 1956)

among the four races studied over a number of litters. Significant racial differences were found regarding the time of nest building. In the correlational analysis a significant relationship was found between the quality of the nest and the percentage of liveborn young suckled on the first day of life. A suggestion was developed that some factor or factors may act in common upon nesting and suckling activities in rabbit maternal behavior.

One of the interesting differences found in comparing the rabbit with other common domestic animals is the apparent absence of retrieving behavior. One report in this series, by Ross *et al.* (1959), describes the failure to find such retrieving on the part of the doe through a series of experimental manipulations. The natural history literature and the observations of highly experienced rabbit breeders were consulted.

Some interpretations were offered in terms of the rabbit's particular adaptation to its environment and the neonate's general independence from extensive maternal care. One of the incidental findings in a later study (Deutsch, 1957), for example, indicates that normal development of the young takes place in spite of a total doe involvement of no more than 2 minutes for a 24-hour period for care, inspection, and nursing.

An analysis was made on cannibalism and scattering aspects of the maternal behavior complex, in an attempt to relate these behaviors to the previously studied relationships (Denenberg *et al.*, 1959) Only in one race was there a significant amount of scattering and cannibalism (Race IIIc). In this race, cannibalism and scattering were found to be significantly related to nest quality and with time of nest building.

The findings of this analysis showed that better nest quality, earlier time of nest building, greater percentage of liveborn suckled on the first day, lack of scattering, and lack of cannibalism were intercorrelated. As a result of these analyses, we have reason to believe that a "maternal-care" behavioral complex can be conceptualized and that this complex appears to be independent of a second group of factors involving interest in the young and aggressive protection.

Endocrine Aspects

- HAIR LOOSENING AND THE
  MATERNAL NEST

It should be emphasized at this time that the pregnant rabbit expresses two types of nesting activity. The first occurs relatively early, and in this instance the animal builds a nest composed of straw, excelsior, or whatever nesting material is available. This we have called a straw nest. The second type of nest is called the maternal nest and is composed of straw and hair. In general, our observations on a colony of Dutch belted rabbits maintained at Purdue and incorporates this into the nest. In addition, it should be pointed out that (1) occasionally the two types of nesting activity occur almost simultaneously and (2)

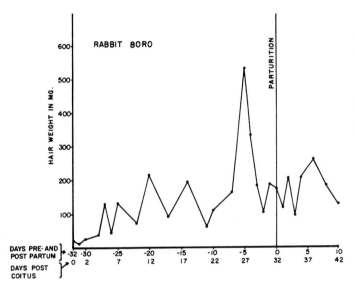

FIG. 13-5. Prepartum hair loosening in the pregnant rabbit (From Sawin et al., 1960).

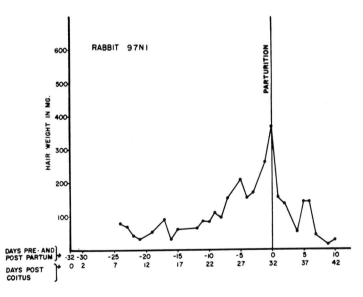

FIG. 13-6. Partum hair loosening in the pregnant rabbit (From Sawin et al., 1960).

University reveal that the pregnant rabbit initially builds a straw nest 1–5 days prior to building the maternal nest. In both instances this is a positive behavior pattern in that the rabbit actively carries straw into the nesting box and actively pulls hair

the straw-nest activity has been noted in nonpregnant rabbits.

These observations plus the report by Tietz (1933) of hair loosening during gestation prompted us to examine this phenomenon in the rabbit. Rabbits were mated,

that additional endocrine factors may be involved (Chu, 1944).

SUMMARY

Maternal behavior in the rabbit is an exceedingly complex phenomenon. Nest building, hair loosening and lining of the nest, nursing, protection and care of the young are among the items involved in this phenomenon. The present report presents data showing that genetic, physiological and experiential factors are important determiners of maternal behavior in this species.

Analysis of data has revealed significant racial differences with respect to the time and quality of nest building. In addition, major differences have been noted with respect to the care and maintenance of the young among the races studied. These racial differences have remained constant over a period of approximately 10 years.

It has been shown that the hair of the rabbit loosens in the latter stages of gestation, suggesting a possible influence of the hormones of pregnancy on this phenomenon. Hair loosening and nest building were also noted in a limited but significant number of pseudopregnant rabbits. Cesarean operations and castration during pregnancy have been shown to induce nest building. Finally, treatment with stilbestrol, progesterone, and prolactin can induce nest building in a small percentage of nonpregnant rabbits.

Behavioral studies have shown that the rabbit first builds a straw nest, then lines it with hair plucked from her body. When the quality of nest built is studied as a function of successive litters, it has been found that the quality improves through the first three litters. Other behavioral analyses lead to the conclusion that there is a "maternal-care" complex which is characterized by better nest quality, earlier time of nest building, greater percentage of liveborn young suckled on the first day, lack of scattering, and lack of cannibalism.

REFERENCES

BEACH, F. A., and JAYNES, J. 1956. Studies on maternal retrieving in rats: II. Effects of practice and previous parturitions. *Amer. Naturalist.* 90: 103–110.

CHU, J. P. 1944. The influence of the thyroid on pregnancy and parturition in the rabbit. *J. Endocrinol.* 4: 109–114.

DENENBERG, V. H., PETROPOLUS, S. F., SAWIN, P. B., and ROSS, S. 1959. Genetic, physiological and behavioral background of reproduction in the rabbit. VI. Maternal behavior with reference to scattered and cannibalized newborn and mortality. *Behaviour.* 15: 71–76.

DENENBERG, V. H., SAWIN, P. B., FROMMER, G. P., and ROSS, S. 1958. Genetic, physiological and behavioral background of reproduction in the rabbit. IV. An analysis of maternal behavior at successive parturitions. *Behaviour.* 13: 131–142.

DEUTSCH, J. A. 1957. Nest building behavior in domestic rabbits under semi-natural conditions. *Brit. J. Animal Behav.* 5: 53–54.

RICHTER, C. P. 1959. Rats, man, and the welfare state. *Am. Psychologist.* 14: 18–28.

RIESS, B. F. 1954. The effect of altered environment and of age on mother-young relationships among animals. *Ann. New York Acad. Sc.* 57: 606–610.

ROSS, S., DENENBERG, V. H., FROMMER, G. P., and SAWIN, P. B. 1959. Genetic, physiological and behavioral background of reproduction in the rabbit. V. Nonretrieving of neonates. *J. Mammal.* 40: 91–96.

ROSS, S., DENENBERG, V. H., SAWIN, P. B., and MEYER, P. 1956. Changes in nest building behaviour in multiparous rabbits. *Brit. J. Animal Behav.* 4: 69–74.

SAWIN, P. B., and CRARY, D. D. 1953. Genetic and physiological background of reproduction in the rabbit. II. Some racial differences in the pattern of maternal behaviour. *Behaviour.* 6: 128–146.

SAWIN, P. B., and CURRAN, R. H. 1952. Genetic and physiological background of reproduction in the rabbit. I. The problem and its biological significance. *J. Exper. Zool. 120:* 165–201.

SAWIN, P. B., DENENBERG, V. H., ROSS, S., HAFTER, E., and ZARROW, M. X. 1960. Maternal behavior in the rabbit: hair loosening during gestation. *Am. J. Physiol. 198:* 1099–1102.

SEITZ, P. F. D. 1954. The effects of infantile experiences upon adult behavior in animal subjects: I. Effects of litter size during infancy upon adult behavior in the rat. *Am. J. Psychiat. 110:* 916–927.

SEITZ, P. F. D. 1958. The maternal instinct in animal subjects: I. *Psychosom. Med. 20:* 215–226.

TIETZ, E. B. 1933. The humoral excitation of the nesting instincts in rabbits. *Science. 78:* 316.

WIESNER, B. P., and SHEARD, N. M. 1933. *Maternal Behavior in the Rat.* Edinburgh, Oliver & Boyd.

ZARROW, M. X., SAWIN, P. B., ROSS, S., DENENBERG, V. H., CRARY, D., WILSON, E. D., and FAROOG, A. 1961. Maternal behavior in the rabbit: Evidence for an endocrine basis of maternal nest building and additional data on maternal nest building in the Dutch-belted race. *J. Repro. & Fertil. 2:* 152–162.

14

DEVELOPMENT OF SUCKLING AND RELATED BEHAVIOR IN NEONATE KITTENS

Jay S. Rosenblatt

Gerald Turkewitz

T. C. Schneirla

Social behavior in the domestic cat has its genesis and basis in the neonate's stimulative relations with the mother. The kitten's earliest approach responses to the mother center on the processes of suckling, which play a central role in social development through the entire period of infancy. The first suckling adjustments of the neonate mark the foundation of a behavioral bond between newborn and female; the waning of the suckling adaptation, which usually occurs at the end of the second month in the litter period, indicates the beginning of an important change in social behavior leading to weaning. In the studies to be described, we find that the behavioral bond between the female and her kitten weakens steadily as that among the kittens increases in strength, and that these related behavioral events contribute to the eventual dis-

The experiments on which this summary and discussion is based were supported by grants from the National Science Foundation and from the Rockefeller Foundation.

In addition to the forthcoming detailed reports (Rosenblatt *et al.,*) a discussion of these results in relation to the problems of individual and social development in insects and mammals was published in the *American Journal of Orthopsychiatry.*

solution of the close-knit group and to the more loosely organized social patterns characteristic of postlitter stages.

The first occurrences of suckling are facilitated particularly by thermal and olfactory stimulation from the female, and by tactual stimulation from her as through licking, helping to orient the neonate. The stimulative and the nutritive adjustments of the kitten consequently are closely related from the beginning, so that in the individual's behavioral development no sharp distinction can be made between social responses and feeding adjustments. For the kitten, the female functions both as the source of nutrition and as the center of social activities, and as a consequence, suckling activities change progressively in a manner that is greatly influenced by the character of the kitten's relations with the mother. In turn, the behavioral relationships of kittens and mother depend crucially on how the activities of suckling by the kittens and nursing by the mother can proceed.

The present investigation was designed to compare the suckling behavior and social adjustments of litter-reared kittens with the behavior of kittens returned to the litter and female after periods of isolation introduced experimentally during the first two months of life. The object was to analyze behavioral adjustments in normally raised kittens in the light of comparisons with the adaptation of kittens subjected to specific conditions of social deprivation.

EXPERIMENTAL AND THEORETICAL BACKGROUND

The research program on behavioral development in the domestic cat, of which the results are discussed in part here, was designed to test hypotheses derived from Schneirla's (1946, 1951a, 1951b, 1956) theory which emphasizes the basic role of reciprocal stimulative processes in mammalian social ontogeny, in relation to factors of maturation and of experience postulated as inextricably interrelated in individual development. With reference to the first stage of socialization, studies in our laboratory (Tobach *et al.*, in manuscript) indicate that the behavioral bond between the female and her offspring begins at parturition. We find evidence for a progressive integration of stimuli centering first on adjustments to organic events such as uterine contractions, next on stimuli pertaining to the genital zone (as from fluids), and thereby presently on the neonate itself. Although the neonate participates rather passively and incidentally in the events of parturition, soon afterward, through the early development of suckling and related activities, it enters into progressive stimulus-response processes which become increasingly bilateral and reciprocal.

Research on the subsequent development of social behavior has involved both detailed analytical investigations of group and individual behavior at successive stages in the litter period and tests of related functions such as individual orientation in the

kitten. Studies on orientation have been carried out with several litters from time of parturition through the third week, in relation to studies on social behavior carried through the entire litter period. To summarize the results on an early phase of this investigation, systematic observations of suckling from the time of parturition show that the neonates, although at first inept and variable in their activities, within the first hours accomplish increasingly specific adjustments to the female's mammary surface. Related developments in orientation are indicated by our findings on the neonate's nest-returning behavior. In systematic tests of this behavior carried out in a daily routine, we have found (Rosenblatt *et al.*, in manuscript) steady progress in the neonate's formation of spatial discriminations utilizing olfactory and other nonvisual cues and in its emotional attachment to a familiar site associated with an expanding repertoire of feeding and social activities.

NORMAL DEVELOPMENT OF SUCKLING

Under normal conditions, suckling occurs within the first hour after birth, even before the entire litter has been delivered, and thereafter it occurs regularly at short intervals in nursing sessions that initially may last as long as 45 minutes each. At first young kittens may expend a total of nearly eight hours per day in suckling, until at about the thirty-second day the processes of weaning begin. From this time there is a gradual decline in the frequency and duration of suckling activities to the time weaning is completed. Under normal conditions, weaning is completed by the end of the second month; under special conditions, however, as when the female and young continue to be confined together, weaning of the kittens may not be completed for several months and may not reach an end in certain cases.

In general, we have identified three

STAGE I. In this period, which lasts from birth to the end of the third week, feedings are initiated mainly by the female. She ap-

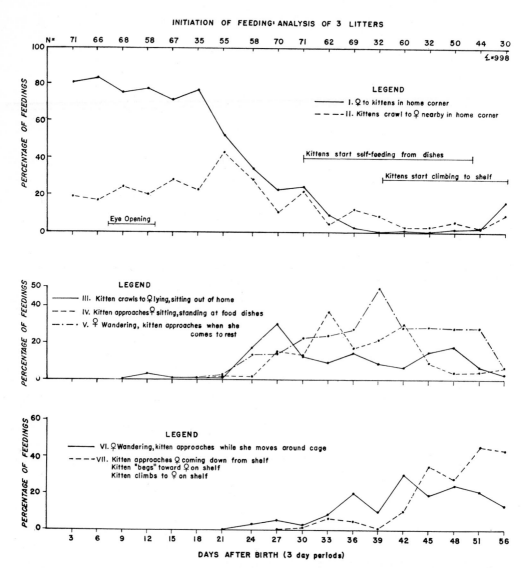

FIG. 14-1. Stages in the initiation of maternal-young feeding relationships in the domestic cat (data from three litters). Graphs show percentage of responses of each type recorded in the daily observations in each three-day period.

principle stages in the development of suckling at the female, with each of these involving important changes in the suckling pattern. These stages, described below, are indicated in Figure 14-1.

proaches the kittens huddled in the home region of the cage, lies down while arching her body around them, and "presents" her mammary zone to them. The kittens, in response to tactual and other stimuli from the female, and to directional influences as from her licking, first become active, then begin variable movements that in the course of time lead into nipple localization, attachment, and suckling. Evidence of early participation of kittens in the initiation of suckling is shown in both their increasing readiness to respond to the nursing approaches of the female by pushing toward her body and in the rapid progress they make individually in locating a nipple. By the fourth day most of the kittens of the litter are able to localize rapidly and to attach to a nipple at the rear, center, or anterior region in the mammary surface. Thereafter, at nearly every nursing, most of the kittens adopt their own individually specific nipple regions for suckling.

STAGE II. The period from the third to the sixth week constitutes the second stage of suckling, in which (as Fig. 14-1 indicates) the initiation of suckling becomes increasingly a mutual activity of the kittens and the female. The kittens now begin to leave the home corner of the cage with increasing frequency and to make approaches to the female even at some distance in the cage with nipple localization and suckling the outcome. Fewer nursing sessions than before begin with the female approaching the kittens; she facilitates suckling, however, by frequently remaining at rest in places outside the home situation or by adjusting her mammary region and permitting suckling on their approach at other times as when she is crouched over the food dish. For the kittens this period involves a transitional process in which their perceptual reactivity is transferred from certain cage localities to the female as the focus of suckling and other orientative adjustments. Also in this period there occurs a rapid development of play activities among the kittens and between the kittens and the female.

STAGE III. Starting at the fifth week and continuing to the end of weaning, initiation of suckling depends more and more and finally altogether upon the kittens. With increasing frequency and for longer intervals they follow the female as she wanders about the cage; when she evades them by leaping to the wall shelf, they remain at the place of her disappearance. When she happens to be accessible to them they persist with increasing vigor in attempts to nuzzle. At times these actions may result in attachment and suckling, but often, as when they are counteracted by the female, they result in little more than a perfunctory social exchange. In this period, also, sucklings are initiated by individual kittens rather than by the group to a greater extent than before, marking for the kittens the approach to a high point in their individual functioning within the social situation of the litter. At the time of this accomplishment, when suckling involves the most intricate and most subtle relationships of the entire association between female and young, the processes of weaning begin simultaneously. Paradoxically, the advance of weaning and self-feeding from artificial sources marks a gradual decrease in the potency of the social bond between the female and her young.

These and other results of our study of the development of suckling in the litter situation provide a normative ontogenetic basis for comparison with the responses to the female of kittens returned from experimental isolation. Our findings suggest that the normal steady increase in the efficiency of suckling and in the complexity of the feeding pattern depends upon more than specific improvements in the motor, perceptual, and motivational capacities of the kittens. We find that necessary adaptations to changes in the behavior of the female in the course of the litter period also involve factors strongly influential in the social development of the kittens. The results are in agreement with the hypothesis (Schneirla, 1946, 1956) that the development of social bonds and of individual socialization centers on reciprocal

FIG. 14-2. Seven-day old kitten suckling at the nipple of the "artificial mother," a brooder enclosed in the incubator in which a subject lived during its isolation period (see text). Rear-guard panel and milk supply are indicated.

stimulative processes including those of feeding. As our results show, in the behavioral ontogeny of the kitten no sharp distinction can be drawn between nutritive and social adjustments, as in the litter period both of these types of adjustment are involved at every stage in a close relationship characteristic of that stage.

ISOLATION EXPERIMENTS

In this research, the aim was to analyze the normal socialization processes by determining the effects of social deprivation inserted at different times on the feeding behavior and other social adjustments of kittens.

The Incubator and Related Procedures

• INCUBATOR AND BROODER SITUATIONS

The experimental kittens were isolated in a special incubator, a cubical enclosure containing a brooder or "artificial mother" (a U-shaped vessel with its open side outward, Fig. 14-2) placed on the floor near the wall. The brooder was designed not only to present a nipple from which the isolated kitten could draw, through its own efforts in suckling, a synthetic formula available at a controlled temperature, but also to offer a model which would be attractive by virtue of its thermal, tactual, and spatial properties as a crude partial substitute for the female.[*] The brooder served these purposes, as well as obviating any important need for substantial amounts of forced feeding by hand and other special attentions which might have been equivalent in some sense to the normal behavioral role of the female.[†]

• SUCKLING DEVELOPMENT IN THE
  INCUBATOR

To start the processes of independent feeding equivalently in different subjects, all of the isolated kittens were helped in a standard way to attach to the brooder nipple. Within three days they were all able to crawl up into the brooder from the incubator floor, locate the nipple, and attach independently. Thereafter, self-initiated

[*] A prototype of the "artificial mother," in the functional U-form and covered with soft toweling, was developed in 1949 in connection with experiments on parturition in the cat (Tobach *et al.*), was modified for further use by Dr. Alan Frank, Fellow of the National Institutes of Mental Health, in our laboratory during 1950–1951, and was further improved for the present experiments.

[†] One other special procedure carried out in this situation as a substitute for normal activities of the female involved a brief manipulation of the isolate kitten daily in the first two neonatal weeks with routine stimulative operations appropriate to the facilitation of defecation and urination.

suckling occurred at regular intervals in these isolated subjects, and in the course of time, gradual changes were observed in their manner of approaching the nipple and attaching.

These changes in brooder feeding paralleled only in a broad way the development of suckling in female-reared kittens. In general, three stages were observed in adjustment to the brooder.

STAGE I. In the first two weeks, each isolated kitten adopted a more or less canalized patch to the nipple leading along one or the other arm of the brooder, in close contact with the soft surface and following the physical contour of the brooder and its guard panels. In this phase, nuzzling movements, at first localized in the general region of the nipple, gradually were confined to the base of the nipple; nipple-grasping, also, although evidently a more difficult task in the brooder than with the female, rapidly became a smoothly performed action.

STAGE II. Beginning in the third week, kittens tended to make a variable approach to the nipple through the open U-shaped area in the brooder and between the arms of the brooder. As the kitten's route through the center of the brooder brought it more and more directly to the nipple, nipple localization improved, and the amount of preliminary nuzzling decreased. Indications were that the transition to this improved mode of approaching the nipple after about 10 days occurred through the increased utilization of visual cues, with proximal cues such as contact used in the local nipple adjustments.

STAGE III. After the fourth week, kittens held in isolation rapidly became more versatile in approaching the nipple, passing to it directly from different angles—over the arms or through the central area of the brooder—and attaching with a minimum

of nuzzling. Approaches to the nipple then were initiated at some distance from the brooder and from any position in the chamber.

No further changes of importance in brooder suckling were observed in isolated kittens until the fifth or sixth weeks, when processes of weaning appeared in several of the subjects. At this time the isolated kittens began to approach the food dishes (which, although present in the incubator for several days, had not been visited before) and for the first time began to dip into them, taking small amounts of milk or meat; at the same time each of the kittens continued to feed at regular intervals from the brooder. Thereafter the brooder continued to be the source of the same food as before while dish feeding also was permitted so that both modes of feeding would be available to the isolates on their subsequent test returns to the female and litter.

* SUCKLING TESTS

The subjects, after their different periods of isolation, were returned individually to the female in the litter situation for detailed observations of their suckling responses to the female, their general cage orientation, and their social reactions to female and litter mates.

Results

* FREQUENCY OF SUCKLING

Suckling appeared, on the first returns of the subject to the female, in all of the kittens isolated from birth to the 7th day, from the 6th to the 23d day, and from the 18th to the 33rd day. In contrast, all but one of the kittens isolated from the 23d to the 44th day and from the 2d to the 44th day failed to suckle from the female. These kittens, moreover, although left contin-

TABLE 14-1   SUCKLING REACTIONS OF ISOLATE KITTENS UPON RETURN TO THEIR FEMALES

ISOLATION PERIOD (DAYS)	NUMBER OF DAYS	NUMBER OF KITTENS	SUCKLING FREQUENCY (%)	MEAN SUCKLING LATENCY	CONTACT LATENCY*	SUCKLING DELAY†
0– 7‡	7	3	100	3 hr. 11 min.	0 hr. 51 min.	2 hr. 20 min.
6–23	18	5	100	19 42	1 2	18 40
18–33	16	2	100	15 10	0 46	14 24
23–44	22	4	25	————||	47 56	————||
2–44	43	4	0	————	38 36	————
34–49§	16	4	100	48 15	0 56	47 39
47–54	8	4	100	2 10	0 12	1 58

* "Contact latency," the interval between the start of a test and the appearance of the first sustained contact with the female.
† "Suckling delay," the interval between contact latency and suckling.
‡ Kittens in these 5 groups were brooder-fed in isolation.
§ Kittens in these 2 groups were fed from dishes in isolation.
|| One kitten of this group suckled after 72 hours, 25 minutes.

uously with the female from the beginning of their tests, never suckled (Table 14-1).

Failure to suckle was not due to an inability to suckle. As noted previously, efficient brooder suckling was observed in all of the isolates not long before their removal for the cage tests. Nor was this failure due to insufficient hunger, as is indicated by the results of two isolates that had failed to suckle with the female. These kittens were left with her for two days without food, while the female was fed outside the cage. With the female as the only source of food in the cage, suckling by two mother-reared kittens occurred promptly each time she returned. The isolates, in contrast, notwithstanding a period of food deprivation extending to 48 hours, never joined the nursing group and displayed no tendencies to suckle.

Two other groups of isolates were tested at the 49th and 54th days after periods in the incubator in which they were fed from dishes without any opportunity to suckle. The results in these tests, in which all of the kittens suckled after their return to the litter situation, indicated that the failures to suckle in the brooder-fed groups were not due to any "natural decline" in suckling—as might be suggested by the fact that suckling normally falls off by the 44th day in litter-reared kittens (Table 14-1).

• OTHER MEASURES OF SUCKLING

Our results for cage-return tests with regard to the relative delay of suckling ("suckling latency") provide a useful measure of the difficulty of accomplishing female suckling after isolation (Table 14-1). The suckling latencies were longer for all of the groups of isolates than for normal kittens, with the single exception of the group isolated from the 47th to the 54th day.

From our findings, the period of suckling latency may be divided into an interval ("contact latency") preceding the appearance of the kitten's first sustained contact with the female and a further interval (the "suckling delay") required for the subsequent more-specific adjustment to her leading to suckling. By comparing the values of these two intervals of adjustment we may ascertain the basis of both prolonged suckling delays and of failures to suckle in isolated subjects.

In the five groups of isolates that finally

suckled in the female tests, short contact latencies of one hour or less indicate clearly that the processes of making a preliminary adjustment to the female had been disrupted only minimally by the period of isolation (Table 14-1). By contrast, the second and more specific adjustment preceding suckling was protracted in all the isolate groups, and suckling was delayed on the average for times ranging from 2½ hours to nearly 48 hours.

In the two remaining groups (Table 14-1), the contact latencies exceeded 38 hours, and the achievement of a sustained contact with the female after these long intervals represented the best performance in adjusting to her of all but one of these kittens. Nearly all of these isolated kittens evidenced a high degree of disturbance in the female tests. Characteristically, from shortly after their return to the litter situation, these kittens displayed an evident tension and a heightened excitement in the proximity of the female, marked by the appearance of hissing, overt withdrawal, and other signs of fear. In these two groups, such disturbed reactions to the female continued for many hours before subsiding. In contrast, in the kittens isolated from the 34th to the 54th day, the only other group to show disturbance in the presence of the female, all signs of disturbance disappeared within the first hour of the test. It is interesting to note, however, that in this last group the suckling latencies were all longer than they were in the other isolate groups that suckled.

• SUCKLING STATUS OF THE ISOLATES

The results we have presented thus far suggest that for the isolate kittens in the tests the principal difficulty lay in the initiation or in the performance of the suckling act, or in both of these, rather than in accomplishing a preliminary adjustment to the female. To carry further our analysis of results for the adjustment of these isolated subjects to the female, toward an understanding of its relation to the characteristics of behavior under normal conditions, we may compare the suckling behavior of the kittens isolated under different conditions with that of female-reared kittens at corresponding ages.

BIRTH–7th day isolates. Kittens tested after an isolation of one week exhibited deficiencies in their cage adjustment which not only prevented them from reaching the regular site of group nursing in the home corner but later on caused them to leave when they happened to reach this place. As a result, in the tests of all of them spent considerable intervals of time alone at a distance from the female and apart from the group of litter mates huddled in the home corner. With these isolate kittens, therefore, the initial contact with the female usually had to occur largely by chance. When one of them happened to brush against the female, this initial contact was usually followed by turning toward her and next by pushing against her body with nuzzling into her fur. But nuzzling in these kittens was not confined to the nipple region as in normal subjects; instead, the week-old isolates nuzzled over the female's entire furry surfaces including even her paws, neck, and back. At first, therefore, the proximal orientation of these isolates to the female was quite generalized and not significantly more efficient than that of neonate kittens. This adjustment in the week-old isolates was markedly different from the highly localized nuzzling of mother-reared litter mates which at the age of 7 days already were able to adopt individually specific suckling positions in the mammary area and attach to the nipple within a few seconds after their nuzzling began.

These isolates, therefore, revealed the handicap of losing the initial week in the litter situation by their cruder orienting movements, their much more variable responses to the nursing approaches of the female, and in particular by the lower efficiency of their actions as compared with normal subjects in localizing nipples.

6th–23d day isolates. The kittens tested after this period of isolation were clearly inferior to normally raised litter mates in the initiation and early performance of suckling. Notwithstanding the fact that these kittens achieved their first sustained contacts with the female early in their test periods, mainly through being attracted visually to her from a distance, the latencies of their first suckling reactions were much longer than were those for the first-week isolates. While the litter mate controls were suckling once or twice each hour, the 6th–23d day isolates each continued for nearly 20 hours in a persistent orientation to the female's face and anterior body but not to her mammary region. These kittens, also, as with the first-week isolates, were generalized in the locus of their nuzzling, all of them spending long intervals nuzzling over the bodies of other kittens and the furry, nonmammary surfaces of the female before localization of the nipple and attachment occurred. Apparently their early suckling experience in the litter situation, prior to isolation, was of little help to them under the new conditions that prevailed in the litter situation at the time of their tests. Our normal studies show that the litter mates, during the interval between the removal and the return of these isolates, had gradually developed the capacity to initiate suckling by approaching the female on a visual basis from different parts of the cage. Furthermore, as we have indicated, the female's behavior had also changed under these conditions. For this group of isolates, however, the intervening period of practice in orienting to the brooder and suckling there was clearly inadequate as a preparation for meeting the different and more complex conditions they encountered in the litter situation on their return.

18TH–33d day isolates. For the kittens returned to the litter situation from isolation in what we have identified as the intermediate stage of normal suckling development, the situation of testing was somewhat different from those described for the younger isolates. Although these subjects, like the 6th–23d day group, were slow in localizing the female's mammary region, they had less difficulty in localizing nipples. Their difficulties centered more on adjusting to the female as an object from which to suckle.

34TH–49th day isolates. These kittens, isolated during the normal weaning period, needed an even longer time than the other isolates to accomplish their first suckling adjustments to the female in the tests. At the time these kittens were tested, their normal litter mates were suckling individually or in small groups at irregular intervals, in nursing sessions initiated actively by them for the most part through their direct approaches to the female from a distance. The deprivation period evidently handicapped the isolate kittens of this group chiefly through having deprived them of the opportunity to modify their suckling orientation to the female under the changed conditions rather than through having affected their specific operations of localizing a nipple and suckling.

47TH–54th day isolates. In their responses to the female, the kittens of this group differed markedly from the subjects in other groups isolated after the sixth day. Although the one-week isolation of these kittens had begun at the time weaning normally is nearly completed, they all accomplished suckling in return tests. Their suckling delays, moreover, were the shortest of those in all isolation groups, although their nipple localizations had to be accomplished while the female was moving around the cage. The interval of isolation, therefore, did not seem to have affected these kittens in their suckling adjustments and their general litter adjustments in the light of those prevailing when the period of isolation began for them. In their case, the litter situation had undergone only a minimal change during the absence in isolation, as our results show clearly that the principal developments in suckling and in general social adjustment normal to the litter period had already taken place.

• FEMALE AND BROODER AS SUCKLING
  OBJECTS

Significant differences appear when the female and the brooder are compared in their effect on the kittens as objects from which to suckle. The results of all tests of isolates with the female indicate that whatever the stage of isolation the brooder was only very partially adequate as a preparation for a readjustment to the female, whose situation and behavior had changed meanwhile. For the kitten, the brooder at best was equivalent only to a minor extent with the complex and varying exteroceptive and spatial properties of the active female. Although for the kittens at early ages the thermal and other stimulative properties of the brooder proved attractive and its spatial (i.e., the functional-U) properties useful as canalizing factors, the limited equivalence of the brooder to the female for them was apparent. In contrast, in the litter situation, orientation to the female and suckling progressed steadily from the first, due particularly to orienting stimulative effects of the female such as licking for which manual guidance in the brooder was an inferior substitute.

That the brooder situation demanded a simpler adjustment for suckling than did the female was suggested, however, by the rapid manner in which older kittens accomplished this adaptation on their first introduction to the brooder, as compared with the far greater difficulties shown by brooder-isolated kittens at corresponding ages in adjusting to the female. It is evidently the simpler and relatively static nature of the brooder situation that explains this difference.

A project was undertaken to test the recall and reinstatement of suckling at the brooder as against that at the female as a means of distinguishing between these two patterns both in their conditions of formation and change and in their possible effects each upon the other. Suckling at the female was tested in kittens that had originally suckled at the female but had suckled at the brooder in isolations starting after the 25th day. Suckling at the brooder was tested in kittens that had originally suckled at the brooder but had been nursed by females during intervals corresponding to the above isolations. In each of these groups, therefore, the test object was the one at which suckling had occurred during approximately the first 25 days. For most of the kittens used in this comparison, the suckling tests came at 40–45 days, or at an age when on other grounds the kitten's adjustments to the two types of suckling object could be considered maximally different.

The difficulty of reinstating suckling at the female on the one hand and at the brooder on the other is represented by the results in Table 14-2. For the reappearance of suckling in tests with the female after brooder isolation, a mean latency of 31 hours was obtained, whereas for the reinstatement of suckling in brooder tests after periods with female and litter the latencies were much shorter, averaging only 12 minutes. Suckling latencies in female tests were shorter for kittens tested

TABLE 14-2   REINSTATEMENT OF SUCKLING AT THE FEMALE AND AT THE BROODER

TEST CONDITION: SUCKLING AT FEMALE		TEST CONDITION: SUCKLING AT BROODER	
PRECEDING PERIOD WITH BROODER (DAYS)	SUCKLING LATENCY	PRECEDING PERIOD WITH FEMALE (DAYS)	SUCKLING LATENCY
17	26 hr., 5 min.	36*	immediate
16	72 25	24	24 min.
16	23 15	24	12
15	93 25	17	3
15	50 35	15	8
15	24 40	14	10
14	7 5	12	21
14	no suckling	10	16
13	5 hr., 35 min.		
8	5 56		
8	9 33		
Mean = 13.7 days	31 hours	19 days	12 minutes

* Part of this period was spent alone in a cage feeding from dishes.

after brooder periods of two weeks or less than they were for kittens that had been isolated for more than two weeks in the brooder.

The duration of absences from the brooder, in contrast, did not seem critical, for the latency scores for suckling in brooder tests were similarly low in the different kittens given these tests after intervals of from 10 to 24 days respectively in the litter situation.

DISCUSSION

The results of our analytical studies of behavioral development in the litter situation in comparison with the status of behavior in isolated subjects are best understood if reviewed in terms of a comparison of the pattern of feeding relationships holding in the two situations at corresponding ages. From comparisons of the conditions prevailing for female suckling at different stages we find that the normal relationship of female and young

through the litter period is a complex and changing one in which the roles of the participants are modified progressively through three very different stages. As a consequence, the litter situation confronting isolates returned from the brooder at different times deviates radically from that prevalent at the earlier time of removal, especially as concerns the general behavior of the female and her responses to the kittens. To meet the different conditions of the new stage, without having participated in their gradual genesis, constitutes an increasingly difficult task for kittens returned at later stages, as it requires a more and more complex and specialized social and nutritive adjustment, diverging increasingly from that formed earlier by the kittens in the litter situation.

On the other hand, adjustment to the brooder after an interval in the litter situation evidently involves meeting a relatively unchanged situation, as our findings show that this situation can be modified in its behavioral and functional relevance *only* in dependence on the kitten itself. The outcome of our test indicates that a relatively simple stereotyped approach-conditioning pattern arose thereby which was not greatly disrupted by intervening adjustments to the female in the litter situation and which could be reinstated without much difficulty on the kitten's return to the brooder.

For the most part, therefore, the disturbed behavior and the deficiencies of adaptive adjustment in kittens isolated late in the litter period may be attributed to their shortcomings for dealing with differences which had arisen in the litter situation during their absence. Both the evidence summarized here and results to be reported in further detail emphasize the necessity of a continued behavioral and functional interchange with female and litter mates if the kitten is to develop an adequate suckling adjustment typical of its age group. As we have mentioned, the feeding adjustment may be considered a central process in behavioral development; this, however, is not just any mode of feeding by suckling, as in the brooder, but one appropriately adapted to the current behavior pattern of the female and to the prevalent social situation.

Our findings lead us to favor a rather different view of the concept of "critical periods" than the one now adopted by many investigators (e.g., Scott and Marston, 1950). For social ontogeny in the domestic cat, our results support instead the interpretation that striking behavioral changes are attributable not only to growth-conditioned processes (i.e., to maturation) but also to factors of experience characteristic of the existing developmental situation. From this standpoint, we are led to emphasize not just one or a few striking time-conditioned changes in the pattern, but to recognize that in general every age-period is *critical* for the development of certain aspects of the *normal, progressive suckling pattern*. Because factors of experience dependent upon the developmental situation are always significant for this pattern, in close relation to growth-dependent factors, we find that isolation from the normal developmental situation so deprives a kitten of developmental advantages available to normal litter mates that it cannot adjust adequately when returned later.

The extent of recovery following a period away from female and litter is so dependent upon the age, the duration of the isolation, and the conditions of the isolation, however, that much further research is essential to clarify what factors of maturation or of experience at any one stage may become critical for specific as against inclusive and highly organized adjustments of the same or of later stages. The entire problem is complicated by questions concerning the equivalence of different kinds of maturational processes and of experience for the specific or for the general attainments of any stage in ontogeny.

It seems clear from our results that understanding the effects of any condition of isolation or deprivation, in relation to those of the standard ontogenetic situation, requires an investigation of developmental processes in both of these situations to ascertain their equivalences and their differences at successive stages.

REFERENCES

ROSENBLATT, J. S., WODINSKY, J., TURKEWITZ, G., and SCHNEIRLA, T. C. Analytical studies on maternal behavior in relation to litter adjustment and socialization in the domestic cat. II. Maternal-young relations from birth to weaning. III. Development of orientation. In preparation.

SCHNEIRLA, T. C. 1946. Problems in the biopsychology of social organization. *J. Abnorm. & Social Psychol. 41:* 385–402.

SCHNEIRLA, T. C., 1951a. A Consideration of Some Problems in the Ontogeny of Family Life and Social Adjustments in Various Infrahuman Animals," in *Problems of Infancy and Childhood, Tr. Fourth Conference,* New York, Josiah Macy, Jr., Foundation, pp. 81–124.

SCHNEIRLA, T. C. 1951b. "An Evolutionary and Developmental Theory of Biphasic Processes Underlying Approach and Withdrawal," in *Nebraska Symposium on Motivation.* Lincoln, Nebr., University of Nebraska Press, pp. 1–42.

SCHNEIRLA, T. C. 1956. "Interrelationships of the 'Innate' and the 'Acquired' in Instinctive Behavior, in *L'Instinct dans le Comportement des Animaux et de l'Homme,* ed. by GRASSE, P. P. Paris, Masson & Cie, pp. 387–452.

SCOTT, J. P., and MARSTON, M. 1950. Critical periods affecting the development of normal and mal-adjustive social behavior of puppies. *J. Genet. Psychol. 77:* 25–60.

TOBACH, E., FAILLA, M. L., COHN, R., and SCHNEIRLA, T. C. Analytical studies on maternal behavior in relation to litter adjustment and socialization in the domestic cat. I. Parturition. In preparation.

15

ELIMINATIVE RESPONSES IN MICE AND RATS
AND THE PROBLEM OF "EMOTIONALITY"

Ethel Tobach

T. C. Schneirla

In 1932, Yoshioka (1932) observed that food-deprived rats placed in an enclosure with food accessible often responded in early trials by defecating and urinating but not by feeding. Introduced successively to the same situation, however, most of the animals began to feed, and eliminative responses in the enclosure ceased. Hall (1934c) viewed this phenomenon not in the context of learning theory, as had Yoshioka, but in relation to individual differences in adjustment. He (1938) gave the following four facts as evidence for characterizing these responses as "emotional":

1. They occur in situations recognized to be emotionally arousing in character.
2. They are linked with other reactions set off by impulses traveling over the autonomic nervous system.
3. They disappear as the originally strange situation becomes familiar.
4. As the number of animals defecating and urinating decreases, the number of animals eating increases.

According to Hall (1938), the proof that such behavior affords a valid measure of

The preparation of this paper was supported by Grant No. M1441 from the National Institute of Mental Health.

individual differences is that the same animal that defecates in the novel situation does not feed, whereas the nondefecating animal does feed.

In later work by Hall and co-workers, and by others, Criteria 3 and 4 were modified or dropped (Anderson, 1939; Bindra and Thompson, 1953; Broadhurst, 1957a, 1957b; Hall and Whiteman, 1951; Lindzey, 1951; Martin and Hall, 1941; Stern, 1957; Willingham, 1956). The second criterion has received relatively little attention. No studies have been reported in which other autonomic activities were measured in correlation with defecation and urination. Rather, in this respect, the research has been indirect, involving either operative procedures aimed at the clarification of the role of the adrenal medulla (Fuller, Chambers, and Fuller, 1956; Moyer, 1958) or pharmacological investigations of drug effects, with the defecatory reaction as the dependent variable (Broadhurst, Sinha, and Singh, 1959; Jones, 1944; Ryall, 1958; Taeschler and Cerletti, 1959).

Although Hall uses the term "emotional," he prefers the word "emotionality," considered "a convenient concept for describing a complex of factors . . . a group of organic, experiential, and expressive reactions . . . a general upset or excited condition of the animal" (1934c). He has also referred to such behavior as "timidity" or "fearfulness," a view which has found some support (Anderson, 1938; Geier, Levin, and Tolman, 1941), but which other investigators (Billingslea, 1940, 1942; Bindra and Thompson, 1953; Hunt and Otis, 1953; Willingham, 1956) have considered related to other aspects of behavioral organization.

Hall's first criterion for the phenomenon is that it must occur in "emotionally arousing situations." There have been two approaches to the problem of defining "emotionally arousing situations" which can elicit the defecatory reaction. In one, the intensity of the stimulus situation presented to the animal in the open-field test has been investigated. Hall (1938) specified that the animal in the open-field test should be stimulated by a high intensity of light. Later investigators (Broadhurst, 1957a; Evans and Hunt, 1942) found that the open-field test becomes a more reliable indicator of emotional defecation when its stimulative intensity is increased.

Another approach to studying the relation between noxious stimulation and the defecatory response has been to stimulate young mice and rats at various stages of development and later to test them in the open-field situation. Hall and Whiteman (1951), working with offspring of crosses between C57 and dba mice, found that animals subjected to a noxious auditory stimulus defecated more than did control pups. Stanley and Monkman (1956), working with dba/1 mice, did not find a comparable effect when animals were shocked during the litter period. Griffiths and Stringer (1952), with rats, used several forms of noxious stimulation during the litter period

but found no differences in defecation in adulthood.

Other investigators have used "manipulation" of the animal as an early experience designed to affect the incidence of defecation or number of boluses in the open-field test. The noxious character of this treatment is less readily defined than is that of shock or auditory stimulation, but its general, over-all stimulative effect is apparent. It is not clear from the literature on "manipulation" studies (Bovard, 1958) how this treatment acts as a disturbance to the animal. Although Weininger (1956) showed that rats handled outside their home cages defecate less than nonhandled controls in their home cages, Ader (1959) and Mogenson and Ehrlich (1958) found no differences in defecation between handled and nonhandled rats in the open-field test. Levine (1959) also, who manipulated mice prior to weaning, observed no differences in amount or incidence of defecation in a runway situation designed to study "aggression." In an earlier study with rats, however, he found that handled rats defecated less than nonhandled rats (1956).

The second approach to clarifying the concept "emotion" as related to the defecatory reaction has been to "validate" the "emotionally arousing situations" which elicit the response. Parker (1939) used various forms of noxious stimulation designed to arouse the emotions of "fear" and "escape behavior" and found that the defecation scores of rats in all of these situations intercorrelated significantly and positively. Hall (1934b) presented food behind a wire-mesh barrier in an open-field test and found a significant decrease in defecation, which he took to indicate the effect of "frustration." O'Kelly (1940) also created a "frustration" situation by using a barrier to prevent rats from leaving a brightly lit area as they had been doing and found a significant increase in defecation and urination. The crucial factors may concern differences in the nature or in the degree of frustration, in the techniques used, or in all of these.

Hunt and Otis (1953) have shown that a defecatory reaction can be conditioned in an "anxiety"-producing situation. The only attempt to test the hypothesis that the defecatory reaction is related in some way to "anxiety" was a study on rats by Moyer (1957) in which he found no correlation between defecation and the "anxiety" advanced by Mowrer as a factor in conditioned-escape responses.

"Anxiety" has been defined experimentally for man by the work of Welch and Kubis (1947) on the basis of Pavlov's (1927) finding that more excitable dogs condition more quickly than phlegmatic animals. Their report that human subjects judged "anxious" in a psychiatric examination condition more rapidly than normal subjects was substantiated by Bitterman and Holzman (1952) and by Taylor (1951). Runquist and Ross (1959), using a physiological measure of emotionality in human subjects, also found a correlation between conditioning scores and emotionality. James (1953) pointed to a need for experimental investigation of the relationship between "emotionality" and conditioning and cited several examples of the possibility of such a relationship in dogs.

Levine (1959), although not studying the problem in the context outlined above, did find a correlation between the defecatory reaction and conditioning rate in Sprague-Dawley rats. The relationship was a positive one, so that animals which conditioned quickly in the avoidance situation were low in amount of defecation. If the

concept of human anxiety is in any way related to that of emotionality in the defecatory reaction, the correlation should have been a negative one, i.e., animals high in amount of defecation should condition quickly.

Although Hall does not include in his list of criteria his genetic characterization of the defecatory reaction, the idea is implicit and explicit in his work and in that of others, that the behavioral pattern is "something quite fundamental to the animal" (1938), an innate factor related to the functioning of the autonomic nervous system which is more constitutionally than situationally determined. Hall (1938) bred two strains of rats selectively: "emotional" rats which defecated consistently in the test situation and "nonemotional" rats which did not defecate in the test situation. According to Hall (1938), the fact that such a breeding program could be carried out supports his psychogenetic view of the defecatory reaction. Recently, Broadhurst (1959) has stated that the "rat's defecation in the open field is determined by a polygenic system having a low degree of dominance and a moderate heritability . . ." suggesting that defecation indicates a "high degree of susceptibility to environmental effects . . . ."

Although Broadhurst's statement might imply a disagreement with Hall's (1938) position that experience is not an important variable in the defecatory response mechanism, it is clear that he considers defecation in the generalized open-field situation a genetic trait, i.e., an innate characteristic. If the level of defecatory reaction is thus held to be constitutionally characteristic of the individual, two questions are raised: (1) Are there any measures of the level of defecatory response which may differentiate individuals as to this characteristic at

TABLE 15-1 EXPERIMENTAL DESIGN

	I. DEVELOPMENT ASPECT						II. ENVIRONMENTAL ASPECT						III. CONTROL	
GROUP	UPUS						VPUS		UPVS		VPVS		MC	
LITTER-PERIOD ENVIRONMENT														
"Physical" aspect (cage)	Unvarying (standard laboratory cage)						Varying		Unvarying		Varying		Unvarying	
"Social" aspect (dam and litter)	Unvarying						Unvarying		Varying		Varying		Unvarying	
SUBGROUP	Pups of each litter equally assigned to the following subgroups						Pairs of litter mates assigned to the following subgroups						Pups of each litter assigned to each subgroup	
	A		B		C	D	A	B	A	B	A	B	1	2
	1	2	1	2										
OBSERVATIONS														
Litter period	Open-area test daily (4 min.)		Kept in container during testing of Subgroup A		Open-area test daily (2 hr.)	Open-area test on 1 day only (4 min.)	Open-area test daily (4 min.)	Kept in container	Open-area test daily (4 min.)	Kept in container	Open-area test daily (4 min.)	Kept in container	Cage cleaned every 5 days; no other treatment	
Postweaning period	Open-area test and approach impedance (4 min.) Avoidance conditioning	Avoidance conditioning	Open-area test and approach impedance (4 min.) Avoidance conditioning	Avoidance conditioning			All animals in all groups tested after weaning in the standard open-area situation, and subjected to approach impedance						Open-area test and approach impedance (4 min.) Avoidance conditioning	Avoidance conditioning
Number of subjects	10	10	10	10	18	385	10	10	10	10	10	10	12	12

all stages of development? and (2) Is this activity really characteristic of an individual animal in all situations?

Although a developmental study using both cross-sectional and longitudinal methods is required to answer these questions (Schneirla, 1956), no studies are found in the literature involving developmental indicators of the defecatory reaction. Schneirla (1956) has pointed out the need for an experimental analysis in which external and internal factors are viewed as interrelated and as differently integrated at all stages of development. Despite Hall's (1951) plea for a strictly genetic approach, the existence of an interaction between phenotypic physiological characteristics and the developmental situation is tacitly accepted in his insistence upon the maintenance of a *constant* environment, and by his own work with Whiteman (Hall and Whiteman, 1951). Clearly, experimental investigations are needed of the effects of different types of experience on the type of individual response under study here.

Two aspects of the phenomenon seem to lend themselves to such experimental study. First, as rodents do not defecate and urinate spontaneously at birth, onset of defecation presents itself as an early indicator of phenotypic variation perhaps responsive to various types of experience during development. Second, the defecatory response seems to be most easily and reliably elicited in a situation not specifically experienced earlier by the animal. Consequently, it would seem that an animal experiencing novel situations frequently in early life might defecate less than otherwise in a novel test situation encountered in later life.

Other aspects of the problem of "emotionality" will be considered, in regard to the defecatory reaction in situations designed to be "emotionally arousing," and in

regard to a needed validation of the "anxiety" concept of this behavioral pattern. Thus, by observing the same animals in many different situations, we may also investigate the hypothesis that defecatory reactivity is constitutional on an innate basis.

SUBJECTS

B Albino C mice were used, the colony derived from breeding pairs from the Roscoe B. Jackson laboratory.

METHODS AND PROCEDURE

The methods used in this investigation combine the longitudinal and cross-sectional types of investigation. Subjects representing all groups were studied concurrently, and the experiment involving a particular group was repeated until the prescribed number of subjects was obtained. Where possible, litters were assigned to different groups. The replication of experiments took approximately five months (July 1, 1956 to November 20, 1956).

Table 15-1 shows the experimental design.

Development of Defecatory Response

To study the development of the defecatory response, litters were assigned to one group which was raised in an environment unvarying as to its principal physical and social aspects. In each litter in this group, some animals (Group UPUS-A; see Table 15-1) were observed daily in a modified open-area situation from their day of birth until weaning. To control for the effects of the manipulation involved, some animals from each litter (Group UPUS-B) were kept meanwhile in a carrier without being exposed to the bright light of the testing situation. The fact that mice, like many other mammals, do not defecate spontaneously for an appreciable time after birth recommended the inclusion of another group (UPUS-C), to find whether the four-minute duration of the open-area test was sufficient to elicit the response and also whether the animals would defecate and urinate spontaneously despite the lack of any stimulation by the dam over an extended period. This "extended period" was set at two hours, as pilot experiments revealed that mice could be removed from the litter for a period of two hours daily without seriously affecting their viability or growth rate. To control for the effects of these types of daily manipulation, the remaining litter mates (UPUS-D) were tested in the open-area situation on one day only. Litters were standardized as to size because of possible effects on the defecatory response after weaning (Seitz, 1954). In this way, a litter of seven or eight in this group would be assigned as follows:

Subgroup A: Observed daily in the open-field test—2 pups.

Subgroup B: Kept in container while litter mates A observed—2 pups.

Subgroup C: Kept for two hours daily in an open-field situation—2 pups.

Subgroup D: Tested only once in the open-field situation—1 or 2 pups.

Pups were marked individually on the day of birth by a system of ear clipping.

To supplement the regular UPUS-D pups obtained from the assignment of the experimental litters to the various subgroups, additional pups were taken from regular colony litters. All animals in the UPUS-D group were left with the female at all times, except for the one test.

To further control the effect of a high amount of manipulation during the litter period, another group (the manipulation control—MC—see Table 15-1) was incorporated into the design. These animals were handled once every five days in the course of cage cleaning only.

Effect of Varying the Aspects of Environment During the Litter Period

To observe the development of the defecatory response and the effects of a varying litter environment, four groups were set up as follows.

Group UPUS: *u*nvarying *p*hysical and *u*nvarying *s*ocial aspects of the environment.

Group VPUS: *v*arying *p*hysical and *u*nvarying *s*ocial aspects of the environment.

Group UPVS: *u*nvarying *p*hysical and *v*arying *s*ocial aspects of the environment.

Group VPVS: *v*arying *p*hysical and *v*arying *s*ocial aspects of the environment.

In each of the four groups, litter mates were assigned to Subgroups A and B as described above, with the exception that the first group (UPUS) also contained Subgroups C and D.

All scheduled environmental changes in the social or physical aspects of the environment, or in both of these, were made daily. Pups to be tested were removed from the home cage, and at the end of the test period were placed in the new situation, i.e., one in which either the physical or social aspects, or both of these, had been altered.

Postweaning Tests

At weaning, all animals were placed in individual maintenance cages with food and water. On the day after weaning, all animals in the VPUS, UPVS, and VPVS groups were presented with the open-field test described below. In Groups UPUS and MC, only half of each group was tested (see Table 15-1).

• OPEN-FIELD TEST AND APPROACH
  IMPEDANCE

Upon return to the maintenance cage after observation in the open-field test on the day after weaning, subjects were deprived of water. Three hours after the observation, they were given water for one minutes, the interval timer rang once more, and the animal was removed. One trial was given daily for 10 days. On Days 11 and 12, the water bottle placed in the enclosure was empty. On Day 11 the animal was not given any water in its home cage, so that at the time of observation on Trial 12 it had been without water for 44 hours.

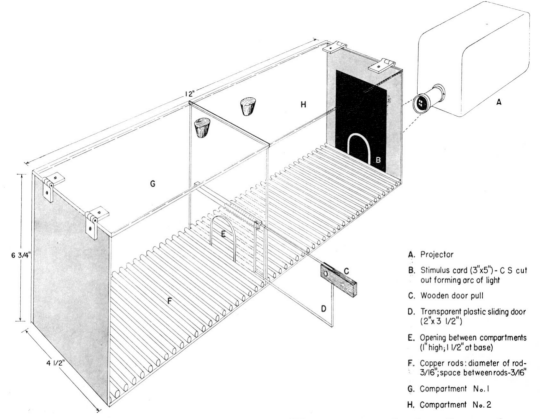

A. Projector

B. Stimulus card (3"x5")- C S cut out forming arc of light

C. Wooden door pull

D. Transparent plastic sliding door (2"x 3 1/2")

E. Opening between compartments (1" high; 1 1/2" at base)

F. Copper rods: diameter of rod- 3/16"; space between rods-3/16"

G. Compartment No.1

H. Compartment No. 2

FIG. 15-1. Avoidance conditioning apparatus. (Diagram courtesy American Museum of Natural History, New York)

hour. This routine was continued so that in this part of the experiment each animal was deprived of water for 20 hours before each observation.

For this test, the animal was placed in the center of the enclosure. Two minutes after its entry, an interval timer rang, and a water bottle was placed at the center of the open-area enclosure. At the end of two

This procedure of presenting a dry water bottle after water deprivation proved significant for testing impedance of a bottle-approach response (Ghent, 1957; Siegel and Stuckey, 1947).

• AVOIDANCE CONDITIONING

After the defecatory reaction had been studied in the open-area situation, animals from Groups UPUS-A-1 and B-1, and from MC-1 so studied, together with their litter mates (UPUS-A-2, UPUS-B-2, and MC-2) not experienced in this open-field testing, were conditioned to give an avoidance response to a lighted arc with electric shock as the unconditioned stimulus (Fig. 15-1).

For a conditioning trial, the animal was placed in Compartment 1, and the door was opened. If the subject entered Compartment 2 before the CS was given, it was shocked until it re-entered Compartment 1. If an animal entered Compartment 2 after the CS was presented, and before shock, a CR was noted as made. After Compartment 2 was entered, the animal was returned to Compartment 1, and the next trial was begun. The criterion of conditioning was reached when an animal made five successive CR's.

Intervals between "door-opening" actions ranged from 15 to 45 seconds. The first trial (each door opening, CS, and shock equal one trial) started 35 to 120 seconds after the animal was placed in Compartment 1 at the beginning of each day's session. Daily sessions lasted approximately 12 minutes.

APPARATUS

The various types of cages and nesting materials used are described in Table 15-2.

The open-field enclosure used for tests in the litter period was a solid metal cage $10 \times 6 \times 5$ inches high, painted a flat gray. A 100-watt bulb was suspended over the center of this cage. The open-area enclosure used for postweaning tests had a circular wall of metal 24 inches high and 30 inches in diameter standing on a metal floor 30 inches in diameter. The metal was painted a flat gray. A 300-watt bulb hung over the center of the enclosure.

The conditioning apparatus consisted of two adjoining chambers, connected by a door and floored with parallel copper rods

TABLE 15-2 CAGES USED FOR VARIOUS GROUPS AND ANIMALS

Standard laboratory cage: solid metal cage, wire-mesh cover; gravity-type water bottle; measurements: $7\frac{1}{4} \times 9\frac{3}{4} \times 8$ inches. Groups UPUS and UPVS. Sawdust.

Glass tank: standard two-gallon aquarium, wire-mesh cover; gravity-type water bottle; measurements: $10 \times 8\frac{1}{2} \times 6\frac{3}{4}$ inches. Groups VPVS and VPUS.

Glass dish: a round glass dish with convex sides; wire-mesh cover; gravity-type water bottle; measurements: $9\frac{1}{4}$ inches in diameter and 5 inches high. Groups VPVS and VPUS.

Round cage: an all-mesh metal cage with a solid metal cover; a water bottle is inserted through the mesh sides; measurements: 9 inches in diameter and $7\frac{1}{4}$ inches high. Groups VPVS and VPUS.

Large cage: a solid metal cage with wire-mesh cover; gravity-type water bottle; measurements: $16 \times 11\frac{3}{4} \times 5\frac{1}{4}$ inches. Groups VPVS and VPUS.

Individual laboratory cage: a solid metal cage with wire-mesh cover; gravity-type water bottle; measurements: $10 \times 6 \times 8$ inches. (Postweaning maintenance.) Sawdust.

Nesting materials: sawdust; fine gravel; nonsterile absorbent cotton; packing material (an absorbent paper cloth); strips of $\frac{1}{2}$-inch white crepe paper. Groups VPVS and VPUS.

Food loose on floor in all cages.

for electrical conduction (Fig. 15-1). The entire apparatus was enclosed and lighted from within, creating a one-way screen for viewing the animal. An Applegate constant current stimulator was used to deliver 130 microamperes of current to the floor of the apparatus at all resistances of the circuit.

GENERAL LABORATORY CONDITIONS AND TESTING PROCEDURES

The colony was maintained on a reversed lighting schedule so that the animals could be observed during their active period. Observations took place in rooms other than the colony room. With the exception of the postweaning period during the open-field testing, food and water were always present. After weaning, animals were maintained in individual cages. Weaning took place at 21 days of age.

All equipment and the enclosures and apparatus were swabbed with 95 per cent alcohol between observations.

BEHAVIORAL DATA RECORDED

In the open-area observations prior to weaning, written records were made of the animal's activity, with times noted as far as possible. The occurrence of eliminative responses was recorded both during the tests and when the animal was in the carrying case before and after the tests.

For postweaning tests in the open-area situation, an Esterline-Angus reaction recorder with the Aronson (Clark and Aronson, 1951) keyboard was used to record ambulatory activity, circling, and the following important responses: washing and grooming, number of fecal boluses and occurrence of micturition, time to reach wall, all crossings of open area, all movements to center from wall or to wall from center, approaches to the water bottle, duration of drinking acts, standing up to or climbing leg of apparatus, nosing and drinking drops of water on the floor, standing up at wall, and jumping. In addition, the number of boluses and occurrence of micturition in the container before and after observations were recorded.

In all conditioning trials, data were taken on a check sheet as to jumping, number of fecal boluses, micturition, washing, grooming, complete or partial entries into Compartment 2, rigidity or freezing, and conditioned responses with times noted as far as possible.

RESULTS

No sex differences were found on any of the measures analyzed, except that in the incidence of micturition during the open-field tests after weaning, as discussed

below.[*] No significant correlations were found between defecation and micturition at any stage of the experiment. Comparisons of the behavior of animals raised under the "split-litter" conditions as well as of the litter mates assigned to different groups showed that differences among the various groups were due to treatment rather than to litter differences. Table 15-3 shows the results obtained in all the subdivisions of the experiment.

DEVELOPMENTAL DATA

Onset of Spontaneous Defecation and Micturition

Mice, like most mammals, for an appreciable period after birth require urogenital stimulation for elimination to occur. In this study, significant differences were found among the groups with regard to the first appearance of defecation and micturition.

Using as the "score" the day on which defecation was first seen, with techniques for analysis of matched samples, no differences were found between animals tested in the open-area situation and their litter mates kept in the carrying case (Groups VPUS and VPVS). In Groups UPUS and UPVS, the animals observed in the open-field test started defecating spontaneously at an earlier age than their litter mates kept in containers. It was also found that UPUS-A mice showed spontaneous defecation later than UPVS-A animals, and that UPUS-B animals started defecating later than UPVS-B mice.

Eliminative Responses Throughout the Litter Period

The four groups studied in litter situations of varying stability may be compared not

[*] Information about statistical results, excluded from the article by requirements of space, is available on request.

Differences Among Groups with Different Experience

MEASURES	OPEN-FIELD TESTED PUPS (SUBGROUP A) VS. CONTAINER-HELD PUPS (SUBGROUP B) (DURING THE LITTER PERIOD)	COMPARISONS AMONG ALL GROUPS	BETWEEN-GROUP COMPARISONS	WITHIN-GROUP COMPARISONS
Litter period:				
Age at which defecation first seen in open-field test	UPUS-A < UPUS-B UPVS-A < UPVS-B	Significant	UPVS-A < UPUS-A UPVS-B < UPUS-B	
Number of pups giving response on each day of litter period	Not significant		Day 11: UPUS-D > UPVS Day 12: UPUS-D > UPUS-A & B Day 13: UPUS-A & B < UPVS 　　　UPUS-C, UPVS, VPUS > UPUS-D Day 14: UPUS-A & B, UPUS-C, UPVS, VPUS > UPUS-D Day 18: UPUS-A & B > UPUS-D	UPUS-D: Day 10 > Day 9 Day 12 > Day 13 Day 12 > Day 14
Post-weaning period: (mean defecation rate)				
A. Open-field test				
Trial 1, Part 1	Not significant	Significant	UPUS = UPVS < VPUS < VPVS	
Trial 1, Part 2	Not significant	Significant	VPVS > VPUS	
Trials 2–11, Part 1	Not significant	Not significant		
Trials 2–10, Part 2	UPVS-A < UPVS-B	Significant		
B. Approach-impedance trials				
Trial 11, Part 2	Not significant	Not significant		
Trial 12, Part 1	Not significant	Not significant		
Trial 12, Part 2	Not significant	Significant	VPVS = UPVS < MC-1; VPUS = UPUS > MC-1	
Trial 11, Part 2: increase over median Trials 2–10, Part 2			UPUS = VPUS = UPVS > MC-1	
C. Avoidance conditioning				
"Door-only" trials				
"Door-only" and CS trials	} Not significant	} Not significant		
Conditioning trials				

Correlations Between Measures Within Groups

MEASURES	MEAN DEFECATION RATE TRIALS 2–10, PART 2	APPROACH-IMPEDANCE REACTION SCORE	CONDITIONING RATE	
Onset of defecation		VPUS-A −.776*		
Approach-impedance reaction score	UPUS-B-1 −.717*			
Conditioning rate	UPUS-A-1 +.731*			
Defecatory reaction on first trial of "door-open" and CS			MC-1 +.809†	
Mean defecation rate on conditioning trials			MC-1 −.685†	

No other correlations were found to be statistically significant.

* N = 10; RHO = .564; "p" = .05; RHO = .746; "p" = .01.
† N = 12; RHO = .506; "p" = .05; RHO = .712; "p" = .01.

only with one another but in particular with two control groups—the two-hour group (UPUS-C) and the cross-sectional group (UPUS-D). It is not clear from the present experiment whether the two-hour separation from the female should be characterized as disturbing or as analogous to what might happen in the nest situation. Although in this experiment no observations were made in the nest situation, observations of litters in the colony room seemed to indicate protracted periods during which the female neither licked nor nursed the pups, and when spontaneous defecation and urination may have taken place in the home cage. These intervals, when female and pups were separated in the home cage, were very short at the beginning of the litter period but lengthened gradually, the longer intervals probably coming at about the tenth day (cf. Williams and Scott, 1953). In any event, the data of the two-hour group make an interesting standard against which to compare the other groups.

In the case of the cross-sectional group, the comparison is more tenable. These animals were taken from regular colony litters and tested only once as a control on the effects of continuous testing of the same animal. Some of the animals came from litters which were handled daily (UPUS-D group), and an analysis disclosed no difference between these animals and those from colony litters.

In the following analyses, animals in the group tested in the open area were first compared with those kept in the container, but no differences were found among them as to the number of animals defecating on any one day. Accordingly, the animals were combined into six groups: the UPUS, VPUS, UPVS, VPVS, UPUS-D, and the UPUS-C groups.

Starting on Day 10, significant differ-

ences begin to appear among the groups in the number of animals defecating. Generally these differences among the groups are a reflection of the characteristics of Groups UPUS-C and UPUS-D. Group UPUS-C reached a maximum earlier than any of the other groups and maintained it throughout the litter period. Group UPUS-D showed a significant increase on Day 10 and continued significantly higher than other groups until Days 13 and 14. On these days, not only was this group significantly lower than the other groups, but the decreases from Day 12 to Day 13 and to Day 14 were statistically reliable. (A two-by-two chi-square analysis—Siegel, 1956—was significant at less than the 5 per cent level of probability.) From Day 15 until weaning there were no more significantly different relationships among the groups, except on Day 18 when UPUS-D had a lower frequency of animals defecating than UPUS-A and UPUS-B.

Throughout the litter period no differences were found among the four groups with varying degress of environmental stability, except on Day 13 when UPUS-A-1, UPUS-A-2, UPUS-B-1, and UPUS-B-2 had less animals defecating than Group UPVS.

Time of Eye Opening

The eyelids of the mouse normally fuse in utero approximately five days before birth and then reopen about Day 14 (Bennett and Gresham, 1956; Takebe, 1939), with some variation as we have found. In this study, "day of eye opening" was marked as that day when both eyes were open.

Although there were no differences between the subgroups (A and B) of each group, or among the four main groups (UPUS, VPUS, UPVS and VPVS), all of these groups opened their eyes earlier than the animals in UPUS-C.

Two-by-two χ^2 analyses of defecation

and eye-opening frequencies on Days 13 and 14 revealed no relationship between the two phenomena. That is, an animal that had opened its eyes on a given day would not be more likely to defecate than an animal that had not yet opened its eyes.

POSTWEANING OBSERVATIONS IN THE OPEN-FIELD SITUATION

Defecatory Reaction

Each trial was divided into four intervals: Pretesting (animal in the case to the observation situation); Part 1 (animal in the enclosure without the water-bottle apparatus); Part 2 (in the enclosure after the water-bottle stand was introduced); and Postobservation (animal in the case to the home cage). Counts were made of the number of fecal boluses in the case before and after the observation and in the enclosure in each part of the observation, and each occurrence of micturition was noted. As each of these parts of the trial varied in duration, a defecation rate was calculated by dividing the number of boluses by the duration in seconds of each part of the trial.

The first trial in the open-field situation was run before any deprivation was introduced, and the data from this trial are treated apart from both the trials in which the animals were deprived and from the behavioral-impedance trials (i.e., the second part of Trial 11 and Parts 1 and 2 of Trial 12).

The incidence of defecation in the carrying case before and after the trials was random, although defecation was more frequent before trials than after. On Trial 1, however, enough animals defecated before the observation to warrant an analysis. No reliable differences were found among the groups or their subgroups. As defecation was too sporadic before the observations in

the subsequent trials, these data were not analyzed. The one reference to the rate of defecation before observations (Yeakel and Rhoades, 1941) reports no relationship between preobservation defecation and defecation during the observation.

Defecation after the trials was not frequent enough to admit an analysis of data for Trial 1 or for subsequent trials.

Using the Friedman two-way analysis of variance technique it was found possible to arrive at average defecation rates for each animal for the first part of Trials 2 through 11 and the second part of Trials 2 through 10, as there were no significant differences among the days or the groups.

The data for the first trial reveal significant differences among the groups for Part 1 and for Part 2 of the test. For Part 1 of Trial 1, no differences were found between animals observed in the open field prior to weaning and their controls kept in the containers. They were, therefore, combined and treated as one group. The differences among all the groups were significant (Kruskal-Wallis analysis of variance, "p" $= .02 - .01$).

MEAN RATE OF DEFECATION—TRIAL 1, PART 1

(Mann-Whitney "U" Tests)

GROUPS	MEAN RATES	
UPUS-A-1 and UPUS-B-1	20.45	Differ from all groups except UPVS
UPVS	23.20	Differs from all groups except UPUS
VPUS	26.65	Differs from all groups
VPVS	30.55	Differs from all groups
MC-1	12.90	Differs from no other group

A similar analysis conducted for Part 2 of Trial 1 showed no differences between the groups tested in the open-field situation during the litter period and their controls; hence these were combined. There was an over-all difference due mainly to differences between VPUS and UPVS animals. The VPUS group was lower than the UPVS group.

Micturition

Micturition took place so rarely as to exclude analysis. There was a slight (not statistically significant) tendency for females to urinate more frequently than males. In each group between seven and nine animals urinated on a mean of 1, 2, or 3 trials. When urination did take place there was also a slight but not significant tendency for it to occur in Part 2 rather than Part 1.

APPROACH-IMPEDANCE REACTION

Defecatory Reaction

In Part 2 of Trial 11, the animals were presented with an empty water bottle. Using the median defecation rate on Days 2 through 10 for all groups, each animal in a group was rated for Part 2 of Day 11, as above or below the median. Below are listed the number of animals in each group above or below the median:

	UPUS	VPUS	UPVS	VPVS	MC-1
Above median	10	13	10	7	3
Below median	6	7	8	12	9

The discrepancy in total number of animals in each group is due to cases with rates equivalent to the median in Part 2 of Day 11.

From these results, it was found that Groups UPUS and VPUS differed significantly from Group MC-1 ("p" = .05 — .02). Group UPVS when compared with Group MC-1 showed a higher frequency above the median ("p" = .10 — .05). In general, it would appear that Groups UPUS, VPUS,

and UPVS were fairly similar in that there was an increase in defecation when the empty water bottle was presented, but Groups VPVS and MC-1 were more alike in showing a decrease in defecation.

The animals were then deprived of water for a period of 44 hours before Trial 12. In Part 2 of Trial 12 they were again presented with an empty water bottle. Again, no statistically significant difference was found among the groups in defecation rates on Part 1 of Trial 12. The difference among the groups on Part 2 of Trial 12 was statistically significant, however (Kruskal-Wallis test; "p" < .01).

DEFECATORY REACTION IN PART 2 OF TRIAL 12

(Second approach–impedance situation)

GROUPS	MEAN DEFECATION RESPONSE
UPVS	5.7
VPVS	7.4
MC-1	9.8 (differs from all groups)
UPUS	11.1
VPUS	12.3

The main source of the group differences centered on Group MC-1 which differed from all other groups. No other comparisons between pairs of groups were significant.

When the defecation rates in each group were analyzed in two-by-two comparisons, as to the number of animals showing a decrease from Trial 11 in defecation rate, Groups VPUS, VPVS, and MC-1 did not show a significant decrease in defecation rate in Part 2 of Trial 12, whereas Groups UPUS and UPVS did. The factor of lack of fecal material may be discounted (Broadhurst, 1957a; Hall, 1936).

A further analysis of the behavior of the animals in Trial 12 revealed a significant relationship between defecation and attempts at drinking from the empty water bottle. A Mann-Whitney "U" test was performed between the defecation rates of the following two groups (whatever their pre-weaning experience): (1) all animals that were consistent drinkers and also attempted to drink on Trials 11 and 12 were compared with (2) all animals that were consistent nondrinkers and did not attempt to drink in Trials 11 and 12. "Consistency" was determined by applying the one-sample runs test to each animal. The latter group (i.e., the nondrinkers) had a significantly higher defecation rate than the drinking animals. Furthermore, there was no statistically significant difference between random drinkers that attempted to drink on Trials 11 and 12 and random drinkers that did not.

Locomotion

Although there were no group differences in the absolute duration of locomotion in Trials 11 and 12, a statistically significant number of animals in each group increased in locomotor activity in Part 2 of Trial 11 above the mean locomotion level for Trials 2 through 10. A chi-square comparison of consistent drinkers, consistent nondrinkers and random drinkers revealed that a significant number of nondrinkers decreased in locomotor activity in Part 2 of Trial 12, whereas drinkers and random drinkers increased in locomotion in the second approach-impedance test.

In the open-area test some animals exhibited a pattern involving locomotion between the wall and the center of the enclosure, with or without reaching the center or wall. In some instances this was done shortly before the water-bottle apparatus was introduced. This activity was exhibited primarily, however, by animals that showed random drinking and random "wall going." In Part 2 of Trial 12 there was a change in the animals exhibiting this pattern.

Correlation Between Defecatory Reaction and Reaction to Approach-Impedance

Seven behavioral indices were used to qualify an animal's reaction to the empty water bottle: a change in wall-going or in center-staying behavior, wall-to-center locomotion with or without reaching wall or center, biting the tube, climbing tube more than momentarily, standing up at wall (if not done in earlier trials), urinating in Part 1 of Trial 12 and in Part 2 of Trials 11 and 12 (if not in earlier trials) and failure to drink in Trial 12 (if animal was a consistent drinker and an attempt to drink had been made in Trial 11).

Animals in each group were ranked by these indices, and the rankings were correlated with several defecatory indices: onset of defecation prior to weaning, defecation rate in Part 1 of Trial 1, mean defecation rate in Part 1 of Trials 2 through 11, in Part 2 of Trials 2 through 10, and in Part 2 of Trial 12. Two significant rank-order (RHO) correlations were found: in Group VPUS-A animals, a negative correlation was found between onset of defecation and severity of reaction in the approach-impedance trials, i.e., animals defecating early tended to react more severely to approach-impedance. Group UPUS-B-1 showed a negative correlation between severity of reaction and defecation rate in Part 2 of Tests 2 through 10, i.e., animals which reacted severely in the approach-impedance trials tended to be low in defecation rate during the postweaning open-field testing under water deprivation conditions. (See Table 15-3.)

AVOIDANCE CONDITIONING

No statistically significant differences were found among any of the groups in conditioning rate, in defecatory reaction, or in other behavioral measures observed.

CORRELATIONAL ANALYSIS

None of the correlations among the defecatory reactions in any of the various test situations reached statistical significance. Significant correlations were found, however, between the conditioning rate and defecatory reaction. For Group UPUS-A-1 animals a positive correlation was found between conditioning rate and mean defecation rate in Part 2 of Trials 2 through 10. For Group MC-1 the correlation was positive between conditioning rate and defecation rate on the first day of presentation of "door-open" plus C3, and it was negative between conditioning rate and defecation rate in conditioning trials.

DISCUSSION

The Defecatory Response as a Fundamental Characteristic of the Organism

This research has been directed particularly at the properties of the defecatory reaction in rodents, widely accepted as a measure of "emotionality." We have noted especially the view of Hall, according to which this reaction is considered a constitutionally fixed process, a basic trait running through behavior, differentiating individuals in disturbing situations at different stages of development.

We do not exclude hypothetical characteristics of maturation and experience that may be sufficiently pervasive to render certain reactions of an animal more constant than seems possible for defecatory reactions as studied under our conditions. By adopting the view that the defecatory reaction is highly dominated by the animal's perception of conditions in the prevalent situation, and that this reaction may therefore vary considerably under different conditions of

stress, apparent inconsistencies in our results are resolved. Thus, individuals may have different thresholds for the defecatory response in different situations or may be more comparable in terms of patterns of defecatory reactivity than in terms of the simple occurrence or nonoccurrence of defecation.

It is evident from our experimental design that introducing the mice to new situations at different ages may have confounded the developmental changes of the defecatory response with responses to a specific treatment. In further investigations, a control for this factor should be included. Nonetheless, because both developmental and cross-sectional techniques were used in this study, certain comparisons are admissible, and conclusions may be drawn from them. The differences between groups at different stages of development, the lack of significant correlations within individuals during the same period of the experiment, and the longitudinal comparisons within particular stages of development are all reliable. At first sight, the finding of certain relationships at some stages but not at others may seem contradictory. It is our belief, however, that this type of finding throws light not only on certain contradictory results in the literature but also on the complexities of open-system phenomena such as behavioral development that do not seem consistent with hypotheses of constitutionally determined constancy.

Experiential Factors in the Defecatory Response

One outcome of the view that the defecatory reaction is a basic and pervasive individual characteristic has been to limit investigations of the role of experience in the development of individual patterns and levels of this reaction. From our results, it is clear that when the physical aspects of environment vary, defecatory reactions under disturbing test conditions increase and that when both physical aspects and social aspects vary the level of defecatory reactions is higher.

The possibility must be considered that varying the physical aspects of environment has effects upon mice equivalent to those of lowering response thresholds to noxious stimulation, rather than increasing the effects of adaptivity to disturbances. This interpretation involves the unproved assumption that the defecatory response necessarily indicates disturbance and must be adaptive. Now it is known that mice to an appreciable extent organize their home-cage areas into feeding zones distinguishable from defecation zones (Warne, 1947; Williams and Scott, 1953). In females subjected to our conditions, when this propensity for living-area organization operated against the necessity (as in the physical-change group) to rebuild nests and re-organize living areas daily, the general level of disturbance may have been raised very considerably. The possibility of ramifying disturbance effects in female and young is suggested by the finding of Carrière and Isler (1959) that frequent housing changes in a group of C3H mice resulted in a lowered thyroid function, although without detectable changes in adrenal weight.

Although Anderson and Anderson (1938) found no differences between "emotional" and "nonemotional" subjects, Yeakel and Rhoades (1941) reported heavier thyroid glands in the Hall strain of "emotional" rats than in the "nonemotional" strain. On the good possibility that frequently enforced housing changes reduce thyroid function appreciably, and that in mice and rats a comparable relationship exists between thyroid weight (and possibly function) and defecatory response, it follows that our

mice raised under constant environmental conditions would be expected to show a higher defecatory rate in the tests than those raised under conditions of physical instability. Under our conditions, this did not prove to be the case.

Furthermore, the lack of evidence for the prediction that a preweaning environment in which the physical aspects were frequently varied would result in a lowered defecatory response supports the suggestion of Anderson (1937–1938) and Lebo (1953) that the defecatory response can become habituated to specific situations without there being any generalized habituation to "strangeness" as such. This means, in effect, that rather than habituating mice to "novelty" our preweaning manipulation had so exposed them to disturbances differing in kind and in degree that the effects of such disturbances later waned after their initial appearance in a given test situation.

The Definition of "Emotional" Defecation

It might be objected that, in the present study with mice, the techniques used and the results obtained may indicate that we are not dealing with "emotional" defecation as defined by Hall, and that evidence of individually consistent defecatory patterns otherwise admissible was somehow excluded. Hall (1938) stated that "emotional" defecation refers only to that defecatory reaction which ceases under conditions of familiarity with the situation first stimulating the response. Under conditions such as those in our open-field tests, mice, in contrast to rats, do not cease their defecatory response. This reaction may, therefore, prove useful as an index of generic- and species-specific adjustments to disturbing conditions, as with Farris and Yeakel's (1945) finding that strains of rats can be distinguished by differences in the continuance of their defecatory responses.

Characteristics of Situations Eliciting the Defecatory Response

A stricture offered (Hall, 1938) for situations that elicit the defecatory reaction concerns their "emotion"-arousing characteristics. Three of the techniques used in our experiment that could be so interpreted are: the open-field tests during the litter period, the approach-impedance test, and the avoidance conditioning test. Although our investigation did not test the concept of "emotion" in animals, and although we are not undertaking a theoretical critique of this concept, our evidence indicates that in studying the defecatory response we are dealing with the upper and disruptive part of a continuum of excitatory stimulative intensities. Accordingly, we find significant differences among the mice in regard to some aspects of the defecatory response in two of the situations—that is, the open-field testing during the litter period and the approach-impedance situation—but do not find a statistically significant difference in the defecatory response with the introduction of electric shock.

In the results from open-field tests given in the litter period, there were no signs of individual differences in measures such as, first, incidence of defecation prior to weaning or, second, the number of days of recorded defecation up to the time of eye opening. In three different group comparisons, however, reliable differences in onset-of-defecation were found under conditions indicating that the differences were related mainly to the prevalent intensity of stimulation. Thus, the UPUS and UPVS animals presented with the open-field tests began their spontaneous defecation earlier than did litter mates held in containers during the test periods, and the UPUS animals (raised under unvarying physical and social environmental conditions) were later in their onset-of-defecation than the UPVS animals (raised under unvarying physical but varying social conditions). If onset-of-defecation is more related to the processes underlying defecatory reactivity in stressful situations than to specific aspects of growth (e.g., motor properties), it would appear that in mice subjected to disturbance during the litter period there is a hastening of the appearance of the defecatory response in ontogeny.

In analyzing the effects of the approach-impedance test on mice, we find an increase of locomotor activity. This result was observed not only in Part 2 of Trial 12 but also in Part 2 of Trial 11, and it seemed directly related to the drinking or non-drinking proclivities of the animals. Consistent drinkers and random drinkers increased in their locomotion, whereas consistent nondrinkers decreased. Furthermore, the type of locomotion was striking in its character as specifically related to this situation. Under these impedance conditions, increases were common not only in general locomotion but also in partial movements either to the center or to the wall. When this behavior was analyzed in relation to responses of licking or not licking the water bottle, it was found that animals approaching the bottle evidenced more of this vacillatory locomotion than did animals not attempting to drink.

Accordingly, in analyzing the responses of mice to the approach-impedance test, we find that alterations thereby entailed in the open-field test had the effect of inducing behavior of an evidently non-directive and unstabilized character not as frequently observed in the open-field situation itself. Thus, the animals did not keep to one locality or to one type of response, but alternated in these respects in phases of short duration. These activities and their described changes, clearly apparent and readily quantified, may be accepted as reliable indicators of disturbed behavior.

Accompanying these changes in locomotor behavior was a decrease in defecation rate in most animals. If approach-impedance tests such as ours are sufficiently disturbing to initiate a condition of frustration, our results are consistent with those of Hall (1934b) in tests with rats presented with a wire-mesh barrier around food in the open-field situation.

The last of the three situations which might be considered "emotion"-arousing was that of avoidance conditioning. In this test, we introduced electric shock, more clearly noxious than any characteristics of other testing situations used. Despite this fact, no reliable changes were found in defecatory reactivity under these conditions as against those in other tests, either in the frequency of defecation or in the number of boluses. It is of course conceivable that the shock was not sufficiently intense to have produced distinct differences in this respect; this idea, however, is opposed by the fact that in all significant behavioral respects the animals indicated strong reactions of withdrawal in this situation.

"Emotionality" or the Defecatory Response and "Anxiety"

The dominant experimental interest in this area has concerned finding a technique for investigating disturbed behavior in lower animals—and particularly one which might aid the understanding of disturbed behavior in man. In the complex literature, often the existence of a relationship between conditions such as "emotionality" and "anxiety" has been assumed without supporting evidence. Because we have found such questions abstruse, in this investigation we have employed operationally the occur-

rence of "defecatory reactions" as a more objective term than "emotionality," and have used the term "anxiety" as an expedient only to introduce the more exact concept of a "conditioning rate." One notable precedent for this step is Pavlov's delineation, from his work with dogs, of a relationship between conditioning rate and degree of emotional excitability.

Although, in general, no correlation was found in our study between the defecatory reaction and rate of conditioning, the three significant correlations found involved two of the three groups tested in the open-area situation prior to conditioning, (i.e., MC-1 and UPUS-A-1). Two of these correlations were positive: (1) conditioning rate as against defecatory reactivity in Part 2 of Trials 2 through 10 and (2) defecatory reactivity on the first day that *"door-open" and CS* were presented as against *conditioning rate.* The second correlation means that animals that conditioned quickly tended to rank low in defecatory reactivity on the first day of conditioning. The only value to correlate negatively with conditioning rate was defecatory reactivity during the actual pairing of the conditioned and unconditioned stimuli. If it were permissible to consider defecatory responsiveness in rodents somehow analogous to human "anxiety," the latter result would make possible equating the defecatory reaction with "anxiety."

In view of our findings, however, of such a negative correlation in only one group of six, it is questionable whether behavioral conditions of the type reported for Pavlov's dogs are analogous to those we have found in mice under conditions of high defecatory reactivity. It is also doubtful whether both conditioning-rate measures and defecatory reactivity may be accepted as criteria of "anxiety" as involved in the disturbed reactions of infrahuman animals. Further study of the two phenomena seems warranted, however, in light of their quantifiable characteristics and in respect to the few suggestive correlations we have found.

To a great extent, we think, the vagueness of terms such as "emotionality" and "anxiety" rests upon untested assumptions of an underlying unity in all individual disturbed behavior, frequently assumed to have a common innate basis. In our judgment, our failure to find inclusive and uniform trends in "defecatory reactivity" at different stages of development and in disturbing situations of different character suggests an inherent weakness in these last assumptions of a *constitutional unity* and a *common innate basis* underlying "emotionality." It seems clear, however, that hypotheses of "innateness" and of "constitutional unity" should be tested independently, with adequate controls on developmental and situational factors.

Our results suggest that the term "defecatory reactivity" is not to be used synonymously with concepts such as "emotionality" and "anxiety," but that aspects of disturbed behavior evidently not appraised adequately by the defecatory-reactivity criterion may be studied advantageously through the use of other objective concepts such as "conditioning rate," under experimentally differentiated types of background and test conditions. Objective standards such as those admitted by criteria such as "defecatory reactivity" should be used for disturbed behavior to the extent that they can be supported experimentally. These two concepts, as examples, may prove valuable as mutually complementary instruments to carry out the types of developmental research that are clearly indispensable to understanding the over-all problem of "emotionality" (or "disturbance") in behavior. It is along these lines particularly that the problems of phyletic similarities and differences in adaptation to disturbing conditions may be studied to best advantage.

CONCLUDING STATEMENT

The defecatory reaction, often considered synonymous to "emotionality" or "autonomic reactivity" as studied in rats, from results on investigations of disturbed behavior in mice is viewed as a situationally specific response rather than an individually generalized pattern resting upon a native or constitutional basis. Developmentally controlled studies show that defecatory reactivity is likely to increase or decrease according to the nature of the disturbing situation and according to the given individual's developmental history, rather than to remain always on a level typifying the individual's measurable responses. Defecatory reactivity, which is therefore not found equivalent to any presumably general characteristic such as "emotionality," is affected by the nature of individual developmental experience, differentiated in this investigation in terms of stability or instability of the physical or of the social aspects of the individual's preweaning environment.

REFERENCES

ADER, R. 1959. The effects of early experience on subsequent emotionality and resistance to stress. *Psychol. Monographs. 73*(2): 1–31.

ANDERSON, E. E. 1937–1938. The interrelationships of drives in the male albino rat. II. Intercorrelations between 47 measures of drives and of learning. *Comp. Psychol. Monographs. 14*(6): 1–119.

ANDERSON, E. E. 1938. The interrelationship of drives in the male albino rat. III. Intercorrelations among measures of emotional, sexual and exploratory behavior. *J. Genet. Psychol. 53:* 335–352.

ANDERSON, E. E. 1939. The effect of the presence of a second animal upon emotional behavior in the male albino rat. *J. Social Psychol. 10:* 265–268.

ANDERSON, E. E., and ANDERSON, S. F. 1938. The relation between the weights of the endocrine glands and measures of sexual, emotional, and exploratory behavior in the male albino rat. *J. Comp. Psychol. 26:* 459–474.

BENNETT, J. H., and GRESHAM, G. A. 1956. A gene for eyelids open at birth in the house mouse. *Nature. 178:* 272–273.

BILLINGSLEA, F. Y. 1940. The relationship between emotionality, activity, curiosity, persistence and weight in the male rat. *J. Comp. Psychol. 29:* 315–325.

BILLINGSLEA, F. Y. 1942. Intercorrelational analysis of certain behavior salients in the rat. *J. Comp. Psychol. 34:* 203–211.

BINDRA, D., and THOMPSON, W. R. 1953. An evaluation of defecation and urination as measures of fearfulness. *J. Comp. & Physiol. Psychol. 46:* 43–45.

BITTERMAN, M. E., and HOLTZMAN, W. H. 1952. Conditioning and extinction of the galvanic skin response as a function of anxiety. *J. Abnorm. & Social Psychol. 47:* 615–623.

BOVARD, E. W. 1958. The effects of early handling on viability of the albino rat. *Psychol. Rev. 65:* 257–271.

BROADHURST, P. L. 1957a. Determinants of emotionality in the rat. *Brit. J. Psychol. 48:* 1–12.

BROADHURST, P. L. 1957b. Emotionality and the Yerkes-Dodson Law. *J. Exp. Psychol. 54:* 345–352.

BROADHURST, P. L. 1959. Application of biometrical genetics to behaviour in rats. *Nature. 184:* 1517–1518.

BROADHURST, P. L., SINHA, S. N., and SINGH, S. D. 1959. The effect of stimulant and depressant drugs on a measure of emotional reactivity in the rat. *J. Genet. Psychol. 95:* 217–226.

CARRIÈRE, R., and ISLER, H. 1959. Effect of frequent housing changes and of muscular exercise on the thyroid gland of mice. *Endocrinology. 64:* 414–418.

CLARK, E., and ARONSON, L. R. 1951. Sexual behavior in the guppy, *Lebistes reticulatus* (Peters). *Zoologica. 36:* 49–66.

EVANS, J. T., and HUNT, J. McV. 1942. The emotionality of rats. *Am. J. Psychol. 55:* 528–545.

FARRIS, E. J., and YEAKEL, E. H. 1945. Emotional behavior of gray Norway and Wistar albino rats. *J. Comp. Psychol. 38:* 109–118.

FULLER, J. L., CHAMBERS, R. M., and FULLER, R. P. 1956. Effects of cortisone and ad-

renalectomy on activity and emotional behavior of mice. *Psychosom. Med. 18:* 234–242.

GEIER, F. M., LEVIN, M., and TOLMAN, E. C. 1941. Individual differences in emotionality, hypothesis formation, vicarious trial and error and visual discrimination learning in rats. *Comp. Psychol. Monographs. 17:* 1–87.

GHENT, L. 1957. Some effects of deprivation on eating and drinking behavior. *J. Comp. & Physiol. Psychol. 50:* 172–176.

GRIFFITHS, W. J. JR., and STRINGER, W. F. 1952. The effects of intense stimulation experienced during infancy on adult behavior in the rat. *J. Comp. & Physiol. Psychol. 45:* 301–306.

HALL, C. S. 1934a. Defecation and urination as measures of individual differences in emotionality in the rat. *Psychol. Bull. 31:* 604.

HALL, C. S. 1934b. Drive and emotionality: factors associated with adjustment in the rat. *J. Comp. Psychol. 17:* 89–108.

HALL, C. S. 1934c. Emotional behavior in the rat. I. Defecation and urination as measures of individual differences in emotionality. *J. Comp. Psychol. 18:* 385–403.

HALL, C. S. 1936. Emotional behavior in the rat. II. The relationship between need and emotionality. *J. Comp. Psychol. 22:* 61–68.

HALL, C. S. 1938. The inheritance of emotionality. *Sigma Xi Quart. 26:* 17–27.

HALL, C. S. 1951. "The Genetics of Behavior," in *Handbook of Experimental Psychology*, ed. by STEVENS, S. S. New York, Wiley, pp. 304–330.

HALL, C. S., and WHITEMAN, P. H. 1951. The effects of infantile stimulation upon later emotional stability in the mouse. *J. Comp. & Physiol. Psychol. 44:* 61–66.

HUNT, F. H., and OTIS, L. S. 1953. Conditioned and unconditioned emotional defecation in the rat. *J. Comp. & Physiol. Psychol. 46:* 378–382.

JAMES, W. T. 1953. Morphological and constitutional factors in conditioning. *Ann. New York Acad. Sc. 56:* 171–183.

JONES, M. R. 1944. Some observations of effects of phenobarbital on emotional responses and air-induced seizures. *J. Comp. Psychol. 37:* 159–163.

LEBO, D. 1953. A simplified method for measuring emotional defecation in the rat. *Science. 118:* 352–353.

LEVINE, S. 1956. A further study of infantile

handling and adult avoidance learning. *J. Personality. 25:* 70–80.

LEVINE, S. 1959. Emotionality and aggressive behavior in the mouse as a function of infantile experience. *J. Genet. Psychol. 94:* 77–83.

LINDZEY, G. 1951. Emotionality and audiogenic seizure susceptibility in five inbred strains of mice. *J. Comp. & Physiol. Psychol. 44:* 389–394.

MARTIN, R. F., and HALL, C. S. 1941. Emotional behavior in the rat. V. The incidence of behavior derangements resulting from an air blast stimulation in emotional and non-emotional strains of rats. *J. Comp. Psychol. 32:* 191–204.

MOGENSON, G. J., and EHRLICH, D. J. 1958. The effects of early gentling and shock on growth and behaviour in rats. *Canad. J. Psychol. 12:* 165–170.

MOYER, K. E. 1957. Relationship between emotional elimination and the persistence of an anxiety motivated response. *J. Genet. Psychol. 90:* 103–107.

MOYER, K. E. 1958. Effect of adrenalectomy on emotional elimination. *J. Genet. Psychol. 92:* 17–21.

O'KELLY, L. I. 1940. The validity of defecation as a measure of emotionality in the rat. *J. Genet. Psychol. 23:* 75–87.

PARKER, M. M. 1939. The interrelationship of six different situations in the measurement of emotionality in the adult albino rat. *Psychol. Bull. 36:* 564–565.

PAVLOV, I. P. 1927. *Conditioned Reflexes,* trans. and ed. by ANREP, G. V. London, Oxford University Press.

RUNQUIST, W. N., and ROSS, L. E. 1959. The relation between physiological measures of emotionality and performance in eyelid conditioning. *J. Exper. Psychol. 57:* 329–332.

RYALL, R. W. 1958. Effect of drugs on emotional behavior in rats. *Nature. 182:* 1606–1607.

SCHNEIRLA, T. C. 1956. "Interrelationships of the 'Innate' and the 'Acquired' in Instinctive Behavior," in L'Instinct *dans le Comportement des Animaux et de l'Homme,* ed. by GRASSÉ, P.-P. Paris, Masson & Cie, pp. 387–452.

SEITZ, P. F. D. 1954. The effects of infantile experiences upon adult behavior in animal subjects: I. Effects of litter size during infancy upon adult behavior in the rat. *Am. J. Psychiat. 110:* 916–927.

SIEGEL, P. S., and STUCKEY, H. L. 1947. The diurnal course of water and food intake in the normal mature rat. *J. Comp. & Physiol. Psychol. 40:* 365–370.

SIEGEL, S. 1956. *Non-parametric Statistics for the Behavioral Sciences.* New York, McGraw-Hill, 312 pp.

STANLEY, W. C., and MONKMAN, J. A. 1956. A test for specific and general behavioral-effects of infantile stimulation with shock in the mouse. *J. Abnorm. & Social Psychol. 53:* 19–22.

STERN, J. A. 1957. The effect of frontal cortical lesions on activity wheel and open-field behavior. *J. Genet. Psychol. 90:* 203–212.

TAESCHLER, M., and CERLETTI, A. 1959. Differential analysis of the effects of phenothiazine-tranquilizers on emotional and motor behavior in experimental animals. *Nature. 184(1):* 823.

TAKEBE, K. 1939. Experimental hypoplasy and hyperplasy of the centers of vision in the mouse. *J. Fac. Sc. 5:* 165–189.

TAYLOR, J. A. 1951. The relationship of anxiety to the conditioned eyelid response. *J. Exper. Psychol. 41:* 81–92.

WARNE, M. C. 1947. A time analysis of certain aspects of the behavior of small groups of caged mice. *J. Comp. & Physiol. Psychol. 40:* 371–387.

WEININGER, O. 1956. The effects of early experience on behavior and growth characteristics. *J. Comp. & Physiol. Psychol. 49:* 1–9.

WELCH, L., and KUBIS, J. 1947. The effect of anxiety on the conditioning rate and stability of the PGR. *J. Psychol. 23:* 83–91.

WILLIAMS, E., and SCOTT, J. P. 1953. The development of social behavior patterns in the mouse, in relation to natural periods. *Behaviour. 6:* 35–64.

WILLINGHAM, W. W. 1956. The organization of emotional behavior in mice. *J. Comp. & Physiol. Psychol. 49:* 345–348.

YEAKEL, E. H., and RHOADES, R. P. 1941. A comparison of the body and endocrine gland (adrenal, thyroid, and pituitary) weights of emotional and non-emotional rats. *Endocrinology. 28:* 337–340.

YOSHIOKA, J. G. 1932. Learning vs. skill in rats. *J. Genet. Psychol. 41:* 406–416.

PART III

EARLY EXPERIENCE

16

IS EARLY EXPERIENCE DIFFERENT?

John L. Fuller

Marcus B. Waller

Recently interest in the effects of early experience upon later behavior has increased greatly among psychologists and animal behaviorists. At first thought, such research may seem to deal with a trivial problem. Obviously, behavior in later life is a function of prior experience. The demonstration that a particular type of experience has lasting effects is not really very impressive. The point is, of course, that the investigators in this area are concerned with the possibility that frightening experiences, affectionate handling, or opportunities to explore a rich environment may affect young animals much more drastically than older ones. Thus experience crowded into a few months, weeks, days, or even hours may determine an entire life history.

This point of view is, of course, familiar to psychiatrists; emphasis on early experience as an etiological factor in neuroses is an important part of psychoanalytical theory. It should be pointed out, however, that Freud did not ascribe all neuroses to early experience. He writes of neuroses, for example (Freud, 1935, p. 318): "Then there are others in which all the accent lies on

Supported in part by the Ford Foundation and by Grant No. MY1775 from the U.S. Public Health Service.

the later conflicts, and the analytic emphasis upon the childhood-impressions seems to be the effect of regression alone."

Freud's general view was that the young organism was more susceptible than the adult to psychological trauma. He also believed that human beings were particularly likely to be traumatized during certain periods of life, for example, at the time at which oedipal object choices were giving way to adult forms of libidinal expression. This belief is very similar to Scott's hypothesis of critical periods in the development of social behavior in animals (Scott and Marston, 1950; Scott, 1958).

EXPERIMENTAL CONTROL OF LIFE HISTORIES

As we turn from Freud to current research on the effects of early experience upon animals, we find no definite agreement on how early treatments must be applied to produce *early experience* (King, 1958). Variations in procedure make comparisons between experiments difficult, but standardization at present would be premature. It is convenient to divide research in early experience into experiments involving intermittent treatment and those involving continuous treatment. Intermittent treatments may be very short or distributed over a period of days or weeks. During any one treatment session, however, one may reasonably neglect maturational changes in the organism. Intermittent treatments can usually be specified rather objectively and simply. "The subjects were removed daily from their living cages by means of forceps and placed in a box 4 inches square for five minutes"; or "The subjects were held in the left hand against the experimenter's body and stroked gently for 10 minutes daily."

Continuous treatments involve the whole environment and are inevitably more complex since provision must be made for the

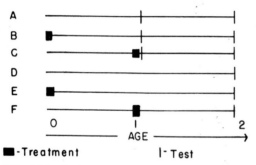

FIG. 16-1. A six-group design for analyzing the effects of intermittent treatment at two stages.

subjects to remain alive and healthy. Subjects may be raised in groups or singly, in open cages or in cages which restrict vision. They may have a great variety of objects to manipulate or may be provided with the minimum possible for survival, even to the extent of providing a liquid diet and a grill through which fecal pellets fall out of reach. Obviously, it is impossible to specify the subjects' responses completely in the continuous-treatment situation, and one cannot neglect maturational changes occurring during the treatment. One of the major points of this paper is that the effects of intermittent treatments must always be interpreted with reference to the mode of rearing outside the formal experimental

situation. All experiments include a continuous-treatment component.

The general design of experiments on early experience is similar for both intermittent and continuous treatments. Two or more experimental groups are given the same treatment at different ages, and the groups are compared on a test given at a later age. A control group which has not been treated previously may also be tested to determine if the treatment is effective at any age. This design inevitably confounds treatment age, test age, and treatment-test-interval. Because of this confounding of factors, experimenters must include a number of control groups and

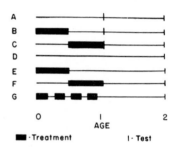

FIG. 16-2. A seven-group design for analyzing the effects of continuous treatment over two age ranges.

determine the effects of each factor by looking for internal consistencies in the data. If differences in treatment-test-interval are confounded sometimes with treatment age, and sometimes with test age, it may be possible to conclude that this variable is not of critical importance.

In Figure 16-1 we have shown a set of designs suitable for comparing the effects of the same treatment at two ages. Six groups are the minimum necessary to determine the effects of treatment age, treatment-test-interval, and test age. Table 16-1 summarizes the combinations which can be compared in testing for internal consistency. For example, if no significant difference is

TABLE 16-1   ANALYSIS OF THE FIGURE 16-1 DESIGN

ROW	GROUPS	TEST AGE	TREATMENT AGE	TREATMENT-TEST-INTERVAL
1	(A)B C	(1,1,1) Same	(—,0,1) Different	(—,1,0) Different
2	(D)E F	(2,2,2) Same	(—,0,1) Different	(—,2,1) Different
3	(A)B C	(2,2,2) Same	(—,0,1) Different	(—,2,1) Different
4	A D	(1,2) Different	(—,—) Same	(—,—) Different
5	B E	(1,2) Different	(0,0) Same	(1,2) Different
6	C F	(1,2) Different	(1,1) Same	(0,1) Different
7	B F	(1,2) Different	(0,1) Different	(1,1) Same

found between the groups in Rows 4, 5, and 6, one can safely conclude that test age and treatment-test-interval were not significant factors. If differences between the paired groups are found, further analysis is needed to separate the effects of test age and treatment-test-interval. Unfortunately, it is impossible to have two factors the same and the third different.

In Figure 16-2 we have presented similar diagrams of designs involving continuous treatment lasting over a substantial portion of the life span. For the most part, results obtained by this scheme can be handled by the comparison system outlined in Table 16-1. However, it is desirable to include an additional group such as G, in which treatment time is equivalent to A, B, C, or D, but is distributed over a longer period of time.

EXPERIMENTAL HAZARDS

One difficulty in comparing the effectiveness of treatments given at different ages is that it is sometimes literally impossible to handle subjects at different stages of maturation in the same manner. A newborn rat removed from its nest cools down more rapidly than a larger one. If cooling stress happens to be an important factor in producing any effects from such manipulation, removal of a larger rat from its nest for an equal period of time will not impose the same degree of stress. An attempt to equal-

ize the amount of body cooling would lead to complicated variations in time of exposure or in the ambient temperatures. As another example of the difficulty of giving the same treatment at different ages, contrast the stroking (gentling) of an infant animal which remains quiet with the stroking of a juvenile which must be forcibly restrained. The unavoidable addition of restraint may change the nature of the treatment drastically.

We have already referred to another complication of the design—the effect of the mode of handling subjects during the pretreatment period and the treatment-test-interval. Some of the divergencies between experimentors now working in the area of early experience have been attributed to weighing or not weighing control animals during weekly inspections. The importance of such background conditions was emphasized for our group in a recent pilot experiment using dogs. We were interested in whether certain psychopharmacological agents would produce persistent behavioral deficits like those produced by social isolation. Basing our procedure upon the statement by Scott (1958) that the period of primary socialization for dogs extends from the fourth to the seventh week, we isolated puppies at the beginning of the fourth week and removed them from isolation at 8 and 12 weeks of age. We were surprised to find that these older puppies could be easily socialized when removed from isolation for less than 15 minutes per day. All came readily to a human handler, and played vigorously with a litter mate.

We do not consider that this experiment disproves the evidence for an earlier critical period for socialization under other conditions. The original arguments were based upon difficulties in forming dog-human relationships with puppies which had been left with their mother and litter mates in large enclosures. Under these conditions, dogs apparently learn a set of responses appropriate to a free-ranging wild creature and avoid human beings. Our subjects, constrained within an area of 5 square feet, had developed no such responses and learned quickly to approach and to make contact with the experimenters.

The impossibility of putting animals on a shelf and maintaining them without any experience makes critical tests of the critical-period hypothesis, extremely difficult. At the heart of the difficulty is the problem of separating effects of maturation, which are relatively invariant functions of age under all circumstances, from effects of a particular rearing system and experimental treatments adopted by an investigator. Often it is difficult to say whether a particular age is critical in the development of a function, or whether a particular sequence of events is critical. Our personal preference is to speak of the effects of *schedules of experience* rather than of critical periods. The study of schedules of experience includes the phenomena of imprinting, socialization, perceptual learning, modification of emotionality and of learning—in short, all the areas in which experience at particular ages has been postulated to be more important than experience at another age. Obviously, critical periods may be postulated to occur at any age, but emphasis

has been placed upon those which occur early.

SPECIAL FEATURES OF EARLY EXPERIENCE

Two aspects of early experience appear to underlie its presumed special importance. First, the effects of early experience are considered often to be less readily reversible than those of later experience. Irreversibility has been specifically attributed to the imprinting phenomenon in birds (Lorenz, 1935), although this view has been challenged (Moltz and Rosenblum, 1958). The idea of irreversibility is implicit in some of the reports on apparently permanent behavior deficits in animals subjected to sensory deprivation during youth (Thompson and Heron, 1954). Melzack and Scott (1957), for example, have reported that Scottish terriers raised in a restricted environment are almonst insensitive to burning matches thrust in their faces. Somehow or other, in this view, the behavior mechanism jells at a certain age, and its characteristics are henceforth fixed. New learning is possible—the jelly is not rigid—but the essential form cannot be changed.

A second dimension concerns the specificity of the relationship between early experience and its later effects. The adult rat, shocked for eating from a white dish, learns to avoid white dishes but is otherwise much the same as before. The younger rat shocked in a roughly similar manner shows excessive emotionality in many situations. The effects of early treatments are often not readily predictable and may be detected by behavior tests quite unlike the original treatment. (For example, Denenberg, 1958; Levine, 1957). To the extent that generality rather than specificity characterizes the results of early treatments, one may argue for the operation of factors other than learning based on contiguity of stimuli or reinforcement of particular responses.

EARLY AND PRIOR EXPERIENCE

The experimental evidence for more pronounced effects of earlier treatments is less adequate than one would hope. Ader (1959) has pointed out that many so-called effects of early experience have never been shown to be more than the effects of *prior* experience. Ader's own experiment involved a number of treatments administered to rats just after weaning or at 4 months of age. Some types of handling rendered his subjects less emotional, but these procedures were as effective with old as with young rats. Other workers (Baron, Brookshire, and Littman, 1957) found that exposure of young rats to severe electric shock made them, as adults, better learners in a shock-avoidance test. However, treatments at 20, 36, and even 120 days were approximately equal in effectiveness. Eingold (cited by Woods, 1959) is reported to have found that rats fail to benefit from an enriched environment when the opportunity to explore such an environment is given before 46 or after 65 days of age. Contrariwise, Woods (1959) found that exposing previously isolated rats to an enriched environment from 66–158 days brought them almost to the level of rats who had lived continuously in an enriched environment since weaning.

On the other hand, Levine (1958) has reported opposite effects of shock upon drinking behavior in infant and adult rats. Handled and shocked infants developed into adults who were more tolerant of stress than nonhandled adults. Shock administered to adults (previously nonshocked) reduced their capacity to adapt to stressful situations. The same investigator (Levine and Lewis, 1959) found a critical period for the effectiveness of manipulation in accelerating the maturation of a physiological response to stress. Unmanipulated rats show no depletion of adrenal ascorbic acid before 16 days of age. Manipulation during Days 2–5 speeds up development so that the response is present by 14 days of age. Manipulation during Days 6–9 or 10–13 is not effective in the same manner. Denenberg and his students (personal communication) have reported critical periods for effects of manipulation on later learning in mice. Experimental evidence for critical periods in socialization of dogs has been reported by several investigators (Scott, Fredericson, and Fuller, 1951; Freedman, Elliot, and King, 1958). Dogs, isolated for seven to ten months in the McGill experiments failed to perform as well as normally reared subjects even after prolonged training (Thompson and Heron, 1954).

Some of the reasons for contradictory results certainly arise from variations in procedure. When rats are treated previous to weaning, results are obtained which have not been duplicated at later ages. Postweaning experience has not been particularly more effective than experience in early adulthood. Some change in reactive capacity at about weaning age is clearly suggested. We have referred previously to complications arising from routine management of "nonhandled" controls in some experiments. Our own results with semi-isolated puppies demonstrate that young animals effectively utilize brief exposures to a complex environment and organize their behavior about as adequately as do puppies having continuous access to such environments. Taking into account these methodological differences, we conclude that there is a sufficient body of evidence to support the belief that schedules of experience do make a difference and that young animals are more sensitive to certain kinds of treatments. However, more behavioral research is essential in order to define critical periods for different processes in different species. It is unlikely that one can define *the* critical period for psychological or social development.

EXPLANATORY CONCEPTS

Thus far, our attempts to answer the question, "Is early experience different?" have been at the descriptive level. It should be clear that there is no single answer to the question; at least, the variety of results obtained by investigators in different places argues against a unitary explanation. Beach and Jaynes (1954), in a review of early experience studies, grouped explanatory concepts under three headings: persistence of first-formed habits, influence of early perceptual learning, and critical periods for the development of particular responses. We shall review these, together with other ideas which have been proposed since the appearance of Beach and Jayne's paper.

Perhaps the simplest way of explaining the effects of early experience is to assume that prior responses pre-empt the nervous mechanisms and thus continue to be made throughout life. Alternative courses of action simply are not tried providing the initial response is adequately reinforced. By itself, this principle makes prior experience, but not necessarily experience during youth, more critical than later experience.

The idea of critical periods involves a similar pre-emption by prior responses, but adds a factor of age changes in the probabilities of eliciting a particular response by a novel stimulus. Hess (1959), for example, has used this type of explanation to account for the critical period of "imprinting" chickens by an artificial model.

Very young chicks approach an unfamiliar moving object, and approach and following are reliably produced when the same stimulus is presented again. If experience with moving objects is delayed a few days, Hess finds that an avoidance response is evoked. Under these conditions, the following response which is used as a measure of imprinting does not develop. Using the language of operant conditioning, we might say that the response "shaped up" in a particular test situation is a function of the subject's age. The ideas of pre-emption and "shaping up" of age-specific responses can also be applied to critical periods in the social development of mammals (Scott, 1958). An organism is ready at certain stages to emit social responses, and it makes them to any competent stimulus which happens to be present. Usually the stimulus is a member of the same species, but an experimenter can manipulate this so that social responses are given to members of other species or even to inanimate objects (Harlow and Zimmerman, 1959).

A third explanatory concept is the idea that organization of perceptual processes is possible only during a limited period of life. By perceptual learning we mean the organization process which enables an animal to respond differentially and appropriately to complexes of stimuli (Hebb, 1949). Certainly the organization of an animal's perceptions must await the maturation of its sense organs. Chemical and tactile senses are generally present from birth, but the distance receptors are quite variable in rate of development. Although we can logically correlate the beginning of perceptual learning with sense-organ maturation, its end is less clearly defined. We have no biological basis by which we know that an organism is jelled to the point that perceptual learning is impossible. Perhaps, strictly speaking, perceptual learning never ceases, but the results on animals raised in a restricted environment (Thompson and Heron, 1954) indicate that eventually the capacity for benefiting by training decreases. We know very little about the time requirements for perceptual learning. Experiments in progress at our laboratory suggest that less than 10 minutes per week in an enriched environment suffices for the normal development of responses to a wide variety of stimuli. In these experiments, enriched environment has been presented only intermittently in contrast to the usual experiment (Forgays and Forgays, 1952; Forgus, 1954) in which the subjects have access to complex stimuli continuously. There are differences between our semi-isolated puppies and subjects reared with more outside contacts, but these can be interpreted as well in terms of sensory deprivation affecting drive states as in terms of perceptual deficits.

Another concept which has been supported by Levine and his co-workers is that early stimulation accelerates maturation of physiological systems. Extremely mild manipulation has been shown to increase the rate of maturation of the pituitary-adrenal system (Levine and Lewis, 1959). Manipulation at later ages was ineffective. One possible explanation for the critical period found by these workers is that stimulation is required for neuro-endocrine functional maturation. The source of stimulation may be external or internal. When the young rat begins to stir "spontaneously," self-stimulation is sufficient to start and maintain development, and the added stimulation from manipulation is superfluous. Thus, in only the newborn rat can maturation be accelerated by relatively mild stimulation.

Much more specific than Levine's theory is Bovard's (1959) argument that handling in infancy shifts hypothalamic dominance forward, thus increasing the secretion of pituitary growth hormones and lessening the activity of the pituitary-adrenal cortex and sympathetico-adrenal medulla system. These effects are in turn referred back to sensory inputs relayed through the amygdaloid complex. There is little direct evidence for this theory, but it is consistent with a considerable body of neurophysiological and neuro-endocrine data. Bovard has suggested a number of experiments which could be used to test his ideas. In order to be a theory of early experience and not a general theory of neuropsychology it is clearly necessary to assume that the postulated shifts in hypothalamic dominance are relatively permanent if they occur in young animals and that such shifts cannot be effected in later life.

Physiological data also provide a basis for the belief that early experience is more potent because drive states are more intense and learning, under greater drive reduction, is facilitated. Certainly the homeostatic controls of young animals are less effective than in adults, and biases on the control systems for such functions as eating and drinking are presumably greater. If one assumes that there are neurological states associated with exploratory and manipulative drives which are analogous to those for food and water drives, one can use the same concept to explain the more severe effects of sensory deprivation in young animals. Early experience in an enriched environment cannot be replaced by later experience because the older animal cannot be as strongly deprived of exploratory and manipulative experience. The mature animal doesn't hunger for new sensations.

Still another factor pertinent to the problem of early experience is change in learning ability with age. We have been studying the acquisition of conditioned avoidance responses in young puppies for several years.

In a first report (Fuller, Easler, and Banks, 1950) we were unable to obtain conditioned responses before 3 weeks of age. Now, using more refined techniques, we have evidence that the critical age must be lowered to about 14 days when daily sessions of 10 trials are given from 4 days on (Fuller & Christake, 1959). However, it still appears that the capacity for avoidance conditioning goes up sharply at about 3 weeks of age, and conditioned cardiac acceleration has not appeared reliably before about 32 days. In contrast, learning based on sucking has been demonstrated in the first week of life and probably begins immediately after birth.

Obviously, learning has a rather complex course of development in the dog. We can demonstrate discrimination learning based on food reinforcement very early; no avoidance conditioning can be demonstrated during the first 10–12 days of life, but exposure to the test situation apparently facilitates acquisition at about 14 days of age. Rapid avoidance conditioning (often with 5–8 pairings of conditioned and unconditioned stimuli) comes in the fourth week, and autonomic conditioned responses still later—in the fifth or sixth week. Learning may be a unitary process in terms of neurology, but it is not a unitary function in development. Experiments on the learning of the rhesus monkey have yielded results in complete accordance with this view (Harlow, 1959).

Finally in this list of factors, we have the explanatory concept of susceptibility to trauma. Although this term is familiarly used in psychiatry, it is difficult to specify what is meant by psychological trauma. A number of studies have shown that the nervous system of the young animal is in fact more readily injured by physical agents. Duffy and Murphree (1959) showed, for example, that 8-day-old rats injected with encephalitis virus became ill and were much inferior in maze learning at the age of 150 days. Rats injected at 10 days showed no clinical disease, but they also learned less well at 150 days. Rats injected at 14 days or over, however, showed neither clinical symptoms nor delayed psychological effects. A number of experimenters (Thompson, 1957; Doyle and Yule, 1959) reported that subjecting mothers to "anxiety" during pregnancy made their offspring more emotional. No postnatal treatment effects could be found. Presumably, therefore, the results depend upon some chemical agent transmitted from the mother to the sensitive offspring.

A SIMPLIFIED MODEL

These hypotheses do not exhaust the possibilities, but they will suffice for the present purposes. Obviously, the concepts are not mutually exclusive, and perhaps all of them have some merit. We wish at this time to venture a few suggestions toward a general concept of the differentness of early experience. It must be borne in mind that the developmental courses of species are so different that few statements can possibly apply to all organisms. The guinea pig and the sheep can locomote independently soon after birth—the human infant and the puppy can merely wiggle.

Our first postulation is that the cells of young organisms are very sensitive to direct physical and chemical changes and that they may be exposed to wide fluctuations in body chemistry because of imperfect functioning of homeostatic mechanisms. Thus, hormones from an anxious mother diffusing through the placenta, changes in ambient temperatures, vibration, infection with encephalitis virus—all may act in a nonspecific manner to alter cell metabolism during maturation and to effect persistent modifications in function. The duration of this period in the rat may extend to about 10 days of age, and in the puppy to about 20 days. We regard the duration as relatively invariant within a given species, at least within the limits of conditions which permit normal growth. In summary, our first postulate states that young organisms are physiologically unstable so that metabolism is easily disturbed. Permanent alterations in physiological function follow, and these may have nonspecific psychological consequences.

Second, we postulate a gradual shift with age in the probability that any specified response will occur when an animal is confronted with a novel stimulus. These probabilities are functions, but not invariant functions, of age. Thus freezing, hopping, and running occur with different frequencies when mice are given shock-avoidance training at different ages (Denenberg, 1958). We believe that in general the variety of the response repertory (the free operant responses) and the total probability that some response will be given rises after birth to a maximum and declines thereafter. The period of maximum response is the stage of playfulness in mammals. The psychological consequence of this postulate is that the effectiveness of a given experience may be at a maximum during rather vaguely limited critical periods. However, we believe that the boundaries of such periods can be shifted within limits by modifying the level of general stimulation. It is probable that response systems jell later if they function less.

The third component of our model involves progressive changes in the possible complexity of stimulus control of behavior. Newborn mammals, at least mice, dogs, and monkeys, show distinct changes in learning capacity as they mature—often correlated with sense-organ development.

The maturation of learning ability may be truly continuous, but our methods of measurement show stepwise cumulative increases in capacity.

Obviously, exposure to a situation whose later effects are dependent upon complex associative learning will be less effective in young animals. Hence the beginning of a critical period might be determined by

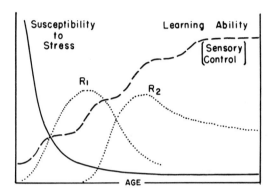

FIG. 16-3. A diagram of a three-component model illustrating unique features of early experience. Susceptibility to stress is high in young animals and decreases sharply to a relatively constant level. The probability of eliciting response R_1 is high in young animals but low in older animals, who are more likely to give response R_2. As animals age, the probability of all responses (when no prior training has occurred) decreases gradually. Learning ability is represented as increasing progressively in stepwise fashion—and eventually reaching a constant level.

the maturation of a particular capacity. However, it seems unlikely that such capacities decrease until degenerative organic changes occur in the nervous system. The failure of experience-deprived animals to profit from delayed training is more likely to be caused by the fixation of incompatible responses than by an upper age limit for the development of learning.

We have combined these three components in Figure 16-3. This three-function model is adequate to account for almost any relationship between schedules of experience and the psychological consequences of experience. Critical periods of varying onset and duration can be accommodated. The formal adequacy does not mean, of course, that we have chosen the best model. Only direct experimental tests of each component will confirm or disprove the theory. Such tests must be based upon intensive and extensive studies of different species, with attention to comparisons between species and to physiological mechanisms. We predict that the study of schedules of experience will continue to provide data useful for psychiatry. In fact, we would strongly urge that research on child development be framed in terms which will facilitate comparison with studies on animals.

CONCLUSION

To conclude, we have found that early experience is different, and we have proposed a model for early-experience effects based upon biological and psychological principles. We also propose a *rapprochement* between research workers concerned with "schedules of reinforcement" and those interested in "schedules of experience." We can program life histories as well as reward and punishment, and both types of control are effective.

REFERENCES

ADER, R. 1959. The effects of early experience on subsequent emotionality and resistance to stress. *Psychol. Monographs. 73:* 1–31.

BARON, A., BROOKSHIRE, K. H., and LITTMAN, R. A. 1957. Effects of infantile and adult shock-trauma upon learning in the adult white rat. *J. Comp. & Physiol. Psychol. 50:* 530–534.

BEACH, F. A., and JAYNES, J. 1954. Effects of early experience upon the behavior of animals. *Psychol. Bull. 51:* 236–263.

BOVARD, E. W. 1959. The effects of social stimuli on the response to stress. *Psychol. Rev. 66:* 267–277.

DENENBERG, V. H. 1958. Effects of age and early experience upon conditioning in the C57BL/10 mouse. *J. Psychol. 46:* 211–226.

DOYLE, G., and YULE, E. P. 1959. Grooming activities and freezing behaviour in relation to emotionality in albino rats. *Animal Behav. 7:* 18–22.

DUFFY, C. E., and MURPHREE, O. D. 1959. Maze performance of mature rats recovered from early postnatal infection with Murray Valley encephalitis virus. *J. Comp. & Physiol. Psychol. 52:* 175–178.

FORGAYS, D. G., and FORGAYS, J. W. 1952. The nature of the effects of free environmental experience in the rat. *J. Comp. & Physiol. Psychol. 45:* 422–428.

FORGUS, R. H. 1954. The effect of early perceptual learning on the behavioral organization of adult rats. *J. Comp. & Physiol. Psychol. 47:* 331–336.

FREEDMAN, D. G., ELLIOT, O., and KING, J. A. 1958. Developmental capacities for socialization in puppies. *Am. Psychologist. 13:* 327.

FREUD, S. 1935. *A General Introduction to Psychoanalysis.* New York, Liveright.

FULLER, J. L., and CHRISTAKE, A. 1959. Conditioning of leg flexion and cardioacceleration in the puppy. *Fed. Proc. 18:* (Part 1) 189.

FULLER, J. L., EASLER, C., and BANKS, E. M. 1950. Formation of conditioned avoidance responses in young puppies. *Am. J. Physiol. 160:* 462–466.

HARLOW, H. F. 1959. The development of learning in the rhesus monkey. *Am. Scientist. 47:* 459–479.

HARLOW, H. F., and ZIMMERMAN, R. R. 1959. Affectional responses in the infant monkey. *Science. 130:* 421–432.

HEBB, D. O. 1949. *The Organization of Behavior: A Neuropsychological Theory.* New York, Wiley.

HESS, E. H. 1959. Imprinting. *Science. 130:* 133–141.

KING, J. A. 1958. Parameters relevant to determining the effects of early experience upon the adult behavior of animals. *Psychol. Bull. 55:* 46–58.

LEVINE, S. 1957. Infantile experience and consummatory behavior in adulthood. *J. Comp. & Physiol. Psychol. 50:* 609–612.

LEVINE, S. 1958. Noxious stimulation in infant and adult rats and consummatory behavior. *J. Comp. & Physiol. Psychol. 51:* 230–233.

LEVINE, S., and LEWIS, G. W. 1959. Critical period for the effects of infantile experience on the maturation of a stress response. *Science. 129:* 42–43.

LORENZ, K. 1935. Der Kumpan in der Umwelt des Vogels. *J. Ornithol. 83:* 137–213, 289–413.

MELZACK, R., and SCOTT, T. H. 1957. The effects of early experience on the response to pain. *J. Comp. & Physiol. Psychol. 50:* 155–161.

MOLTZ, H., and ROSENBLUM, L. A. 1958. Imprinting and associative learning: the stability of the following response in Peking ducks (*Anas platyrhyncous*). *J. Comp. & Physiol. Psychol. 51:* 580–583.

SCOTT, J. P. 1958. Critical periods in the development of social behavior in puppies. *Psychosom. Med. 20:* 42–54.

SCOTT, J. P., FREDERICSON, E., and FULLER, J. L. 1951. Experimental exploration of the critical period hypothesis. *J. Personality. 1:* 162–183.

SCOTT, J. P., and MARSTON, M. V. 1950. Critical periods affecting the development of normal and maladjustive social behavior in puppies. *J. Genet. Psychol. 77:* 25–60.

THOMPSON, W. R. 1957. Influence of prenatal maternal anxiety on emotionality in young rats. *Science. 125:* 698–699.

THOMPSON, W. R., and HERON, W. 1954. The effects of restricting early experience on the problem solving capacity of dogs. *Canad. J. Psychol.,* 1954, *8:* 17–31.

WOODS, P. J. 1959. The effects of free and restricted environmental experience on problem solving behavior in the rat. *J. Comp. & Physiol. Psychol. 52:* 399–402.

17

PSYCHOPHYSIOLOGICAL EFFECTS
OF INFANTILE STIMULATION

Seymour Levine

Living organisms are born into, develop, and survive in a complex dynamic external environment. Evidence for the effects of this environment on physiological processes is extensive. Numerous studies in the areas of psychosomatic medicine, stress physiology, classical Pavlovian conditioning, and periodicity all emphasize the importance of organism-environment relationships on physiological functions. For the most part, these investigations have used an approach which involves the testing of environmental effects that shortly precede, or are concomitant with, the physiological events being investigated.

We propose that the external environment in which the organism develops exerts a profound effect on its subsequent physiological reactivity. Although there is little question that organism-environment interactions are a continuous dynamic process throughout the life of the organism, we contend that environmental factors during infancy are more profound in their effects than environmental factors during any other period in the organism's history. In fact, the extent and manner to which an organism reacts to later environmental events is determined to a large extent by the environmental conditions which prevail during infancy.

METHODS

The general method used to investigate organism-environment interactions during infancy is one which involves extra stimulation of the infant either during the entire period from parturition through weaning or during specific "critical periods" in infancy (Levine and Lewis, 1958). When one examines the environmental conditions in which most laboratory animals exist, it is apparent that such environments are strikingly barren. Ideally, most animal quarters are temperature- and humidity-controlled; light cycles are rigidly regulated; and in general, variations in the environment are greatly minimized. There are a variety of reasons for these conditions; among these is the assumption that environmental constancy along with genetic constancy reduces variability. "Environmental constancy is both an object and an artifact of research" (Goldstein and Ramey, 1957). When environmental constancy becomes the subject of investigation it is apparent

These investigations were supported by Research Grant No. M1630 from the National Institute of Mental Health of the National Institutes of Health, U.S. Public Health Service.

that this very environmental constancy has far-reaching physiological consequences.

A variety of methods have been utilized to introduce extra stimulation into this barren environment. Predominant among these methods in the program which will be described is the technique called "manipulation" (Levine, 1957*a*). This technique simply involves removing the infant animal from the nest, in most cases the rat, placing it once daily in a small compartment for three minutes, and returning the infant to the nest. When observers have witnessed this procedure we invariably see an incredulous expression followed by some remarks of amazement that such a seemingly innocuous procedure can produce the consequences which have been and will be reported. That this procedure is effective is attested to not only by its subsequent psychophysiological results but by the fact that the effects produced by manipulation cannot be differentiated from those produced by seemingly more extreme procedures such as electric shock and violent shaking (Levine and Lewis, 1959).

DEVELOPMENT, MATURATION, AND INFANTILE STIMULATION

In order to evaluate the environmental influences on growth and development we have studied the effects of infantile stimulation* on various aspects of physiological development. In the first of these studies the effects of manipulation on the maturation of the hypothalamo-hypophysial system were investigated using the onset of adrenal ascorbic acid depletion to severe cold as our measure of the functional status of the system (Levine, Alpert, and Lewis, 1958). The results of this study are presented in Figure 17-1. It can be seen that

* Throughout this paper, stimulation refers to the experimental treatments in infancy. Non-stimulation refers only to the absence of experimental manipulation of the infant.

the manipulated infant showed a significantly earlier depletion of adrenal ascorbic acid and achieved an adult level of response earlier than the nonmanipulated infant. A subsequent study (Levine, 1959) indicated that the appearance of body hair and the opening of the eyes occurred earlier by several days in the stimulated infant. A still further study (Levine and Alpert, 1959) revealed that the process of myelination of the central nervous system appears

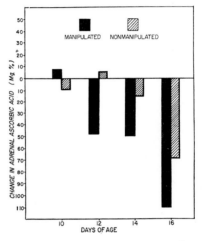

FIG. 17-1. Adrenal ascorbic-acid depletion in manipulated and nonmanipulated infant rats.

significantly earlier in manipulated infants. These results are presented in Figure 17-2.

Thus infantile stimulation results in an acceleration of the physiological development of gross morphological, functional physiological, and structural characteristics of the organism. Although only a very few developmental factors have thus far been investigated we are confident that many facets of development are profoundly affected by infantile stimulation.

What bearing do these data have on the problem of maturation? Gesell (1954) defines maturation as follows:

From the moment of fertilization, intrinsic and extrinsic factors cooperate in a unitary manner; but the original impulse of growth and the matrix of morphogenesis are endogenous rather than exogenous. The so-called environment whether internal or external, does not generate the progressions of development. Environmental factors support, inflect, and specify, but they do not engender the basic forms and sequences of ontogenesis . . . . We apply the term "maturation" to this intrinsic and prospective aspect of ontogenetic patterning.

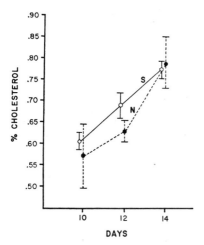

FIG. 17-2. Per cent cholesterol in whole brain of stimulated and nonstimulated infants. The circles represent the mean of the groups and the bars, one standard deviation.

Proponents of the maturation concept as presently held would find the results of these studies consistent with the maturation point of view, for although the nonstimulated infants show a slower developmental rate, they do develop and develop according to the "basic forms and sequences of ontogenesis." However, and fortunately, organisms do not develop in an environmental vacuum. In fact, quite the contrary occurs. We would like to propose (1) that the "so-called environment," far from having merely a supporting role in development, is a potent and profound force and (2) that although patterns of ontogenesis are most likely genetically

determined and phylogenetically limited the emergence of these patterns is dependent upon a favorable environment.

Gesell (1954) states, "The function of the nervous system is to maintain the integrity of the organism and to anticipate the specific demands of the environment with provisional and preparatory arrangements. These forereference arrangements are not determined by stimulation from the outside world."

Gesell therefore places the genetic horse before the environmental cart. Ingle (1954) has demonstrated the "permissive" action of steroids for a wide variety of nonsteroid mediated responses. The main features of this phenomenon are (1) that steroids impart to the animal the capacity for making highly variable and directional responses to stress and (2) that the small amount of steroids required does not, of itself, elicit any of these responses, but supports these responses to specific environmental changes. The role of environment in the process of development can be viewed as exerting a similar permissive action. Thus, given the genetic and phylogenetic substrates, the environment imparts to the animal the capacity to develop and supports a variety of developmental processes. Therefore, environmental influences in the extreme determine whether the process of development can continue and produce an organism—and within reasonable boundaries—provide substance, energy and milieu for the unfolding of the organism potentialities.

INFANTILE STIMULATION OF ADULT PHYSIOLOGICAL RESPONSES

In addition to altering the course of development, infantile stimulation produces an organism which markedly differs in its physiological responses to environmental conditions later in life. These differences are manifested in the organism's responses to stress, transplantable leukemia, seizure-producing stimuli, and brain lesions.

Differential Responses to Stress

Early in the course of this research program it was observed that when stimulated rats were placed in an open field, which consisted of an enclosed table top, they showed significantly less defecation, urination, crouching, and wall-seeking behavior than did nonstimulated subjects. Insofar as defecation and urination are gross indicators of autonomic responses, it seemed reasonable to assume that nonstimulated rats were generally more reactive to stressful situations than their stimulated counterparts. If this was the case, then we would expect other physiological responses to stress—including adrenal weights, hematological changes such as leukocytolysis, and steroid production—to differ between stimulated and nonstimulated animals following stress.

Several experiments tended to support the hypothesis that nonstimulated rats were more reactive to stress than stimulated animals. Stimulated rats show significantly less mortality following 120 hours of total food and water deprivation than do nonstimulated subjects (Levine and Otis, 1958). Further, adrenal hypertrophy 24 hours following an injection of hypertonic glucose was significantly greater in nonstimulated animals (Levine, 1957b). However, subsequent experiments have led us to question the hypothesis stated above. If one examines Figure 17-1, it is apparent that stimulated infants are hardly less reactive to stress and in fact show an earlier and significantly greater response than nonstimulated infants. In a recent unpublished investigation we studied the effects of infantile stimulation on circulating adrenal steroids, principally corticosterone, following electric shock to the feet in adulthood.

These results are shown in Figure 17-3. Although there was no difference in the circulating steroids between the stimulated and nonstimulated subjects in the absence of shock, the stimulated animal showed more rapid rise in corticosterone output and a consistently greater production of steroids for the 15-minute period following one minute of electric shock. These data give very little support for the concept of less reactivity to stress in the stimulated

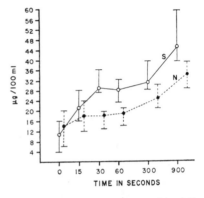

FIG. 17-3. Circulating corticosteroids following electric shock in stimulated and nonstimulated rats. The zero time is the control value without shock. The circles represent the means of the groups; the bars indicate the range.

subjects. Unfortunately at this time steroid values for later than 15 minutes following shock have not been obtained, and it is possible that the nonstimulated subjects, although slower in their initial responses, may show higher sustained levels. However, even if this were to be so this would not alter the fact that 15 seconds following shock the stimulated subjects show a significant rise in steroids, whereas the nonstimulated animals do not show a significant rise in circulating steroids until five minutes following shock. Therefore, instead of being less reactive, the stimulated subjects seem to be far more sensitive to noxious stimulation. To further complicate the picture, a

18

IMPRINTING AND THE "CRITICAL PERIOD" CONCEPT

Eckhard H. Hess

THE PROCESS OF PRIMARY SOCIALIZATION

Imprinting refers to the primary formation of social bonds in infant animals. The nature of the first social experience that a young animal has is important in determining the character of the social behavior of that animal in its later and adult life. For example, ducklings will follow the first moving object with which they come into contact and thereafter regard it as its parent. If this object is not its natural mother it will maintain filial contact with this object rather than with its natural parent. In maturity, social behaviors such as mating may be directed toward this object rather than toward a female of its own species.

Sexual fixations of animals upon objects which are not appropriate species members had been noted by Craig (1908) at the turn of the century. He found that in order to be able to cross two species of wild pigeons the young of one species had to be reared with foster parents of the other species. Upon reaching adulthood, birds so reared were found to prefer mates

that were of the same species as their foster parents. Other interspecies sexual and social fixations were later observed in birds by Heinroth and his wife (1910, 1924–1933), who reared several species of European birds by hand and found that filial and social responses became directed toward the keeper rather than to species members. The European ethologist, Konrad Lorenz, extended these experiments, using graylag geese.

Lorenz called this phenomenon *Prägung*, or "imprinting," since it appeared to be a process in which there was a rapid "stamping in" of the impression of the mother object in the young animal which resulted in the observed fixation. He pointed out that there seemed to be a "critical period" early in the life of an animal during which this experience had to occur in order to result in such an attachment. He also postulated that the first object to elicit a social response on the part of a young animal at the "critical period" later released not only that response but also related responses such as sexual behavior. Imprinting was therefore related not only to the problem of social behavior in animals but also to the general biological problem of evolution and speciation (Lorenz, 1935).

We have carried out extensive laboratory studies, using chicks and ducklings, and

The work described herein was supported in part by Grant M776 of the National Institutes of Health, U.S. Public Health Service; by the Wallace C. and Clara A. Abbott Memorial Fund of the University of Chicago; and by the Wallace Laboratories, New Brunswick, New Jersey.

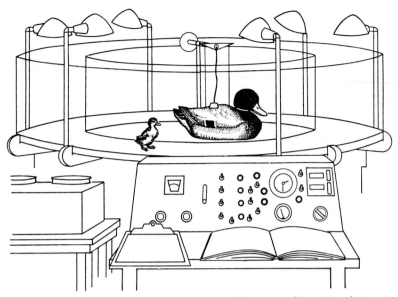

FIG. 18-1. Apparatus used for imprinting ducklings. At the appropriate age, the duckling which has been kept in darkness from the time of hatching is placed in the apparatus where the decoy is offered to it as the first moving object in its experience. The decoy then moves around the runway, emitting a "GOCK, gock, gock, gock" call. The duckling follows the model for a certain distance and then is returned to darkness until testing for strength of imprinting, 24 hours later.

determined the location of the "critical period" in these animals (Hess, 1957). This "critical period" lies in the first 32 hours after hatching, with maximum effectiveness for an imprinting experience between the thirteenth and sixteenth hour after hatching (Hess, 1957).

Evidence has been found suggesting that "critical periods" for the formation of social bonds also exist in other animals such as fish (Baerends and Baerends-van Roon, 1950), insects, (Thorpe, 1944), sheep (Grabowski, 1941), buffalo (Hediger, 1938), guinea pigs (Hess, 1959), and monkeys (Harlow, 1959).

Complete social isolation during the first few days of life in young chicks has been found to result in abnormal behaviors. Such chicks show a variety of aberrant behaviors: some become immobile and give no response to social stimulation; others become

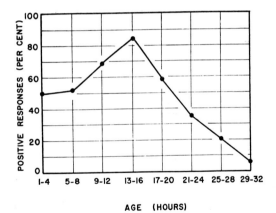

FIG. 18-2. Mean scores made in testing, 24 hours after the imprinting experience, by animals which had been given the imprinting experience at different ages. A score of 100 per cent is regarded as perfect.

flighty and are highly excited upon social exposure; still others in the same situation show hostile behavior, vigorously attacking

FIG. 18-3. Interior of apparatus testing pecking preferences in young chicks. The 1.1-inch in diameter stimuli shown in the upper right-hand corner have $\frac{1}{4}$-inch holes punched in the center, with tissue paper placed in back of these holes. If a hollow holder is used and filled with grain, the chicks can peck through the tissue paper and obtain grains of feed. Each stimulus is connected to a microswitch which is tripped when a chick pecks at the stimulus. The pecks are then recorded by automatic counters.

the outstretched hand of the experimenter (Hess *et al.*, 1959). These behaviors are quite similar to the apathetic, nervous, or hostile behaviors manifested by orphanage children.

PECKING BEHAVIOR IN CHICKS

The concept of the "critical period" is now being utilized with regard to other types of behavior, in particular pecking behavior in young chicks. By observing the pecking behavior of naïve chicks, we find that they prefer to peck more at some objects than at others. We make use of the Hess Pecking Preference Apparatus (Hess, 1956) in order to determine these preferences.

For example, Leghorn chicks prefer pecking at white circles on a blue background rather than at white triangles on a green background. Blue is preferred to green, and circle is preferred to triangle. The mean response to green-triangle over blue-circle is 17 per cent of all pecks—a figure based on more than 300,000 pecks delivered by about 400 chicks. There is a range of variability which is found from group to group, but the direction of preference for a particular breed can be reliably predicted. In addition, color preferences differ between breeds. Another breed, Vantress Broiler, with which we have been working, prefers yellow to blue or red.

These pecking preferences are obviously unlearned behavior since they are determined without the use of any kind of reward condition but are established on the basis of free behavior on the part of the chicks.

These innate preferences, however, can be modified. By using a hollow holder in back of each stimulus and filling it with fine grain, the chicks can be allowed to peck through the hole and obtain food. If

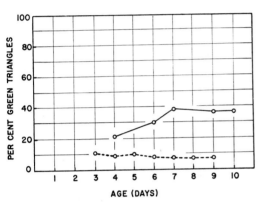

FIG. 18-4. Cumulative total preference, in terms of percentage of pecks made to green-triangle, by two groups of naïve chicks over a period of seven days.

chicks are given food for pecking at green-triangle but not for pecking at blue-circle, they will peck more at the innately less preferred stimulus, green-triangle, not only during reinforcement, but also during extinction when we no longer give them food for pecking at green-triangle. The effect of reward upon the pecking behavior is relatively stable and can last as long as 10 days of extinction.

DISCRIMINATION LEARNING VS. PREFERENCE MODIFICATION

In such a situation the chicks have learned what object is to be pecked at to get food. This would seem to be very much like ordinary discrimination-learning situations

such as having to learn which of two differently colored food boxes contains feed.

Further work, however, has shown that this learning differs a great deal from such discrimination-learning situations. The first indication of the difference is an experiment where we varied the *age* at which the reinforcement experience was given. The two stimuli were white triangle on a green background and white circle on a blue background, the same as those discussed

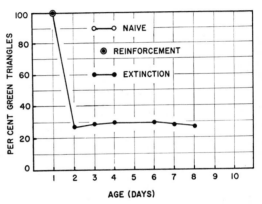

FIG. 18-5. Responses made to green-triangle over a period of eight days by chicks given reinforcement for pecking at green-triangle at the age of 1 day. The responses during the extinction period are given in terms of cumulative total per cent of pecks.

above. All groups of Leghorn chicks were given two hours of reinforcement experience for pecking at the innately less preferred stimulus, green-triangle, at the appropriate age, and were tested without the presence of any food reward for daily two-hour periods prior to and after the reinforcement period.

In the first group, the chicks were 1 day old when they were given the reinforcement experience. During reinforcement, they were presented with green-triangle only, but were tested with both green-triangle and blue-circle present. These chicks made 16,000 reinforced responses to the green-triangle; yet, for six days follow-ing reinforcement, there was no effect on the innate pecking behavior. More than 16,000 responses were made over the six testing days with an average response to green-triangle of 27 per cent, which is within the control limits for green-triangle preference.

The second group was reinforced at the age of 2 days for pecking at green-triangle but not for pecking at blue-circle. In the

of the 1-day or 2-day group. Forty-five thousand reinforced responses, or 99 per cent of all responses, were made to green-triangle during the reinforcement period which occurred at the age of 3 days. Dur-ing the seven days of extinction, the re-sponse to green-triangle remained at a very high level, never dropping below 93 per cent of the cumulative total of nearly 83,-000 responses. Even at the last day of the testing, responses to green-triangle were

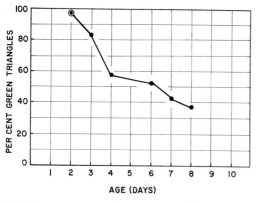

FIG. 18-6. Per cent of responses made to green-triangle by chicks given the reinforcement ex-perience at the age of 2 days, in terms of cumulative total per cent of responses.

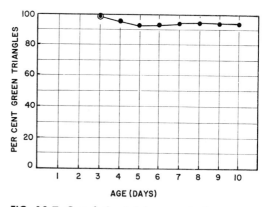

FIG. 18-7. Cumulative total per cent of responses made to green-triangle during extinction by chicks given the reinforcement experience at the age of 3 days.

reinforcement situation, over 27,000 re-sponses were made, with 98 per cent of them to green-triangle. In subsequent test-ing there was a short-term effect of rein-forcement upon pecking behavior; on the first extinction day, 83.5 per cent of the responses were to green-triangle. However, preference rapidly dropped from this level; after five days of testing, the total response to green-triangle was 38 per cent. On the last two days of testing, the total responses to green-triangle were 16 and 24 per cent to green-triangle for each of these days. Since these were at the control level, the effect of reward was therefore completely extinguished by that time.

The 3-day-old group, on the other hand, showed behavior quite different from that

94 per cent. The effect of reinforcement was therefore quite strong and permanent for this age group.

The fourth group had their preference tested for two days at the ages of 3 and 4 days prior to the reinforcement experience. During this time, they performed at the control level, giving 23 per cent of their responses to green-triangle. At the age of 5 days, they were given reinforcement for pecking at green-triangle. During this time they gave 98 per cent of their responses to green-triangle, or 40,000 responses. During the five subsequent days of extinction, we see that there was definitely an effect of reinforcement upon their pecking behavior, but also that it was not as strong as that for the 3-day-old group. The preference for green-triangle gradually declined over the period of extinction to a total of 79 per cent of cumulative responses. On the last day of testing, 69 per cent of the responses were to the green-triangle.

The fifth group, reinforced at the age of 7 days shows no effect of reinforcement upon their preference. Their preference was tested at the ages of 4, 5, and 6 days; during these three days they made a total

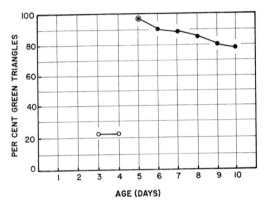

FIG. 18-8. Preference for green-triangle shown by chicks tested at the ages of 3 and 4 days and given reinforcement at the age of 5 days, and cumulative total preference for green-triangle during extinction.

of 35 per cent of their responses to green-triangle. During the three days of extinction following reinforcement, their preference was even lower than their own prereinforcement control level—14 per cent of the total cumulative responses were made to green-triangle.

The last group, reinforced at the age of 9 days, likewise shows no effect of reinforcement upon their pecking behavior. Their preference for green-triangle during the four days of prereinforcement testing was 10 per cent of all responses; after withdrawal of reward, they pecked 20.5 per cent at green-triangle.

These results are summarized in Figure 18-11. Here we have plotted by age groups

the cumulative total per cent of responses to green-triangle during the extinction period. The resulting curve suggests very strongly that there is a period of maximum

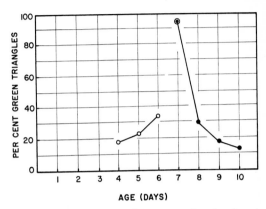

FIG. 18-9. Preference for green-triangle shown by chicks tested at the ages of 4, 5, and 6 days and given reinforcement at the age of 7 days, and cumulative total preference for green-triangle during extinction.

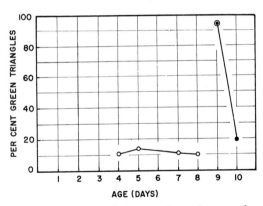

FIG. 18-10. Cumulative total preference for green-triangle shown by chicks tested at the ages of 4, 5, 6, 7, and 8 days, with reinforcement at the age of 9 days, and preference shown during extinction at the age of 10 days.

effectiveness of reinforcement upon modification of pecking preference, the peak of which appears to be the third day of age. It may be that the peak is in fact at the fourth day of age, and that we would have an even smoother curve if we had data for reinforcement at the ages of 6 and 8 days as well. However, the general conclusion is inescapable: there is a "critical period" during which food reinforcement is most effective in modifying innate preferences for pecking at certain objects. Other ages which we have tested are less and less effective the farther they are from the age of 3 days.

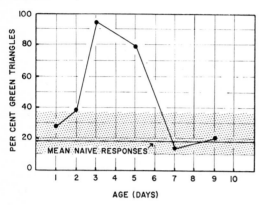

FIG. 18-11. "Critical period" for pecking preference modification in young chicks. The shaded area indicates the control limits set by preferences for green-triangle opposed to blue-circle as shown by several naïve groups. The 17 per cent horizontal line indicates the average preference of about 400 chicks which delivered over 300,000 responses. Only animals reinforced at the ages of 3 or 5 days can be said to show the effects of the reinforcement experience.

Results indicating a period of maximum effectiveness in terms of permanence of behavior modification have never been found for ordinary learning problems using food as a reward and requiring discrimination between two different visual stimuli; this is indeed a major finding setting the process of pecking preference modification apart from these usual learning situations. That there should be a "critical period" for the learning of food objects seems reasonable since at the age of 3 days a chick no longer has resources from the yolk sac and

must acquire food by pecking at appropriate objects.

The second indication of this difference is the effect of carisoprodol and meprobamate upon the retention of this learning. Meprobamate is a tranquilizing drug, and carisoprodol, which is chemically related, acts almost purely as a muscle relaxant. In this experiment (Hess *et al.*, 1959), the subjects were 170 Leghorn chicks, 3 days old at the start of experimentation. They were divided into four groups: 45 were

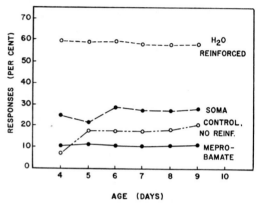

FIG. 18-12. Cumulative total percentage of pecks to green-triangle during the extinction period by four groups of chicks. Only the group not given a drug shows the effect of the reinforcement experience, whereas those that had been given either carisoprodol or meprobamate behave essentially like control animals.

given 16 mg. of carisoprodol one and one-half hours before being given reinforcement; 45 were given 16 mg. meprobamate one and one-half hours previously; 40 were given .2 cc. water one and one-half hours prior to introduction to the apparatus; and 40 served as control animals. The latter were given neither drug nor reinforcement of any kind, whereas the first three groups were given reinforcement for pecking at green-triangle and not for blue-circle for a period of two hours in the apparatus, after having been given a drug or water.

On each of six days following the reinforcement experience, all experimental groups were given two hours of extinction, or experience with the stimuli without food reward for pecking. The control animals were placed in the apparatus for two hours on each of these days without the presence of food reinforcement at any time.

Figure 18-12 shows the results we obtained, in terms of percentage of pecks to green-triangle, during six days of testing without reinforcement or the administration of drugs. All three experimental groups had been pecking at green-triangle during the reinforcement period at a level of precisely 99 per cent. The control group pecked at green-triangle between 7 and 21 per cent during the six-day testing period, while the group given water shows the effect of reinforcement by pecking between 55 and 58 per cent at green-triangle. The other two experimental groups, those given carisoprodol or meprobamate, however, show a performance that is much closer to the control level than that of the group given water; the animals that had been given carisoprodol performed at a level between 21 and 29 per cent for green-triangles, while those that had been given meprobamate pecked at a level of 10 to 12 per cent at green-triangles. It can be easily seen that the animals that were trained under the influence of either drug behaved during the extinction period essentially as if they had never been reinforced at all.

With ordinary discrimination-learning situations, on the other hand, there is no interference with retention of learning if that learning has taken place under carisoprodol or meprobamate. An example of this is the following experiment (Hess *et al.*, 1959). Fifteen Leghorn chicks were divided into three groups of five animals each; one group learned under the influence of meprobamate; the second group learned under the influence of carisoprodol; and the third group was given neither drug. All had been deprived of food but not water for about five hours prior to experimentation. All three groups learned equally efficiently. Those that had been given carisoprodol took 50 trials to reach the criteria (16 out of 20), and those given meprobamate took 45 trials, as compared with the control group's 47 trials. Furthermore, of the animals run the following day without having been given drugs, all ran at least 8 correct responses out of 10 trials; again, there was no difference between the three groups.

DISCRIMINATION LEARNING VS. PRIMARY SOCIAL LEARNING

Not only is there a "critical period" determining the effectiveness of the imprinting experience, but the effectiveness is also a function of the amount of effort expended by an animal in following an imprinting object. In other words, the more effort a naïve animal makes in following an object during the imprinting experience, the better it remembers the details of that object, and the more likely it is to prefer it to other objects later on. It is the degree of effort, not the amount of time spent with the imprinting object as such that determines the strength of imprinting. This relationship we have summarized in a Law of Effort, which states that the strength of imprinting is equal to the logarithm of effort expended, or $I_s = \text{Log } E$ (Hess, 1957). The importance of this law is demonstrated by our experimentation (Hess, 1957; Hess *et al.*, 1959) in which chicks and ducklings were imprinted while under the influence of meprobamate or carisoprodol, whose muscle-relaxing effects have already been noted. We tested animals as follows: (1) imprint when under the influence of meprobamate, test when drug had worn off; and (2) imprint normally, test under the influence of meprobamate later. Control animals were given ⅓ cc. of distilled water, while the drug dosage was 14–30 mg./kg. body weight. The animals that had been exposed to the imprinting situation while under the influence of meprobamate did not show any evidence of having been imprinted, while those imprinted normally and tested under the drug showed perfectly normal imprinting.

In later experimentation, chicks were imprinted under the influence of carisoprodol, and were found to imprint even less than animals that had had meprobamate, as compared to control animals which had been given only water.

It is clear that when the imprinting experience had taken place under the influence of either meprobamate or carisoprodol, there was no retention of this experience; the animals behaved as if they had never been imprinted. However, there was no such interference when imprinting had taken place under normal conditions but was tested for under the influence of either drug. Apparently, then, the muscle-relaxant effects of these two drugs resulted in the loss of efferent consequences and therefore there was no retention of the learning taking place in imprinting. These results are exactly like those we obtained for the modification of pecking preference when the reinforcement experience had taken place under the influence of a drug, and the same interpretation applies also.

PREFERENCES IN PRIMARY SOCIALIZATION

So far there is a strong indication that the modification of pecking behavior is more like the imprinting process than it is like ordinary discrimination processes. Furthermore, there are still other factors which point to the similarity between the two

processes. One of these is the relative effectiveness of stimulus characteristics such as color or form in the imprinting situation. It has already been pointed out that different colors and forms have different capacities to elicit pecking behavior in chicks.

In this experiment we had eight spheres, about 7 inches in diameter, in the colors red, orange, yellow, green, and blue and in the achromatic shades of near-black, neutral gray, and near-white. Each of the 95 Vantress Broiler chicks was offered one of the spheres as an imprinting object during the "critical period." It was found that the spheres ranked in their effectiveness for eliciting following from the highest to the lowest were: blue, red, green, orange, gray, black, yellow, and white. These colors, in the same order, were increasingly less effective in terms of the scores made during subsequent testing (Schaefer and Hess, 1959). Then we took these same spheres and added superstructures of the same coloring, so that they had heads, wings, and tails. These were used to determine form preferences in imprinting objects. The addition of superstructures had a definite effect on the ease with which the following reaction could be elicited: the plain ball was found to be the most efficient; the ball with wing and tail-like superstructures, less so; and the ball to which wings, tails and head had been added, least efficient.

SUMMARY

The two processes, imprinting and pecking preference modification, then, have many things in common. The following summarizes these similarities:

1. Both involve innate behavior patterns.
2. Both involve visual releasers for a muscular response.
3. Both involve innate preferences in that in both cases there are some visual

stimuli which are more effective than others in determining the strength of the response; both imprinting and pecking preference have been found to be a function of color and shape variables (Schaefer and Hess, 1959), and color preferences of Vantress Broilers for each case are inversely related.

4. Both have a "critical period" of maximum effectiveness for the learning.

5. Both can be modified in the sense that the motor behavior pattern can be directed to an object which is different from that to which the behavior is naturally directed.

6. In both cases, retention of the learning is nullified when it has taken place under the influence of meprobamate or carisoprodol; these drugs do not have this effect in ordinary discrimination-learning situations in which food is used as a reward.

All of the above characteristics distinguish pecking preference and imprinting from ordinary learning, where superficially similar motivations can be utilized, including, for example, food reward or escape from a noxious stimulation such as shock. There may well be other types of behaviors in which a "critical period" is important in determining the character of that behavior subsequent to the "critical period"—habitat preferences, for example. This mechanism, as well as the others described above, would distinguish the development and modification of such behaviors from ordinary learning processes which have been the prime concern of psychologists. It also points to the possibility of a tremendous range of new experimental work using a wide variety of animals and behaviors.

REFERENCES

BAERENDS, G. P., and BAERENDS-VAN ROON, J. M. 1950. An introduction to the ethology of cichlid fishes. *Behaviour. 1* (Suppl.): 1–243.

CRAIG, W. 1908. The voices of pigeons regarded as a means of social control. *Am. J. Sociol. 14:* 86–100.

GRABOWSKI, U. 1941. Prägung eines Jungschafs auf den Menschen. *Ztschr. f. Tierpsychol. 4:* 326–329.

HARLOW, H. F., and ZIMMERMANN, R. R. 1959. Affectional responses in the infant monkey. *Science. 130:* 421–432.

HEDIGER, H. 1938. *Wild Animals in Captivity.* London, Butterworth.

HEINROTH, O. 1910. Beitrage zur Biologie, namentlich Ethologie und Physiologie der Anatiden. *Verhandl. Fünfte Internat. Ornithol. Kong.,* pp. 589–702.

HEINROTH, O., and HEINROTH, M. 1924–1933. *Die Vögel Mitteleuropas.* Berlin, Lichterfelde.

HESS, E. H. 1956. Natural preferences of chicks and ducklings for objects of different colors. *Psychol. Rep. 2:* 477–483.

HESS, E. H. 1957. Effects of meprobamate on imprinting in waterfowl. *Ann. New York Acad. Sc. 67:* 724–732.

HESS, E. H. 1959. Imprinting. *Science. 130:* 133–141.

HESS, E. H., POLT, J. M., and GOODWIN, E. 1959. "Effects of Carisoprodol on Early Experience and Learning," in *The Pharmacology and Clinical Usefulness of Carisoprodol,* ed. by MILLER, J. G. Detroit, Wayne State University Press.

LORENZ, K. Z. 1935. Der Kumpan in der Umwelt des Vogels. *J. Ornithol. 83:* 137–214, 289–413.

SCHAEFER, H. H., and HESS, E. H. 1959. Color preferences in imprinting objects. *Ztschr. f. Tierpsychol. 16:* 161–172.

THORPE, W. H. 1944. Some problems of animal learning. *Proc. Linnean Soc.,* London. *156:* 70–83.

19

SOCIAL DEVELOPMENT IN BIRDS AND MAMMALS

Nicholas E. Collias

The object of this presentation will be to bring out the main trends and principles of social development in certain vertebrate animals. There are many convergent resemblances between birds and mammals emphasizing the generality of these principles. Examples will be drawn from field and laboratory. The basic function of field studies is to relate animal behavior in a detailed way to the natural conditions under which this behavior evolved, thus providing the perspective necessary for the formulation of significant problems. The basic function of laboratory studies is to aid the causal analysis of these problems by means of controlled, standardized, and systematically varied conditions. The process of socialization will be considered in six more or less arbitrary stages.

INITIAL PREDISPOSITION TO RESPOND

The process of socialization may be said to begin with the *initial predisposition* of newly hatched or newborn young to respond to certain key stimuli of simple and generalized nature. When a chick of the domestic fowl is lost, cold, or hungry, it gives loud peeps or distress calls. When it is returned to its mother or companions, to a source of warmth, or is fed, it utters light, rapid peeps of very different character that we have termed pleasure or con-

tentment notes (Collias, 1952). A chick on being isolated sometimes delays a minute or more before commencing its distress calls. The fact that an isolated chick does not first go through a period of giving pleasure notes just before commencing to give distress calls indicates that the pleasure notes are not to be interpreted as being merely low-intensity distress calls.

The pleasure notes and the distress calls are not only uttered in opposite situations, they are also *structural opposites* as revealed by sound spectrograms (Fig. 19-1). They are associated with opposite types of posture and indicate opposite tendencies to react. In general, baby chicks move *away* from objects or situations that stimulate distress calls and *approach* objects or situations that stimulate pleasure notes. We believe that these two types of vocalizations provide a good illustration of what Charles Darwin (1890) called the *principle of antithesis* and reflect the balance between what in human terms would be called feelings and expressions of security and insecurity.

In general, we have observed that the functional properties of these vocalizations and initial social responses of baby chicks parallel the properties of the central nervous system as studied by physiologists, exhibiting latency, rhythmicity, fluctuating

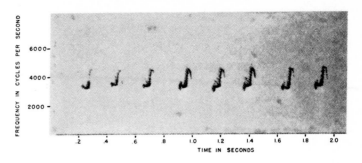

PLEASURE NOTES BY CHICK

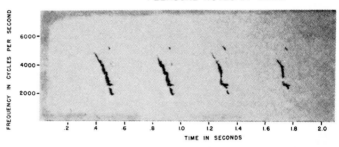

FIG. 19-1. Spectrograms of pleasure notes and of distress cries given by a chick three days after hatching. (From Collias and Joos, 1953)

DISTRESS NOTES BY CHICK

threshold, response-reversal, summation, after-discharge, inhibition, and specific fatigue.

Recently hatched chicks pay no attention to a mount of a broody hen (Fig. 19-2). Maternal guidance to food is of little importance at this time, since chicks do not need to feed the first day. To a newly hatched chick its mother is merely an adaptable complex of warmth, contact, clucking sounds, and movement. This can be demonstrated by hatching individual chicks in isolation under systematically varied conditions related to this complex. The response of such chicks can be quantified by counting the distress calls given under different conditions (Table 19-1).

When chicks were hatched under a warm lamp (100°F.) the number of distress calls given in the first five minutes after hatching was very greatly reduced as compared with chicks allowed to hatch at the subnormal temperature of 78–82°F.

Loss of physical contact, whether with the inside of the eggshell, or with the

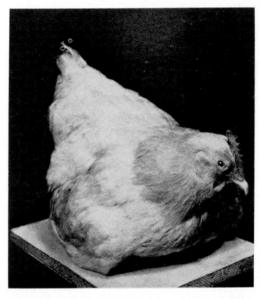

FIG. 19-2. Newly hatched chicks of the domestic fowl were not at all attracted by this mount of a hen in the broody position.

brooding mother, is a very potent stimulus to the freshly hatched chick. But when such a chick was kept warm and the hand of the observer placed over the chick imme-

TABLE 19-1   AVERAGE NUMBER OF DISTRESS CALLS PER CHICK GIVEN ON HATCHING UNDER VARIOUS CONDITIONS*

CONDITION	NUMBER OF CHICKS	1ST 5 MIN.	2ND 5 MIN.	3RD 5 MIN.
Control, 100° F.	12	99	90	
Cool, 78–82° F.	15	280	247	
Contact:	10			
Present		3		
Absent			240	
Clucking:	10			
Absent		238		
Present			102	
Absent				194
Movement:	14			
Absent		244		
Present			187	
Absent				157

* After Collias, 1952.

diately after it had hatched, few if any distress calls were given.

Clucking sounds will also quiet the distress calls of a recently hatched chick. In this test the clucking was begun 5 minutes after the chick had hatched and was stopped at 10 minutes after hatching time. In the subsequent 5 minutes the frequency of distress calls again increased greatly.

The response to moving objects develops somewhat later than do the responses to temperature, contact, and clucking. In these experiments, a moving object (waving hand) induced no consistent cessation of distress calls at 5 to 10 minutes posthatching. However, by one hour after hatching, sight of any object moving nearby usually caused a chick to stop its distress calls. Long ago, Douglas Spalding (1873) observed that chicks as soon as they are able to walk will follow any moving object. It has been shown that young coots and moorhens trained to follow one model readily generalize to others (Hinde, Thorpe, and Vince, 1956).

An example of initial social responses in a *mammal* is the work of David Levy (1934), who has studied the feeding responses of young puppies. Born blind and deaf, young puppies whine loudly if cold or hungry. By feeding them from bottles with either large-hole or small-hole nipples, Levy found that the *need to suck* was quite independent of hunger in these animals. Inadequate satiation of the sucking response before adequate food was secured resulted in prolonged sucking after hunger was satisfied and also in frequent sucking of abnormal objects. Similarly, it has been shown that the development of social attachments of dogs to a person depends more on play contacts than on feeding care (cf. Scott, 1958). Recently, Harlow (1959) has demonstrated that the nature of the physical contact provided to the young by the mother rhesus monkey is the important key to the infant's initial socialization rather than the food she furnishes it.

SELF-REINFORCEMENT OF INITIAL RESPONSES

The next step in socialization is the strong and rapid *self-reinforcement* of initial responses with *social experience* during an *early sensitive period,* leading to the quick formation of social bonds between parent and offspring and between the different siblings. Thus, in the course of routine tests with chicks we noted that, at first, responses of chicks to recorded clucking or to sight of a moving object were very slow, but that after some *minutes* of repeated exposure a chick responded much more rapidly and frequently (Collias, 1950*a*, 1952).

The response of following by both ducklings and by chicks improves very rapidly with practice and with the mere experience of following (Collias and Collias, 1956). This improvement is not a concomitant of domestication causing a weakening of initial endowment in the domestic chick, since wild ducklings hatched in an incubator from eggs collected in the field show a similar improvement in following with experience. In these tests we used ducklings given the opportunity to follow a human observer. A remarkable degree of improvement results after a duckling has merely followed a person moving steadily across a room and back, whether the improvement is measured by latency, amount, or consistency of following. After exposure to about two dozen excursions by the observer, a duckling follows regularly (i.e., for the next 10 trials). Much fewer trials are needed to induce following if the observer imitates the parental attraction calls while moving.

These tests were standardized but somewhat subjective in the sense that mechanical movement was not used for the stimulus object. After we had published our experiments with chicks (Collias, 1950*a*, 1952), Ramsay and Hess (1954) described experiments with both chicks and ducklings in which mechanical objects were used, and they also found considerable improvement in following with the mere experience of following.

We have also studied the socialization of siblings. Newly hatched chicks placed only 6 inches apart do not readily approach one another until they have a few minutes of actual physical contact with one another (Collias, 1950*b*, 1952). Chicks isolated for about ten days after hatching were found to keep somewhat apart from the flock two months later (Collias, 1950*b*). In the case of Mallard ducklings, Weidmann (1958) has observed that individuals isolated for two days after hatching do not later on form normal social contacts with other ducklings.

There is an early sensitive period for development of the response of following a parental object in certain birds, which we demonstrated for domestic fowl (Collias, 1950*a*, 1952) and which Fabricius (1951) demonstrated for the tufted duck and eider duck in Europe. In our experiments, about 100 chicks of various ages were tested individually for response on first exposure to clucking and in another test to first sight of a large, retreating object (person).

The response to clucks was tested in a runway, 1 foot wide and 10 feet long, illuminated within, flanked by cheesecloth walls, and with a loud-speaker at either end of the runway, both loud-speakers being connected with a record player. A toggle switch enabled the recorded clucking to be switched back and forth at will from one loud-speaker to the other. Each chick was placed in the center of the runway and was given 5 or 10 trials during each of which it was exposed to the clucking for one minute. Each trial in which the chick approached to within 1 foot of the loud speaker was considered a positive response. We found a marked decrease in responsiveness to clucking *after the first day* posthatching (Fig. 19-3).

A similar decrease in responsiveness to a person's moving away from the chick was also found (Fig. 19-3). In testing the response to movement, the observer placed the chick at his feet and slowly walked away about 10 feet. This was repeated five times for each chick, and a positive response was taken as a trial in which the chick followed the observer for 3 feet or more. More objective testing by use of mechanical movement would of course be desirable, and than if several days were first allowed to elapse.

The mechanisms underlying this early sensitive period in socialization have not been completely elucidated. However, the changing balance of social attraction with

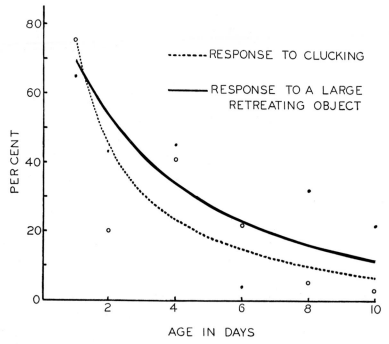

FIG. 19-3. Social responsiveness of chicks on initial exposure to parental stimuli decreases from the first day after hatching (after Collias, 1952). Abscissa refers to age of chicks at first exposure to the specified stimulus. Ordinate refers to the per cent of trials in which a chick approached the source of the stimulus. Each point represents at least ten individually tested chicks; dots refer to responses to movement; circles refer to responses to clucking.

such tests were later supplied by Ramsay and Hess (1954) for ducklings and Jaynes (1957) for chicks. They found a marked decrease in the attractiveness of moving objects after the first day posthatching comparable to our observations with chicks and those of Fabricius with tufted ducklings. Similarly, Hinde, Thorpe, and Vince (1956) found that young moorhens (*Gallinula chloropus*) were more likely to follow a model if tested the first day after hatching fear responses is probably one thing that is involved, as was suggested by Alley and Boyd (1950) in relation to field studies on young coots. Almost a century ago, Spalding (1873, reprinted 1954) observed that three chicks which he had kept hooded apparently from the time of hatching showed marked fear and avoidance responses when he removed the hoods four days later. In chicks and ducklings, fear responses, such as a tendency to avoid any large approaching object are very weak on the day of hatching and become much stronger thereafter. Our chicks, however, when tested to recorded clucking in the runway, showed little or no apparent fear during testing.

After having completed our observations on the development of the response of following in chickens and coincidently with our studies of this response in ducklings, we decided to check the relationship of these responses to those under natural conditions. The most crucial period for the response of following the parent under natural conditions in birds would seem to be the time of leaving the nest. We observed this phenomenon from a blind in two broods of unconfined, wild ducks. We watched a nest of a canvasback, which is a diving duck and nests over water, and a nest of a blue-winged teal, which is a surface-feeding duck and nests on land.

After the first young ones hatched, there was a period of about 24 hours in the canvasback brood and of about 18 hours in the teal brood before the family finally left the nest. This period of association in the nest would appear to provide considerable opportunity for the mother and young to become conditioned and attached to each other, thus affording preparation for the critical time of leaving the nest.

Neither the canvasback nor the teal mother in these instances was heard to give the soft and repetitive attraction calls for the young until after the latter had hatched. These call notes were given with special vigor and frequency when each mother led her brood off the nest. When a duckling became separated from the rest of the brood it gave distress calls; when it rejoined the brood it gave contentment notes. The young do not necessarily follow the mother immediately, as was seen in the case of the teal brood. The mother teal returned to her lagging brood, and not until

her second attempt was she successful in leading the brood away from the nest.

Scott (1958) has discussed critical periods in the development of social behavior in puppies. In the first three weeks after birth the puppy is highly insulated from its environment by the immature state of development of the sense organs and brain. In its fourth week the puppy has well-functioning eyes and ears and differentiated patterns in its electroencephalogram. Coincident with these changes it shows a greatly increased capacity for habit formation and socialization. About this time the mother begins to leave the puppies unattended. Meanwhile, the puppies develop strong social bonds to each other and Scott suggests that this forms the basis for the later organization of the hunting pack.

A similar dependence of social organization on infantile experience has been described by Bartholomew (1959) for Alaskan fur seals under natural conditions. Fur seal pups are as advanced at birth as dog puppies at 3 weeks of age; their socialization begins at birth, and after the age of 1 week is almost exclusively dependent on other pups. The mothers after the first week following birth of their pups spend not more than one day per week ashore and nurse only their own pups. Until they are several years old the young seals, particularly the males, associate mainly with their own age class.

INCREASING SOCIAL DISCRIMINATION

After the establishment of initial social bonds, the next major step in socialization is an *increasing social discrimination* produced by learned associations based upon various aspects of the behavior of parent or siblings. Normal social experience in particular seems to be strongly self-reinforcing and leads to increasingly specific social bonds. Darwin stated (1890) he had heard

flocks composed of the same hens in a shifting membership, there is less fighting, the average individual gets more to eat, maintains body weight better, and probably lays more eggs. It appears likely, therefore, that a somewhat exclusive membership of flocks may enhance social organization and population growth at low densities.

The principal end of social development among animals is to enable acceptance and effective functioning of an individual as a member of an organized group.

REFERENCES

ALLEY, R., and BOYD, H. 1950. Parent-young recognition in the coot. *Ibis.* 92: 46–51.

BARTHOLOMEW, G. A. 1959. Mother-young relations and the maturation of pup behavior in the Alaskan fur seal. *Animal Behav.* 7: 163–171.

BLAUVELT, H. 1955. "Dynamics of the Mother-Newborn Relationship in Goats," in *Group Processes, Tr. First Conference,* ed. by SCHAFFNER, B. New York, Josiah Macy, Jr., Foundation, pp. 221–258.

CARPENTER, C. R. 1945. Concepts and problems of primate sociometry. *Sociometry.* 8: 56–61.

COLLIAS, N. E. 1950a. The socialization of chicks. *Anat. Rec. 108:* (Suppl.): Abstract 93.

COLLIAS, N. E. 1950b. Social life and the individual among vertebrate animals. *Ann. New York Acad. Sc. 51:* 1074–1092.

COLLIAS, N. E. 1952. The development of social behavior in birds. *Auk.* 69: 127–159.

COLLIAS, N. E. 1953. Some factors in maternal rejection of sheep and goats. *Bull. Ecol. Soc. Am. 34:* 78.

COLLIAS, N. E. 1956. The analysis of socialization in sheep and goats. *Ecology.* 37: 228–239.

COLLIAS, N. E., and COLLIAS, E. C. 1956. Some mechanisms of family integration in ducks. *Auk.* 73: 378–400.

COLLIAS, N., and JOOS, M. 1953. The spectrographic analysis of sound signals of the domestic fowl. *Behaviour.* 5: 175–188.

COLLIAS, N. E., and TABER, R. D. 1951. A field study of some grouping and dominance relations in ring-necked pheasants. *Condor.* 53: 265–275.

CRAIG, W. 1908. The voices of pigeons regarded as a means of social control. *Am. J. Sociol.* 14: 86–100.

DARWIN, C. 1890. *The Expression of the Emotions in Man and Animals,* 2nd ed. London, James Murray.

DOUGLIS, M. B. 1948. Social factors influencing the hierarchies of small flocks of the domestic hen: interactions between resident and part-time members of organized flocks. *Physiol. Zool.* 21: 147–182.

EMLEN, J. T., JR. 1939. Seasonal movements of a low-density Valley Quail population. *J. Wildlife Management.* 3: 118–130.

FABRICIUS, E. 1951. Zur Ethologie junger Anatiden. *Acta Zoologica Fennica.* 68: 1–178.

GUHL, A. M. 1958. The development of social organization in the domestic chick. *Animal Behav.* 6: 92–111.

GUHL, A. M., and ALLEE, W. C. 1944. Some measurable effects of social organization in flocks of hens. *Physiol. Zool.* 17: 320–347.

GUITON, P. 1959. Socialization and imprinting in Brown Leghorn chicks. *Animal Behav.* 7: 26–34.

HARLOW, H. F. 1959. Love in infant monkeys. *Scient. Am.* 200(6): 68–74.

HINDE, R. A., THORPE, W. H., and VINCE, M. A. 1956. The following response of young coots and moorhens. *Behaviour.* 9: 214–242.

HOLZAPFEL, M. 1939. Analyse des Sperrens und Pickens in der Entwicklung des Stars. *J. f. Ornithol.* 87: 525–553.

HOWARD, W. E., and EMLEN, J. T., JR. 1942. Intercovey social relationships in the Valley Quail. *Wilson Bull.* 54: 162–170.

JAMES, H. 1959. Flicker: an unconditioned stimulus for imprinting. *Canad. J. Psychol.* 13: 59–67.

JAYNES, J. 1957. Imprinting: the interaction of learned and innate behavior: II. The critical period. *J. Comp. & Physiol. Psychol.* 50: 6–10.

KABAT, C., COLLIAS, N. E., and GUETTINGER, R. 1953. Some winter habits of white-tailed deer and the development of census methods in the flag yard of northern Wisconsin. *Wisconsin Conserv. Dept. Tech. Wildlife Bull.,* No. 7, p. 1–32.

KING, J. A. 1954. Closed social groups among domestic dogs. *Proc. Am. Philosophical Soc.,* 98: 327–336.

KING, J. A., and GURNEY, N. L. 1954. Effect of early social experience on adult aggressive behaviour in C57BL/10 mice. *J. Comp. & Physiol. Psychol.* 47: 326–330.

KUO, Z. Y. 1930. The genesis of the cat's response to mice. *J. Comp. Psychol. 11:* 1–30.

LEVY, D. M. 1934. Experiments in the sucking reflex and social behavior of dogs. *Am. J. Orthopsychiat. 4:* 203–224.

LORENZ, K. 1937. The companion in the bird's world. *Auk. 54:* 245–273.

LORENZ, K. 1952. *King Solomon's Ring.* London, Methuen.

NICOLAI, J. 1956. Zur Biologie und Ethologie des Gimpels (*Pyrrhula pyrrhula* L.). *Ztschr. f. Tierpsychol. 31:* 93–132.

RAMSAY, A. O., and HESS, E. H. 1954. A laboratory approach to the study of imprinting. *Wilson Bull. 66:* 196–206.

REYNOLDS, H. C. 1952. Studies on reproduction in the opossum (*Didelphis virginiana virginiana*). *Univ. California Publications Zool. 52*(3): 223–275, Plates 3–7.

SCOTT, J. P. 1958. Critical periods in the development of social behavior in puppies. *Psychosom. Med. 20:* 42–54.

SPALDING, D. 1873. Instinct, with original observations on young animals. *MacMillan's Mag. 27:* 282–293. Reprinted, 1954, *Brit. J. Animal Behav. 2:* 2–11.

WEIDMANN, U. 1958. Verhaltensstudien an der Stockente (*Anas platyrhynchos* L.): II. Versuche zur Auslösung und Pragung der Nachfolge—und Anschluszreaktion. *Ztschr. f. Tierpsychol. 15*(3): 277–300.

WHITMAN, C. O. 1919. The behavior of pigeons, ed. by CARR, H. A. *Carnegie Institute of Washington Publications. 3:* 1–161.

YERKES, R. M. 1943. *Chimpanzees, a Laboratory Colony.* New Haven, Yale University Press, 321 pp.

PART IV

SOCIAL BEHAVIOR

20

SOCIAL BEHAVIOR OF ANTHROPOID PRIMATES: ANALYSIS OF RECENT CONCEPTS

Stuart A. Altmann

The major features of vertebrate social behavior are gregariousness, social communication, territoriality and home range, social hierarchies (such as those based on aggressive dominance and on leadership), sexual behavior, parental care, and—at least among mammals—social play. The primates are no exception.

Many of these aspects of the social behavior of primates have been reviewed repeatedly (e.g., Carpenter, 1942, 1952, 1958; Chance and Mead, 1953; Miller, 1931; Nissen, 1951; Sahlins, 1959; Zuckerman, 1932). The reader is referred to these reviews for a purview that will be assumed in the following discussion. In the years since the publication of these reviews and the research upon which they were based, several field studies of primate social behavior have been conducted, and a number of intriguing concepts of primate sociobiology have developed. No attempt will be made here to cover all aspects of primate social behavior; nor will I attempt to show how widespread are the phenomena

Supported in part by Research Fellowship No. MF9005 from the National Institute of Mental Health, National Institute of Health, U.S. Public Health Service.

that will be discussed. Rather, my purpose will be to establish that certain phenomena exist among at least some anthropoid primates.

From June, 1956, until June, 1958, we carried out a study of the behavior, social organization and population dynamics of the rhesus monkeys, *Macaca mulatta*, that inhabit Cayo Santiago, a small island in the West Indies. Preliminary results of that study will be used as a basis for the discussion; some analogous or homologous cases in other anthropoid primates will be pointed out. All statements about rhesus monkeys for which no reference is cited are based upon personal observations. A full analysis of the results of the study is now in preparation.

SOCIAL COMMUNICATION

Let us consider certain properties of social communication that are, so far as is known, common to all species of anthropoid primates. The members of all primate social groups communicate with one another; that is, certain behavior patterns serve as social messages in that they affect the behavior of other members of the group. Indeed, it is, in part, the presence of such behavior that enables us to designate the groups as "social."

While all social behavior is communicative behavior, the converse relation does not hold: there are behavior patterns that affect the behavior of other members of the group and therefore are, by definition, communicative, yet that are not classed as "social behavior" in the usual sense of the term. Primate social behavior is communicative behavior that has certain additional properties (cf. Morris, 1955).

First, the behavioral repertoire of each species includes a plurality of classes of communicative acts. In the hamadryas baboon, *Papio hamadryas,* for example, there are 70 such elemental classes of communicative behavior (Kummer, 1957). There are about the same number in the rhesus macaque. These are surprisingly small vocabularies for animals with such complex social organizations.

Second, the communicative acts of each species of anthropoid primates are a part of the behavioral repertoire of all members of the society, at least at some stage in their life history. In contrast, although predator and prey communicate with each other, in that each affects the behavior of the other, they do not share a common repertoire of social behavior patterns. Predator and prey are members of the same community but of different societies.

Third, primate social behavior is plurisituational. The same behavior patterns recur continually at various times and places. Thus, by the repetition of items from a small basic vocabulary, the primates are able to produce an endless stream of babble.

Fourth, there are constraints on the ways in which communicative acts are combined. Certain sequences are far more probable than others, and the behavior of a primate depends in part on the previous behavior of other members of the group. Letting i represent any item from a species' repertoire of social behavior, we would, in general, like to be able to specify the joint probabilities, $p(i_1, i_2, \ldots, i_r)$ or the $r - 1$st order transition probabilities, $p_{i_1, i_2, \ldots, i_{r-1}}(i_r)$, taking r up to the length of the longest sequences of behavior that significantly decrease the uncertainty of our predictions when compared with predictions based on sequences of length $r - 1$. For a species with a repertoire of n distinct, socially significant behavior patterns, the maximum number of unique courses of interaction is $\sum_{a=1}^{m} n^a$, where m is the maximum value of r, as indicated above, and a is an arbitrary symbol with the range indicated. The social behavior of primates can thus be treated as stochastic processes.

Fifth, the elements of social communication are interpersonal, that is, all members of the group or even of the species respond in a generally predictable way to each pattern of social behavior, though individual differences may still be of great significance. More specifically, in the terms of our stochastic model, the matrices of sequential probabilities that are based on random samplings of the interactions of all members of a society or species can be used as a basis for predicting the behavior of any member of the group—though, doubtless, partitioning these matrices by age, by sex, or by individuals will increase the accuracy of predictions. This property makes possible the description of patterns of social behavior that are characteristic of the society or species. The selective rationale for this property becomes obvious if one considers the probable fate of a monkey that persistently gave the "wrong" response or that responded randomly to threats, alarm calls, and sexual presentations. His chances of surviving and of reproducing would be nil.

We will discuss in detail the concept of social communication as stochastic processes elsewhere (Altmann, 1961) and will therefore not pursue it further here.

This analysis of universal features of primate social communication may help to clarify our definition of "society" as "an aggregation of socially intercommunicating, conspecific individuals that is bounded by frontiers of far less frequent communication."

METACOMMUNICATION

Primates include in their repertoire a set of social messages that serve to affect the way in which other social messages are interpreted. In a sense, the use of such messages involves communication about communication. It is therefore designated as "metacommunication" (Bateson, 1955; Ruesch, 1953; Ruesch and Bateson, 1951).

For example, preceding and accompanying play encounters, rhesus monkeys went through certain motions (e.g., gamboling, looking at their playmates from between or beside their own hind legs with their heads upside down) that signaled to the other members of the play group that any aggressive behavior in the play situation would not be "real" aggression: the playing monkeys mouthed and nipped each other but did not bite, even though their dentition and jaw musculature were mature enough to do so.

The sequential patterning of responses in play differs from those in nonplay situations: they can be represented by different stochastic processes. The metacommunicative messages that enabled the monkeys to distinguish between play and nonplay acted like mechanisms that somehow switched the monkeys from one entire set of response patterns to another.

Like communication, metacommunication sometimes breaks down. Rhesus monkeys never vocalized during their aggressive play. Not infrequently a play situation became so rough that an infant no longer accepted it as play; the metacommunicative message, "This is play," broke down. The infant squealed. Its mother quickly approached and threatened her infant's playmates, who then fled. Older monkeys "anticipated" the mothers' intervention: they fled from the play area whenever any member of the play group squealed.

There are other examples of metacommunication in anthropoid primates. One of the most obvious and thus one of the most easily overlooked involves the fact that their social messages are almost always directed toward particular individuals or groups. The social messages of primates are seldom of the form, "To whom it may concern." Such directedness is comparable to the statement, "The following messages are intended only for you." Primates indicate such directedness by facing and looking at the recipient of the message, approaching it, or by other postures and gestures. Such metacommunicative signals serve to restrict the responses to a message to something less than the entire group of animals that is within sight or sound of that message.

The means by which relative dominance status is communicated constitute another form of metacommunication in anthropoid primates. Dominant rhesus monkeys can be recognized by a particularly brisk, striding gait, by the posture of the tail (held erect and curled back at the tip), by the fact that they sit calmly, rather than persistently glancing around them as do some of the most subordinate monkeys, and so forth. Similar status indicators have been described in Japanese macaques, *Macaca fuscata* (Itani, 1954); in hamadryas baboons (Kummer, 1956, 1957); and in chacma baboons, *Papio ursinus* (Bolwig, 1959).

THE ABILITY TO PREDICT

During the course of the study of rhesus monkeys, I was greatly impressed by the fact that the monkeys were constantly faced with exactly the same problem that I was, viz., predicting social behavior. The relative success or failure of any individual monkey depended very greatly upon his ability to make the appropriate responses to different individuals under a variety of circumstances. Beyond that, he had continually to revise his behavior in order to cope with the fact that his own behavior and capabilities, as well as those of the other members of his group, were undergoing both long-term changes, as a part of maturity and senescence, and short-term changes, due to illness, wounds, stressful situations, and so forth. For example, an adult male rhesus who could, at times, be approached with impunity constituted, at other times, a definite threat.

Making the appropriate responses required that the monkeys have an ability to observe, to remember, and to predict. Further, the monkeys were capable of basing their actions upon observed, communicative, and metacommunicative behavior in sequences that were of considerable length and that did not have completely determined outcomes; i.e., they dealt with their own social groups as stochastic processes.

GREGARIOUSNESS

Zuckerman, on the basis of the data that were available nearly three decades ago, postulated that "the main factor that determines social grouping in sub-human primates is sexual attraction" (Zuckerman, 1932, p. 31). This theory apparently was based on the conclusion that monkeys, apes, and man—unlike most nonprimates—have

no anestrum but, rather, "experience a smooth and uninterrupted sexual and reproductive life" (Zuckerman, 1932, p. 51).

During the two-year study on Cayo Santiago, mating among the sexually mature rhesus monkeys began rather abruptly each year around the latter part of September and continued for about five months thereafter. A breeding season has been observed also in the Japanese macaques, the infants being born from June to August (Itani, 1954). There was no obvious diminution in the sociability of the females during diestrum or of the group as a whole during the prolonged anestrum.

Virtually all mature rhesus monkeys were attracted to the dominant, adult males, even outside of the breeding season. The young were, in turn, attracted to their mothers, their siblings, and other close associates. The dominant males initiated and directed progressions of their entire group at all times of the year. Whenever the dominant male of a group got up and briskly walked away, sometimes giving a deep, gruff vocalization ("hŭ, hŭ, hŭ . . . "), the other members of the group moved away with him.

At all times of the year, a rhesus monkey that became isolated from the group began actively searching and calling ("cew, cew, cew . . . "). This occurred regardless of the gender, sexual maturity, or phase of the menstrual cycle of the lost monkey.

When two groups approached each other or intermingled at their peripheries, aggressive interactions began as soon as the approach or presence of strangers was noticed. Since this detection requires familiarity with all members of one's own group, it was not done by the youngest members of the group.

A result of the affinities among members of a group and of the aggression toward strangers is that primates live in discrete social groups with highly stable membership.

SEXUAL BEHAVIOR AND REPRODUCTION

The division into discrete, breeding groups with a relatively small amount of mating among the offspring of different groups, characteristic of many species of anthropoid primates, closely resembles the model (Wright, 1940, 1949) for populations capable of both rapid and sustained evolution.

In contrast with the females of most groups of vertebrates, female anthropoid primates characteristically accept or solicit copulation throughout a far longer span of their sexual cycle than can be expected to lead to conception. This extended period of sexual receptivity is of social significance. During estrous periods of several days, female rhesus monkeys associated very closely with one male at a time. Some females associated with only one male throughout one or more estrous periods; others, with a series of two or more males. During these mating associations, the female had almost the same dominance status as that of the male with whom she associated. When she threatened other monkeys, the female's consort interceded for her. Furthermore, intense aggression was rarely directed by a male toward his mate. Attempts to determine the dominance relations between males and their consort females were unusually difficult. Thus, the estrous female is in an advantageous social position, particularly if she becomes the consort of one of the most dominant males of her group. Perhaps this augmentation of the social status of estrous females has been part of the basis for selection of longer sexual receptivity.

Differential reproduction is one of the major factors altering the gene frequencies of populations. We will try to explicate the relation between the dominance status of rhesus males and their access to sexually receptive females. Let us first consider the biological premises of our model. As we acquire more knowledge about this species, doubtless some of these premises will have to be amended. However, they are probably sufficiently accurate for a first approximation. The premises are as follows:

First, the menstrual cycles of the females are independent, i.e., diachronic.

Second, the mean probability (p) that a female is in estrus is one-third; i.e., the period of sexual receptivity of the female is, on the average, one-third of her menstrual cycle (Carpenter, 1942). In contrast, males are continually receptive.

Third, if only one estrous female is available to two males, she will consort with the more dominant male of the two.

Fourth, males do not consort with more than one female at a time.

As shown by Chance and Mead (1953), it follows from the first two premises that in a population of n sexually mature, nonpregnant females the probability that there will be exactly x females in estrus at any one time is

$$f(n,x;p) = \binom{n}{x} p^x (1 - p)^{n-x}.$$

The male of any dominance rank, r, will have access to an estrous female if and only if r or more females are simultaneously in estrus; i.e., the probability that the male of rank r will have access to an estrous female is

$$\sum_{x=r}^{n} f(n,x;p).$$

We have computed the chance that the male of each rank will have access to a receptive female in groups of various sizes. The results are shown in Figure 20-1. These results have several interesting features. First, there is a sharp change in the probability of access to females where the rank of the males equals one third the number of sexually mature, nonpregnant females. The males are sharply demarcated into the "haves" and the "have nots." Second, the equability of the distribution of the receptive females among the males depends upon the total number of females in the group, as well as on the ratio of males to females. To the extent that access to sexually receptive females is directly correlated with reproductive success, the intensity of

infant relations in the rhesus monkey (Harlow, Ch. 10, this volume). Unlike the surrogate mothers that have been used in these studies, the real mother is responsive to the infant. In addition, the relations between mother and infant develop within a broader social context: both mother and infant interact with other members of their group, who are, in turn, highly attracted to the infant.

Let us look briefly at some of these more complex social relations. In the first days

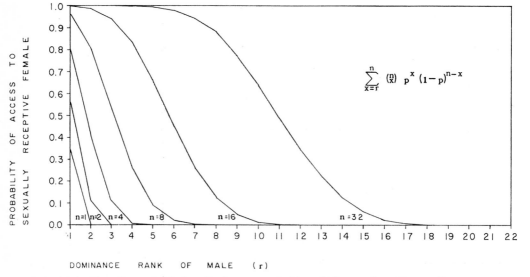

$$\sum_{x=r}^{n} \binom{n}{x} p^{x} (1-p)^{n-x}$$

FIG. 20-1. The effect of relative dominance rank (r) and the number of sexually mature, nonpregnant females in the group (n) on the probability of a rhesus male's access to a sexually receptive female. Based on a model described in the text.

sexual selection can be expected to be a function of the total number of sexually mature females in the group.

Unfortunately, the two groups of monkeys that were on Cayo Santiago do not provide enough data to test this model. Data from a series of groups in their native habitat are highly desirable.

MATERNAL BEHAVIOR AND INFANT DEVELOPMENT

In recent years, there have been a number of excellent laboratory studies of mother-

after the birth of an infant, the female rhesus usually threatens or moves away from other monkeys that attempt to handle the neonate. The neonate, from birth, clings tightly to its mother's fur. Presumably, individual recognition is established during this early period of partial isolation. The infant rhesus certainly gives every indication of being capable of such learning (Harlow, 1959); and very few mistakes are made afterwards, either by the mother, in locating her infant from among a group of infants, or by the infant, in identifying its mother from among a group of adult females.

As the infant rhesus matures and becomes capable of independent locomotion, its mother makes use of two other devices for limiting its social contacts: retrieving the infant as it moves away from her, sometimes pulling it back to her by the tail alone, and threatening other monkeys from the infant, particularly any monkeys that hurt the infant. The older monkeys come to recognize the zone of protection that is provided by the mother; the infant is rarely treated roughly in her immediate vicinity. In striking contrast to the rhesus monkeys, female howling monkeys, *Alouatta palliata*, do very little to interfere with the social interactions of their infants (Altmann, 1959).

In view of the close relation that develops between a dam and her infants, it is perhaps not surprising that the infant rhesus monkey's closest associate, other than its mother, is its next-older sibling.

These facts raise several interesting questions about the degree to which an infant may learn patterns of social interaction from its mother and siblings, thereby inheriting from them its social status. While very little information on this point is now available for nonhuman anthropoids, it should be pointed out that socially learned and transmitted behavior is not completely unknown in these animals. The spread of food preferences through societies of Japanese macaques has been studied over a number of years. Preliminary results indicate that transmission may occur more readily from mother to infant and from dominant to subordinate than in the reverse directions (Frisch, 1959; Itani, 1954).

The rhesus mother frequently grooms her infant. The very young infant does not reciprocate, however. Opposition of thumb and forefinger does not mature until the infant is about 9 months of age (Hines, 1942).

Such social grooming is one of the most frequently seen activities in groups of cercopithecid and pongid primates. As has been demonstrated in the chimpanzee, *Pan troglodytes* (Falk, 1958), and as is doubtless true of other primates, grooming may serve as a "reinforcer," perhaps due, in part, to the salty taste of the detritus that is picked from the fur (Ewing, 1935).

SOCIAL PLAY

Groups of playing monkeys are a conspicuous part of primate societies of many species. The play patterns of the rhesus monkeys that were observed on Cayo Santiago had a number of interesting features. We have mentioned the fact that there were metacommunicative messages that enabled the monkeys to distinguish between play situations and nonplay situations, and that this distinction sometimes broke down.

The play groups seemed to be unstable unless the "games" that were played were "fair" games, i.e., unless each of the participants had approximately equal chances of dominating the play-aggressive situations. This stability was achieved, in part, by what we shall refer to as "self-handicapping": the monkeys that were dominant in nonplay situations were, during play, only about as intense in their play-aggression as were their subordinate playmates.

In the long run, however, the more dominant individuals did play a rougher game. Doubtless, it was in these early play situations that many of the future dominance relations were being established. In general, the larger and older monkeys were the more aggressive. The younger monkeys tended to avoid playing with the older ones. As a result, there was a strong tendency for the play groups to consist of like-aged monkeys. Similar observations have been made on play groups of Japanese macaques (Itani, 1954).

As the monkeys approached sexual maturity, their relative dominance status became more clear-cut. Concomitantly, play became less frequent, perhaps due in part to the inability of the monkeys to accept, even within the context of a play situation, a reduction in status.

SUMMARY

Several recent concepts of primate sociobiology have been discussed, using the rhesus monkey as a paradigm. It is postulated that the social communication of all species of primates is characterized by a number of types of messages that are given and responded to by all members of the society in essentially the same way. The responses are relatively unstereotyped, however, so that the sequences of messages that make up social interactions can be represented by stochastic processes.

In addition, antropoid primates are capable of communicating about their own communication process, that is, their repertoires of behavior include classes of messages that affect the responses to other messages. The use of such messages is called "metacommunication." Metacommunication is used by anthropoid primates in distinguishing between play and nonplay situations, in communicating their social status, and in directing their behavior toward particular individuals.

The ability of primates to cope with their own complex and ever-changing patterns of social communication depends upon their remarkable ability to observe, to remember, and to predict. While sexual attraction is of undoubted importance in primate societies, there are other attractions among anthropoid primates that keep groups together during the females' diestrous and anestrous phases.

Three aspects of primate reproduction—the division into virtually closed breeding groups, the extended period of sexual receptivity of the females, and the relation between the dominance status of the males and their access to females—have been discussed and some of their evolutionary implications considered.

The infant matures within a complex social milieu. Recognition of mother by infant and vice versa may be established during an early period of partial social isolation of the two. The mother sometimes restricts the social contacts of the infant by moving away with the infant clinging to her, by pulling the infant back to her when it moves away, or by threatening others from the infant. Aside from its mother, the infant's closest associate is its next-older sibling. Although the infant is frequently groomed by its mother, it cannot reciprocate until it is physically mature enough to oppose its thumb and forefinger.

Play groups are unstable unless each individual has about the same chance of winning. Stability is achieved by metacommunicative messages, by a tendency toward restriction into like-aged groups, and by "self-handicapping" on the part of older and stronger individuals. In the long run, certain individuals play a rougher game. Future dominance relations may be worked out in these early play groups.

REFERENCES

ALTMANN, S. A. 1959. Field observations on a howling monkey society. *J. Mammal. 40:* 317–330.

ALTMANN, S. A. 1961. The stochastic laws of a primate society. *In preparation.*

BATESON, G. 1955. A theory of play and fantasy. *Psychiatric Res. Rep. Am. Psychiatric A. 2:* 39–51.

BOLWIG, N. 1959. A study of the behaviour of the chacma baboon, *Papio ursinus*. *Behaviour*. *14:* 136–163.

CARPENTER, C. R. 1942. Sexual behavior of free ranging rhesus monkeys (*Macaca mulatta*). *J. Comp. Psychol. 33:* 113–162.

CARPENTER, C. R. 1952. Social behavior of non-human primates. *Colloques Internationaux du Centre National de la Recherche Scientifique. 34:* 227–246.

CARPENTER, C. R. 1958. Soziologie und Verhalten freilebender nichtmenschlicher Primaten. *Handbuch der Zool. 8*(10, article 11): 1–32.

CHANCE, M. R. A., and MEAD, A. P. 1953. Social behaviour and primate evolution. *Symposia Soc. Exper. Biol. 7:* 395–439.

EWING, H. E. 1935. Sham louse-picking, or grooming, among monkeys. *J. Mammal. 16:* 303–306.

FALK, J. L. 1958. The grooming behavior of the chimpanzee as a reinforcer. *J. Exper. Anal. Behav. 1:* 83–85.

FRISCH, J. E. 1959. Research on primate behavior in Japan. *Am. Anthropologist. 61:* 584–596.

HARLOW, H. F. 1959. The development of learning in the rhesus monkey. *Am. Scientist. 47:* 459–479.

HINES, M. 1942. The development and regression of reflexes, postures, and progression in the young macaque. Carnegie Institute of Washington *Contributions Embryol.*, No. 196, pp. 153–209.

ITANI, J. 1954. *Takasakiyama No Saru.* Tokyo, Kobunsha, 284 pp.

KUMMER, H. 1956. Rang-Kriterien bei Mantel-pavianen. Der Rang adulter Weibchen im Sozialverhalten, den Individualdistanzen und im Schlaf. *Rev. Suisse Zool. 63:* 288–297.

KUMMER, H. 1957. Sociales Verhalten einer Mantelpaviangruppe. *Beiheft z. Schweizerischen Ztschr. f. Psychol. und ihre Anwendungen*, 91 pp.

MILLER, G. 1931. The primate basis of human sexual behavior. *Quart. Rev. Biol. 6:* 379–410.

MORRIS, C. 1955. *Signs, Language, and Behavior.* New York, Braziller, 365 pp.

NISSEN, H. W. 1951. "Social Behavior in Primates," in *Comparative Psychology*, 3rd ed., ed. by STONE, C. P., Englewood Cliffs, N.J., Prentice-Hall, 525 pp.

RUESCH, J. 1953. Synopsis of the theory of human communication. *Psychiatry. 16:* 215–243.

RUESCH, J., and BATESON, G. 1951. *Communication, the Social Matrix of Psychiatry.* New York, Norton, 314 pp.

SAHLINS, M. D. 1959. "The Social Life of Monkeys, Apes and Primitive Man," in *The Evolution of Man's Capacity for Culture*, arr. by SPUHLER, J. N. Detroit, Wayne State University, 79 pp.

WRIGHT, S. 1940. Breeding structure of populations in relation to speciation. *Am. Naturalist. 74:* 232–248.

WRIGHT, S. 1949. Population structure in evolution. *Proc. Am. Philosophical Soc. 93:* 471–478.

ZUCKERMAN, S. 1932. *The Social Life of Monkeys and Apes.* London, Kegan Paul, Trench, Trubner, 357 pp.

21

FIELD STUDIES OF A PRIMATE POPULATION

C. Ray Carpenter

One hundred years ago Charles Darwin published *The Origin of the Species*. The theory of evolution formulated principally by Darwin and Wallace, and elaborated by Huxley, Spencer, and others, resulted in an intellectual revolution, especially in biological thought. The well-known theory of evolution, supplemented later by theories of genes and heredity, has stimulated a century of vigorous research. Furthermore, these theories have provided general themes and categories for organizing and ordering large quantities of information, especially on the levels of the taxonomy and morphology of living organisms. In the areas of physiology and behavior, however, these theories have not been as helpful. It has proved to be particularly difficult for scientists to formulate theories and to order systems of information on the evolution of social behavior, and thus to bridge the gaps of knowledge between the biological fundamentals and the basic processes of complex social behavior. The chasm between the social behavior of human and nonhuman organisms remains wide and generally unbridged by integrated systems of both theoretical and factual information. Apparently what is needed is the development of the field of comparative social behavior which would correspond to but extend the areas of comparative anatomy, comparative physiology, physical anthropology, and comparative psychology. This development should eventually integrate facts and principles across the intervening emergents of language and culture.

At present there is a strong resurgence of interest in research on the social behavior of nonhuman primates, both in the field and in the laboratory. These investigations, if conducted intelligently with sufficient vigor over an adequate period of time and on a broad front, may eventually provide valid data and principles for understanding the phylogenetic development of human social adaptations and adjustments. Then we may be able to discard such abstract concepts as Freud's "id," McDougall's "instinct," Horney's "basic anxiety," Jung's "archetype," and other such terms now commonly used both to describe and to explain organic, functional, and biosocial behavior.

The comparative studies of patterns of groupings and systems of social behavior in the nonhuman primates can be viewed as one attempt to describe and to construct *culture-free models* of groups and populations of organisms. Such research could be a part of the broad research strategy concerned with the development of an understanding and perhaps eventually the rational control of complex biosocial behavior. It could be one step toward answering the many important questions which remain unanswered in this area.

We must face the fact that however much we may desire to find solutions to urgent professional problems, including "mental health," personal-social adjustments, and the dynamics of populations, basic science generally must progress by small steps. Our haste and anxiety to have solutions to many critical human problems may have led to many premature generalizations in the behavioral sciences, thus actually retarding rather than advancing the development and formulation of proved principles of sociobiology. Until basic principles have been established by evidence, uncertainties and indecision will characterize the applied professional arts of psychiatry, psychoanalysis, anthropology, and applied psychology.

THEORETICAL ORIENTATION

The purpose of this paper is to apply a general hypothesis and to give the pertinent and available data on the composition of groups of *one* species of primate, the howler monkey (*Alouatta palliata*), in the population of Barro Colorado Island, Panama Canal Zone.

The Hypothesis

Bernard formulated and Cannon (1929) elaborated and supported the illuminating general hypothesis of the *"steady state"* or *homeostasis*. The theory holds that physiological functions and biochemical and neurohumoral regulatory mechanisms operate as systems to maintain dynamic equilibria in the inter l environments of organisms. These homeostatic mechanisms also serve to control cycles of physiological functions

and the related overt behavior. They limit variability within definable ranges of tolerance in normal physiology and behavior. They operate to release energy surges and to activate emergency adjustments under stress and unusual environmental demands. The overt behavioral adjustments of the organisms can be viewed logically as extensions or phases of the physiological adjustive or regulatory mechanisms. If this extension of the general hypothesis is made, then the theory of homeostasis may be tested in its application to the naturalistic activities of nonhuman primates.

Therefore, I propose that the hypothesis of homeostatic regulators be extended to and tested on the level of complex social behavior. In line with this theory it may be shown that the composition and patterns of groups of primates living in a naturalistic context are the resultants of interactive behavioral systems which regulate and maintain norms of ordered adjustments for individuals within structured groups as well as the adjustment of groups within a population of animals. In addition, subhypotheses can be formulated to account for variations in group compositions and patterns which are characteristic of a genus or species. It would appear that variations plus or minus from the grouping patterns characteristic of a species instigate "stress" or motivate behavior which reestablishes the grouping norms. This and similar hypotheses can be tested by adequate field observations.

Three great general theories for motivating and integrating research in sociobiology have been referred to: The theory of evolution, the theory of heredity, and the theory of homeostasis. The third theory challenges the formulation of many subhypotheses bearing on complex social interactions and especially the dynamics of group composition and organization.

THE COMPOSITION OF HOWLER MONKEY GROUPS

Four major field studies have been made on the howler population of Barro Colorado Island, Panama Canal Zone, since 1932. As far as is known, no other nonhuman primate population has been observed so intensively or over such a long period of years. Attempts to make exhaustive censuses of the population and detailed analyses of the composition of all observable groups were made in 1932 and 1933 (Carpenter, 1934), 1951 (Collias and Southwick, 1952), and again in 1959. Furthermore, a sample of 15 groups was also analyzed in 1935 (Carpenter, 1953).

The data for the analyses of group compositions are shown in Tables 21-1 through Table 21-5. The data are arranged to show groups in order of size and five classes of animals: males, females without infants, females with infants, infants, and juveniles. Infants and juveniles are each classified into three subcategories corresponding to stages of growth and maturation. The tables show the patterns of consistencies and variations of the groups, including their size, and other differences for the total sampled populations of each field study.

The analyses of groups made during the 1930's showed that there was a *central grouping tendency* for howlers around which group size and composition varied

TABLE 21-1   CENSUS OF 23 HOWLER GROUPS, APRIL, 1932

GROUPS (ORDER OF SIZE)	MALES	FEMALES WITHOUT YOUNG	FEMALES WITH YOUNG	INFANTS 1	INFANTS 2	INFANTS 3	JUVENILES 1	JUVENILES 2	JUVENILES 3	TOTALS
1	1	3								4
2	1	2	1			1				5
3	1	2	2	1		2	1	1		10
4	2	3	2		1	1	2			11
5	2	3	3	1	1	1	1	1		13
6	3	5	2		1	1	1	1		14
7	2	3	3	1	2		1	1	1	14
8	2	3	3	2	1		1	2		14
9	4	4	1		1	1		3	1	15
10	3	4	2	1	1		2	1	1	15
11	2	2	4	2	1	1		2	1	15
12	4	6	2		2			2	2	18
13	2	5	3	1		4	2	1		18
14	2	5	3	1	1	1	2	2	1	18
15	3	7	2		2		3	1	1	19
16	2	5	3		2	2	1	3	1	19
17	4	6	4	2	1	1	1	1		20
18	3	5	3	1	1	1	4	2		20
19	4	4	2		1	2	2	5	2	22
20	1	5	5		1	6	1	3	2	24
21	6	10	3	1	2	1		1	3	27
22	4	7	5		4	1	3	4		28
23	5	9	5	1	1	3	2	5	4	35
Totals	63	108	63	15	27	30	30	42	20	398

TABLE 212   CENSUS OF 28 HOWLER GROUPS, APRIL, 1933

GROUPS (ORDER OF SIZE)	MALES	FEMALES WITHOUT YOUNG	FEMALES WITH YOUNG	INFANTS 1	INFANTS 2	INFANTS 3	JUVENILES 1	JUVENILES 2	JUVENILES 3	TOTALS
1	1	1	1		1					4
2	2	2						1		5
3	2		2		1	1				6
4	2	4					1	1		8
5	1	1	3	1	1	1		2		10
6	1	2	2	1	1		2	2		11
7	2	4	2		1	1	1	1		12
8	3	4					3		3	13
9	2	2	3		2	1	1	2	1	14
10	2	2	4	1	1	2	1	2		15
11	2	2	3	1	1	1	1	2	2	15
12	3	1	5	1		4	2	1		17
13	3	5	3	1	2		1	2	1	18
14	3	2	5	1	1	3		2	1	18
15	3	3	4	2	2		2	3		19
16	3	3	4	1	2	1	1	2	2	19
17	4	8	2	2				2	2	20
18	3	4	5		2	3	2	1		20
19	3	1	5		5		3	3	1	21
20	3	6	3	1	2		2	3	1	21
21	4	4	4	1	3			3	4	23
22	3	3	5	1	1	3	1	4	2	23
23	4	5	4		3	1	2	3	2	24
24	5	2	7	1	5	1	1	3		25
25	5	5	6	2	3	1	1	1	1	25
26	5	10	3	1	1	1	3	2	1	27
27	3		9	1	3	5	2	2	2	27
28	5	8	4	1		3	2	3	3	29
Totals	82	94	98	21	44	33	37	51	29	489

within limits. The results of the different censuses also showed some degree of consistency in the proportions of animals of different categories in the total population samples (Carpenter, 1952, 1954). Using the data for 66 groups observed in three samplings with a total of 1124 animals and calculating the proportion of animals of the five classes, it was possible to derive a kind of *norm of proportions* of the different categories for the total population samples. Table 21-6 gives these summarized results. For the three field studies made during the 1930's the proportions were: 17 per cent adult males, 40 per cent females, 17 per cent infants, and 26 per cent juveniles.

These proportions, and especially that of adult males to adult females living in groups and having reproductive possibilities, *the sex socionomic ratio*, were assumed to be characteristic of the organized groups of howlers (*Alouatta palliata*) and thus to constitute grouping norms about which variations would occur.

A test of the hypothesis that genera or species of nonhuman primates have char-

TABLE 21-5   CENSUS OF 44 HOWLER GROUPS, JUNE–AUGUST, 1959

GROUPS (ORDER OF SIZE)	MALES	FEMALES		INFANTS			JUVENILES			TOTALS
		WITHOUT YOUNG	WITH YOUNG	1	2	3	1	2	3	
1	1	2								3
2	1	3								4
3	2	1							1	4
4	1	2						1		4
5	1	3					2			6
6	2	2	2		2				1	9
7	2	5	1		1			1		10
8	1	3	2	1	1				3	11
9	3	3	2			2	1			11
10	1	6					2	2	1	12
11	3	5	2	1	1					12
12	3	5	1		1		1		1	12
13	3	5					2	2	1	13
14	3	4	3	1	2					13
15	3	4	2		1	1		2	1	14
16	2	4	4	2	2					14
17	5	5	2	1	1					14
18	2	3	4	3		1			1	14
19	2	3	5	1	2	2				15
20	4	7	1	1			1	1	1	16
21	3	4	5	1	2	2				17
22	4	4	4	1	3				2	18
23	4	8	2		2		1		1	18
24	4	7	2	1	1		1		2	18
25	4	8	2	2			2			18
26	3	6	3	1	2		2		2	19
27	4	8	1	1			2	2	1	19
28	6	7	2	1		1		2	2	21
29	3	5	6	4	2			1	1	22
30	3	3	6	6			1	2	1	22
31	2	6	4	1	3		3	2	2	23
32	3	8	4	1	2	1	2		2	23
33	4	10	2	1	1		3	2	1	24
34	3	3	7	2	4	1	3	1		24
35	3	8	5		5		2	2		25
36	3	7	4	3		1	4	3	2	27
37	8	9	5	1	4				1	28
38	5	12	4	1	2	1		1	2	28
39	5	9	4		3	1	2	1	3	28
40	4	7	7	1	3	2	2	3	3	32
41	3	13	6	1	5		1	4		33
42	4	9	8	1	4	3	3	2		34
43	7	17	3	2		1	2	1	4	37
44	9	17	5	1	4		1	5	3	45
Totals	146	270	132	45	66	20	46	43	46	814

TABLE 21-6 PROPORTION OF DIFFERENT CATEGORIES TO TOTAL SAMPLE AND AVERAGES

YEAR OF CENSUS	MALES	FEMALES		INFANTS	JUVENILES	TOTALS
		WITHOUT INFANTS	WITH INFANTS			
1932	0.16	0.27	0.16	0.18	0.23	398
1933	0.17	0.19	0.20	0.20	0.24	489
1935	0.18	0.24	0.14	0.14	0.30	239
Average proportion	0.17	0.23	0.17	0.17	0.26	
	0.17			0.17	0.26	
		0.40				
1951	0.15	0.42	0.15	0.15	0.13	239
		0.56				
1959	0.18	0.33	0.16	0.16	0.17	814

observed consisted of 4 males, 8 females, 4 infants, and 2 juveniles.

Thus, it can be seen that when the population of howlers increased there was, as predicted, a re-establishment of the group composition approximating but slightly exceeding the predicted central grouping norms.

BEHAVIORAL CORRELATES OF VARIATIONS IN GROUPS

Only qualitative observations are available to support the subhypothesis that the howlers which are living in groups or in isolation but which exhibit the greatest variations from characteristic grouping norms are those animals which are most disturbed or are under stress. Collias and Southwick (1952) called attention to the fact that very small groups had a low proportion of infants. The observations of 1959 confirmed these observations. Small groups and isolated males appear to be more restless, wilder, more easily disturbed, or more de-

fensive than larger groups. If pressed, they become inhibited and either evasive or vocally aggressive. Very large groups, at the other extreme, seem to pay penalties for their size in terms of reduced group mobility and difficulty in maintaining normal group cohesiveness. Thus, the stress hypothesis relative to deviation from characteristic norms seems reasonable but must be supported or rejected on the basis of further research.

A further observation may shed some light on the conditions which are productive of "stress." In areas where groups are concentrated and do not have normally dispersed territorial ranges, the frequency of intergroup conflicts is increased (Carpenter, 1952).

Available evidence suggests that one characteristic of the normal biosocial adjustment and adaptation of the howler monkey and perhaps of other primates living under a natural environment consists of characteristic groups (Altmann, 1959; Carpenter, 1953; Imanishi, 1958). Furthermore, deviations from these typical groups are correlated with motivation and behavioral mechanisms ("stress") which operate to re-establish the group norms.

CONCLUSIONS

The following tentative generalizations seem to be supported by the data presented:

1. In a limited naturalistic population of howler monkeys, norms of proportions of the various categories of animals living in the population can be determined, and these proportions appear to have considerable stability or consistency over time.

2. Reduction in the population of howler monkeys by disease may slightly modify the proportions of males, females, and young and may modify to a greater degree the specific composition of the organized groups.

3. The changes which a reduction of the population produce in the composition of organized groups are counteracted as the population once again increases and the grouping norms characteristic of the species are re-established.

4. The general hypothesis of relative "steady states" or homeostasis is helpful in understanding the dynamic social behavior, group composition, and the maintenance of characteristic "species-specific" patterns of groups in populations of primates living under a limited and protected naturalistic environment.

REFERENCES

ALTMANN, S. A. 1959. Field observations on a howling monkey society. *J. Mammal. 40*(3): 317–330.

CANNON, W. B. 1929. *Bodily Changes in Pain, Hunger, Fear, and Rage.* 2nd ed., New York, Appleton-Century-Crofts.

CARPENTER, C. R. 1934. A field study of the behavior and social relations of howling monkeys. *Comp. Psychol. Monographs. 10*(2):1–168.

CARPENTER, C. R. 1952. Social behavior of non-human primates, structure et physiologie des societes animales, *Colloques Internationaux du Centre National de la Recherche Scientifique. 34:* 227–246.

CARPENTER, C. R. 1953. Grouping behavior of howling monkeys. *Extrait des Arch. Neerlandaises de Zool. 10*(2, Suppl.):45–50.

CARPENTER, C. R. 1954. Tentative generalizations on the grouping behavior of non-human primates. *Human Biol.* 26(3): 269–276.

COLLIAS, N., and SOUTHWICK. 1952. A field study of population density and social organization in howling monkeys. *Proc. Am. Philosophical Soc.* 96(2): 143–156.

IMANISHI, K. 1958. Recent advances in the field studies of primate sociology. *Current Anthropol.*

22

A "BEHAVIORAL SINK"

John B. Calhoun

Unexpected results frequently prove of more interest than anticipated ones. Such has proved to be the case in a study I have pursued during the past two years of social behavior of domesticated Norway rats. In this study rats were reared in slightly different environments. In one, the artificial "burrows" provided (Fig. 22-1) consisted of five nesting boxes connected by a system of tunnels in which alternate routes between any pair of boxes were possible. In the other, the five nesting boxes were lined up in a row along a single straight tunnel. It was my original hypothesis that these two different communication systems would alter the social organization of populations developing under their influence. Actually differences were so slight as to be of little importance.

However, certain similar characteristics of these two slightly different types of environments did produce common effects of profound influence upon the lives of the inhabitants. I shall attempt to show how certain characteristics of the environment led to the development of a pathological aggregation or a pathological togetherness of the inhabitants.

Development of such pathological aggregations led to the formulation of the concept of "behavioral sinks." A brief definition of a "behavioral sink" will facilitate the

gradual unfolding of the evolution of this concept in the account presented below.

Stationary places whose characteristics are such as to lead to securing a reward by the individual who responds there may be designated as *positive response situations*

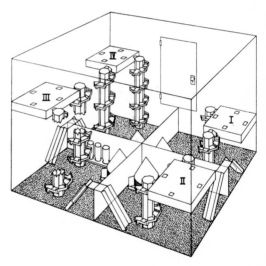

FIG. 22-1. The environment.

(PRS). One or more PRS may be distributed through the environment in such a way that when more than one is present each is sufficiently removed from the others for an animal responding to it to be unable to detect the others. If sufficient animals are present it will frequently happen that one animal will be close to another when they simultaneously respond. Each then serves as a secondary reinforcer for the response executed by the other. In time, each animal redefines the PRS as requiring the presence of another individual. By chance, or under the influence of factors biasing the way the animals move through the environment, some one PRS will have a higher probability of animals arriving at it than will others. The animals will gradually learn that at this particular PRS they will most likely realize their developing redefinition of a PRS which requires the presence of another individual. Thus, more and more animals will gradually increase their frequency of visiting this particular PRS, which may now be designated as the alpha PRS, until very few responses are engaged in at any other PRS. These conditions and processes which culminate in a greater-than-chance reoccurrence of accentuated aggregations of individuals in the vicinity of the alpha PRS comprise a behavioral sink.

THE ENVIRONMENT

Each of the four populations included in this study inhabited a room $10 \times 14 \times 9$ feet (Fig. 22-1). Two-foot high partitions surmounted by a single-strand cattle fence electric guard divided each room into four subareas. Starting from the door into the room these subareas were designated as Pens I, II, III, and IV. V-shaped ramps adjacent to the walls connected Pens I and II, II and III, III and IV, but not Pens I and IV. Thus, insofar as locomotor communication was concerned, the environment was essentially one of four pens in a row. Mounted on the wall in the corner of each pen was an artificial "burrow" designed from a study of many burrows excavated by the author in the Norway rat's natural habitat. Each had a 9-square-foot surface through which four openings gave access

to a trough or "tunnel" underneath. Along this tunnel the rats had access to five 8-inch-square nesting boxes. Two spiral ramps provided communication between the floor and each burrow. Three inches of sawdust covered the floor. A hopper containing 25 pounds of Purina Chow was located in the center corner of each pen. An 8-inch high mesh surface provided access to food around the entire circumference. In Figure 22-1 the food hopper may be identified by its cone-shaped dorsal aspect. Water was available in each pen from a series of two-quart chicken water hoppers placed in a row against one wall. During the winter months, air temperature was maintained at near 65°F. During the summer months the forced air circulating through each room made the temperature closely parallel that outside the laboratory. Each room was lighted from 1000 to 2200 o'clock by four 10-watt bulbs and from 2200 to 1000 o'clock by four additional 100-watt bulbs. A 3×5 foot window on the roof of the room enabled observation.

Strips of paper, which the rats could use for building nests, were placed periodically on the floor in the center of each pen.

Burrows in Pens I and II stood at an elevation of 3 feet from the floor while in Pens III and IV, they were at a 6-foot elevation. This introduced an "income" factor in the environment since rats living in Pens I and II had to expend only half the effort in going to the floor to secure food and water as did rats in Pens III and IV.

These environments formed two types, A and B, which differed only slightly. On one (the A type), the burrow was as shown in Figure 22-1. Its tunnel ran around the underneath side of the 3×3 foot surface. In addition, a tunnel cut across from one side to the opposite one. In the B type the surface was 1 foot wide and 9 feet long. Four openings, equally distributed along this surface gave access to a single straight tunnel underneath, along which there was access to five nesting boxes. We shall not be concerned here with the slight differences in behavior induced by these two types of burrows.

Rooms 1A and 2A contained the A-type burrows. Rooms 1B and 2B contained the B-type burrows.

In all other details the attempt was made to make the environment ideal for the support of a population of not more than 80 rats. The criteria were based upon a three-year study of the ecology and social behavior of wild Norway rats.

SUBJECTS

Osborne-Mendel strain domesticated albino rats from the National Institutes of Health random-bred closed colony formed the original stock. In each room a pregnant female was confined to each pen by removing the ramps connecting pens. At 10 days of age litters were mixed so that in a room each female reared one male and a female progeny from each of the four litters in that room. All 32 young in each room survived to weaning. These 16 males and 16 females in each room were designated as the *1st tier* of rats. These 1st-tier rats were born February 10–20, 1958.

At 45 days of age the mothers were removed, and communication between pens was permitted by placing in the ramps as described above. From the litters born to 1st-tier parents during the latter part of May and the first of June, 1958, four males and four females born in each pen were permitted to survive. These 16 males and 16 females in each room formed the *2nd tier*.

Similarly, a *3rd tier* in each room was formed from young born during the middle of August, 1958. Their parents were either

1st-tier or 2nd-tier rats. Up to the time of weaning of 3rd-tier rats, few deaths of weaned rats had occurred other than those relating to removal of excess young by the investigator.

All rats were individually marked by either metal ear tags or by coded removal of one to three toes. In addition, each rat was marked with two colored dye markings of the pelage which permitted identification from the overhead window.

OBSERVATIONAL PROCEDURES

Each four to eight weeks, or occasionally at shorter intervals, all animals were captured. Each was weighed and measured, and additional data were recorded for each individual: pregnancy, lactation, condition of pelage, number and location of wounds, and various other signs of health. At this time, size, age, and health of litters were noted. Records were kept of complexity of nests and extent of fouling with urine or feces.

Periodically, three to six hours of observation of each room was made through the overhead window. Dictated records, later transcribed for analyses, supplemented tallied records of more frequent and easily categorized behaviors. Emphasis was placed on sexual, aggressive, feeding, drinking, and nest-building behavior as well as movements and place of activity.

A record was maintained of the total amount of water and food consumed in each pen through each consecutive two-week period.

DIFFERENTIAL RESIDENCE

Place of capture during the 12 hours of minimum activity and amount of water consumed both reflect residence. Water consumption as a residence index derives from the typical observed behavior that a

TABLE 22-1   FREQUENCY OF RESIDENCE ACCORDING
TO PEN OF RESIDENCE 1ST- AND 2ND-TIER RATS,
MAY–SEPTEMBER 1958

		PEN			TOTAL
	I	II	III	IV	
Observed	343	467	331	245	1386
Expected (3:4:3:2 ratio)	347	462	347	232	1388

Contingency $X^2 = 1.57$. p of X^2 between .7 and .5.

rat usually drank just after emerging from a period of inactivity and just prior to reinitiating a period of inactivity. Such drinking usually took place in the pen where the rat slept.

During the first few months, frequent movement between pens was the rule. In fact, from watching the activity going on as I sat at the window above the room, I developed a fairly strong impression that there was some interval of time after which if a rat continued to be active it just had to get out of the pen it was then in and go elsewhere. The operation of this process leads to a condition where in time there will be only half as many rats in the two end pens as in the two center ones. A rat in an end pen (I and IV) can only go to a center pen (II or III), whereas a rat in a center pen can go to either the adjoining end pen or the other center pen. Thus more rats will leave the end pens than will be

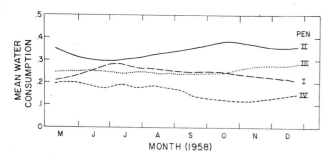

FIG. 22-2. Mean water consumption by pen across Rooms 1A, 2A, 1B, 2B. For each room, every two weeks, the consumption in each pen was converted to the proportion it formed of the total in that room.

Surveys of all rooms from May through September, 1958, provided 735 capture locations for 1st-tier rats and 651 for 2nd-tier rats (Table 22-1). Figure 22-2 shows the mean relative water consumption for a somewhat longer period.

Both sets of data reflect a greater usage of Pen II for residence-related behavior. Pens I and III exhibited nearly equal usage, while Pen IV consistently fell below all the other three pens.

I recognized from the beginning one factor which might contribute to such a differential usage. Use of burrows should be inversely proportional to their distance from the floor. Thus the operation of this factor alone would result in a 2:2:1:1 ratio of usage for Pens I:II:III:IV.

compensated by rats entering from center pens. In time this will lead to a 1:2:2:1 ratio of usage of Pens I:II:III:IV.

Dr. Clifford Patlak has formalized this concept as follows:

1. Consider a ramp connecting two pens.

2. Consider that a rat has a constant tendency per unit time to leave a pen independent of the number of ramps.

3. Therefore, the probability of a given rat in a pen crossing per unit time a particular ramp within that pen is inversely proportional to the number of ramps (r) in that pen.

4. Also, the number of rats in a pen crossing per unit time a particular ramp within that pen is directly proportional to the number of rats (N) in that pen.

5. In the steady state, the number of rats crossing a particular ramp in either direction will be the same.

6. Items 3 and 4 imply that the number of rats in a pen crossing per unit time a particular ramp within that pen will be equal to $\frac{N}{r} \times K$ where K is a constant of proportionality independent of pen.

7. Where the pens are numbered in sequence and N_i is the number of rats in the ith pen and r_i equal the number of ramps in the ith pen, then Items 5 and 6 imply that $\frac{N_i}{r_i} \times K = \frac{N_{(i+1)}}{r_{(i+1)}} \times K.$

8. Therefore $N_i = \frac{r_i}{r_{(i+1)}} \times N_{(i+1)}.$

9. By repeating this procedure for adjacent pens (i and j) it is immediately seen that

$$N_i = \left(\frac{r_i}{r_j}\right) N_j.$$

10. Consider adjoining Pens I and II in the experimental environment. Where $N_I = 1$, $r_I = 1$, and $r_{II} = 2$ it follows from the equation in Item 8 that $N_{II} = 2$. Completing the other comparisons of adjacent pens leads to the ratio of $1:2:2:1$ of number of rats expected per pen across the series I:II:III:IV.

If these two factors which might affect the probability of a rat's selecting a particular pen as a place of residence were of equal importance, their values for each pen might be summated. This produces a $3:4:3:2$ ratio of expected usage of Pens I:II:III:IV. In other words the expected probabilities respectively will be: 0.250, 0.333, 0.250, and 0.167.

As may be seen from Table 22-1 the observed and expected number of rats from each place of capture closely approximate each other. Similarly, water-consumption levels for the four pens vary rather closely about the expected levels. Thus the effort required to reach the burrow from the floor and the departure from one pen to another following the lapse of some average period of time form the most logical, as well as the minimum, assumptions to account for the differential usage of pens as places of residence. For the purpose of considering the development of a behavioral sink, attention must be focused on Pen II with its higher probability of residence.

THE FOOD HOPPERS AS A POSITIVE RESPONSE SITUATION (PRS)

Three types of PRS existed in each pen of each room. They were the water hoppers, the nesting boxes, and the food hoppers. The former two may be summarily dispensed with as potentially being involved in the development of a behavioral sink on the following grounds. The act of drinking required only a few seconds to complete. Thus the chance of two rats drinking side by side was low. Furthermore, the probability of drinking in a pen being visited, but not the rat's pen of residence, was low. Whereas sleeping was a prolonged response, its major duration involved reduced perceptual awareness. Furthermore, the presence of five nesting boxes in each burrow reduced the opportunity of contact with another rat at the time of initiation of sleep.

Eating typically occurred intermittently during most phases of the rat's travels from one pen to another. Securing sufficient food to satiate the rat's hunger required a continuous effort of up to several minutes. The necessity of gnawing through the wire mesh of the hopper called for this greater effort. Thus when one rat was eating there was a fair chance that another rat might join it with an ensuing period of eating side by side.

With this background we many now turn

our attention to the detailed history of food consumption (Fig. 22-3) in Room 2B. The history of the four rooms was somewhat different, but 2B closely reflected the typical changes which occurred in all the rooms.

Initially, in marked contrast to the more uniform distribution of sleeping and drinking, eating was almost entirely concentrated in Pen II. Through the next three months, eating in Pen II declined but never quite reached the level of 0.333 anticipated on the basis of the forces governing probability of determining residence.

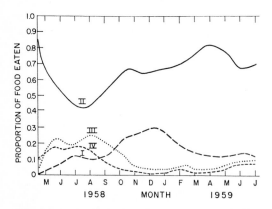

FIG. 22-3. Food consumption, Room 2B. Roman numerals refer to pens.

Initial concentration of eating in one of the four pens has been interpreted as resulting from a "litter-association factor." During nursing each rat gains contact with one or more of its litter mates. Presumably by the time of weaning each rat has defined the food acquisition behavior as requiring the presence of another individual. Behavior of recently weaned rats supports this notion. Most frequently several young rats feed simultaneously, and furthermore, they crowd their mouths together as if attempting to gnaw at the same piece of food—this despite the fact that most of the extensive feeding surface remains bare of any rats eating.

Nearly immediately following insertion of the ramps between pens the young rats concentrated all of their feeding in the one pen where, by the operation of factors previously discussed, they were most likely to find their conditioned definition of a feeding PRS. The pens thus selected were 1AIII, 2AII, 2BII and 1BII. That Pen III might occasionally be selected is not surprising in view of the indeterminancy of the system. However, the probability of Pen IV's ever becoming a major pen of feeding is rather remote. For the rats to maintain their concentrated eating in one pen each rat must experience frequent reinforcements in the form of proximity with another while eating. Obviously such frequency was not sufficient for there ensued a period of continuous decline in amount of eating in the pen originally selected by the weanling 1st-tier rats.

By the end of June, 1958, the 32 2nd-tier rats were weaned, and by mid-September the 32 3rd-tier rats joined the others in free-feeding acts. The same forces affecting residence of the 1st tier also applied to those two younger tiers. On the average, one-third of the rats lived in Pen II. However, the pen where young rats were most likely to find other rats eating was the one where their elders were still concentrating their eating. Thus, sometime between June and September sufficient numbers of rats were present to reinitiate the social definition of the feeding PRS among the older rats and retard its loss among the younger rats. Gradually more rats came to 2BII to feed and simultaneously reduced their eating elsewhere. A common observation was that a rat resident in Pen IV would go down to the floor, perhaps drink, and then cross over and through Pen III to Pen II before engaging in eating.

This latter phenomenon facilitated the development of territoriality. In each pen there were usually one or more very aggressive males who became active later than their subordinates. By the time the dominant male in Pen IV became active he would likely find himself alone. As a subordinate rat living in Pen IV started back over the ramp connecting Pens III and IV after a period of eating in Pen II, he was likely to run into the dominant Pen-IV male as he was starting on his trip to Pen II to eat. These circumstances were ideal for the subordinate rat's associating departure from Pen IV with escape from the dominant male there. Without himself being completely responsible, the dominant male in Pen IV also became territorial. In time the process extended to Pen III so that he was left with a harem of 20 females.

This forms a circular series of events in which the development of the food hopper in Pen II as an alpha PRS facilitated development of a territorial male. In turn, the territoriality of this male increased the effectiveness of the food hopper in Pen II as an alpha PRS. All this time Pen II and, in particular, the immediate environs of its food hopper had developed all the attributes of what I now term a "behavioral sink."

An important facet of this sink is the relative numbers of individuals so involved in comparison with the group size typical of the species. In an unpublished extensive study of wild Norway rats the average group size was 11 individuals. Yet here in proximity to the alpha feeding PRS the size commonly exceeded this figure. Further discussion of this topic will be presented farther on in this paper.

Before turning to consequences of the behavioral sink, a brief comment regarding the other three rooms is in order. In Rooms 1A and 2A, territorial males with associated harems developed in Pen I. As was the case for the pens dominated by the territorial males in Room 2B, these pens could also be designated as "brood pens" since here the females were markedly successful in rearing young in comparison to females residing elsewhere. Room 1B exhibited a very odd history. Following the accidental death by suffocation of seven 1st-tier male residents in Pen II in June, 1958, the major pen of feeding shifted from Pen II to Pen III. But Pen III never gained real ascendency. In fact during the last few months there developed a marked oscillation in relative amount of feeding in each of the four pens. All abnormal behaviors developing in the other rooms became even more accentuated here.

NORMAL BEHAVIOR

Abnormal behavior associated with the development of a behavioral sink must be viewed against the normal. I use the term *behavior* in the following sense. It includes both a perceptual and a motor phase. Sustained attention to one stimulus characterizes the perceptual phase. Similarly, a sustained period of repeating a specific response characterizes the motor phase. Higher levels of behavior require sustained attention toward an object or situation whose identification involves integration of several distinct cues or stimuli. In the motor phase there must be expressed an orderly sequence of discrete but different acts.

The following normal behavior characterized most 1st- and 2nd-tier rats of reproductive age through September, 1958. They exemplify my definition of normal behavior.

• NEST BUILDING

Rats of both sexes build nests, but this behavior becomes intensified by females just preceding and just following parturition. If a rat picks up a strip of paper from the floor and carries it up into a nesting box, it will most likely make several such trips in close succession before engaging in an unrelated behavior. Completion of a nest may require several nest-building behaviors such as the one described. The end product forms a fluffy intermeshed mass of paper strips surrounding a deep cuplike depression, and frequently the mesh work extends dorsally over the cup to form a hood.

• TRANSPORT OF YOUNG

This behavior characterizes females having young under 15 days of age. When such a female, while with her young, is disturbed by either the experimentor or by an invading strange rat, she customarily transports the entire litter from one place to another. Such a transport is not interrupted by any other behavior until the entire litter has been moved to the same place.

• EATING

As described previously the behavior of eating involves quite a long series of gnawings at the surface of the hopper.

• SEXUAL BEHAVIOR

For the present discussion, emphasis will be placed upon the male's behavior. Its culmination involves mounting an appropriate receptive female. However, it includes a passive perceptual phase and an active pursuit phase. In the latter, following the withdrawal of a receptive female into a burrow, the male follows her to the burrow opening but does not pursue her into the burrow. He waits there quietly or with intermittent movements back and forth with his head protruding into the burrow opening. The full sexual dance characteristics of wild Norway rats in their natural habitat did not develop fully on the artificial burrows in the absence of the conical mound of dirt. Eventually the fully receptive female emerges and is pursued by the male until he overtakes her. The chase culminates in intromission as the male mounts the receptive female while holding her with his teeth so gently by the scruff of her neck as not to cut the skin. Simultaneously he exhibits pelvic thrusting as she exhibits lordosis.

The passive sexual behavior is perceptual, involving the integration of a graded set of cues. The male must perceive that the sexual object is an adult, that it is a female, and that it is a receptive female. This formulation of a passive perceptual sexual behavior is an inference derived from the development of inability to select appropriate sex partners as discussed below.

• AGGRESSIVE BEHAVIOR

Males more frequently than females inflict wounds on other rats, usually other adult males. I shall not attempt here to describe the full sequence of related acts which culminates in one rat's biting another. Suffice it to say that there arises a stage in the conflict when one rat turns and flees. At this moment the dominant member frequently bites the fleeing rat on its posterior dorsal aspect. Wounds rarely were noted on other parts of the body preceding development of the behavioral sink. Wounds typically do not exceed 5 mm. in length and rarely extend through the skin.

ABNORMAL BEHAVIOR

Beginning in September, 1958, and continuing to a climax by April, 1959, these behaviors markedly changed in character. The change was gradual both in terms of degree of change characterizing any one individual and with reference to the number of individuals exhibiting more marked abnormality of behavior. This period started with the weaning of the 3rd tier and continued to their full adulthood at 8 to 9 months of age. The average number of 1st- to 3rd-tier adults per room in February, 1959, was 77 (Table 22-3, Row 1).

• NEST BUILDING

Failure to organize paper strips taken into the nesting boxes formed the first indicator of disruption of this behavior. Although many strips were transported they were just left in a pile and trampled into a flat pad with little sign of cup formation. Then fewer and fewer strips reached the nesting box. Frequently a rat would take a single strip, and somewhere along the way it would drop the strip and then engage in some other behavior. In the extreme state of disruption, characterizing at least all major pens of feeding, the nesting material would remain in the center of the room for days. Even when females delivered litters in the burrow in the major pen of eating, no nest was formed; the young were merely left on the bare sawdust periodically placed in every box by the experimentor.

• TRANSPORT OF YOUNG

In the normal condition when females had litters in separate boxes, the litters were maintained intact with no mixing, As the behavioral sink developed, litters became more and more mixed. When only one litter was present in a burrow the young frequently became scattered among several boxes. This resulted from the female's interrupting the transport behavior by some other behavior. The consequence of a reinitiation of transport resulted in even greater scattering because the second terminus of transport was likely to be some nesting box other than the first. In the extreme state of disruption the terminus of transport was undirected. The mothers would take a pup out of the burrow and start toward the floor with it. Anywhere along the way or any place on the floor the mother would drop the pup. Such pups were rarely ever retrieved. They eventually died where dropped and then were eaten by other rats.

• EATING

Unfortunately, no measures of disruption of this behavior were made. I say unfortunate because, as discussed below, alteration of the duration of this behavior—that is, shortening it—should be the first behavior disrupted. See the discussion for elaboration of this point.

• SEXUAL BEHAVIOR

The first sign of disruption involved more frequent attention to and attempts at mounting females who indicated no sign of being receptive. Later, males mounted other males, and a few of these, particularly 3rd-tier males, seemed to prefer other males as sexual partners. In the final phase, young rats, even recently weaned ones of both sexes, were mounted. Such abnormality may best be termed *pansexuality*. In essence, the perceptual behavioral phase of recognition of a sexual partner became so disrupted that fewer and fewer elements of the perceptual pattern were requisite for shifting from the perceptual phase of recognition of sex partners to the active behavioral phase of pursuit, mounting, and pelvic thrusting. Pursuit also became altered. With increasing frequency males who followed a receptive female to the burrow also followed her into and through the burrow. Such intrusion produced further disturbance to lactating females and thus aggravated the already disturbed transport behavior. Another element of disruption of normal sexual behavior involved the scruff-of-the-neck biting act during mounting. As the behavioral sink became accentuated in its influence, many females following their period of receptivity were characterized by literally dozens of nicks about the dorsal aspect of the neck. Males subjected to homosexual advances exhibited similar wounds, but fewer in number.

• AGGRESSIVE BEHAVIOR

Three abnormal aggressive acts developed as the behavioral sink became established. The first of these was tail biting. A peculiarity of this behavior was that males alone exhibited tail biting insofar as I could determine. Furthermore, the population became divided into tail biters and those who were bitten on the tail. The latter category included both sexes. At times it was impossible to enter a room without observing fresh blood splattered about the room from tail wounds. A rat exhibiting tail biting would frequently just walk up to another and clamp down on its tail. The biting rat would not loosen its grasp until the bitten rat had pulled loose. This frequently resulted in major breaks or actually severance of the tail.

The population in each room passed through this phase of tail biting of adults by other adults. Its duration varied from one to three months following the peak development of the behavioral sink. Young weaned during this period received similar treatment from adult biters, although in earlier, more normal states no tail wounds were inflicted on young rats and only rarely were body wounds received until well after sexual maturity. The population in Room 1A was allowed to survive beyond July, 1959, when rats living in the other three rooms were autopsied. A sixth tier was allowed to survive to Room 1A until many of them had reached sexual maturity. And yet from weaning to sexual maturity most of these 6th-tier young received sev-

eral tail bites despite the fact that adults were rarely any longer receiving such wounds. It is difficult to escape the conclusion that the behavior of bitten rats in some way influences the probability of attack by biters. In some way the rats who are subject to being bitten on the tail alter their behavior in such a way as to avoid elicitation of attack by biters. That the biters do not alter their behavior is evinced by the fact that young rats which have not had the opportunity to learn the appropriate alteration to their behavior are attacked by the biters.

The basis of this behavior has so far eluded me. From several very incomplete lines of evidence presently available I can only say that I suspect that tail biting derives from a displacement of eating behavior rather than stemming from modification of aggressive behavior.

Inflicting small nicks about the shoulders during sexual mounts becomes an aggressive behavior insofar as the recipient is concerned. The third aberration takes the form of slashing attacks. Gashes ranging from 10 to 30 mm. may be received by either sex on any portion of the body. The depth of such wounds frequently extend down into the muscles or through the abdominal wall.

CHANGES IN REPRODUCTIVE PHENOMENA

A general survey of all the records supports the conclusion that there was a reduction in conception or at least a reduction in pregnancies continued to the age when embryos could be detected by palpation. However, as yet no detailed analysis has been prepared. Also, pregnant females exhibited difficulty in continuing pregnancy to term or in delivering full-term young. Both phenomena were noted only after the behavioral sink began developing. Several females were found near term lying on the floor with dark bloody fluid exuding from the vagina. I never found any evidence that these females delivered. One died while I watched her from the overhead observation window. She was immediately autopsied. Extensive dark hemorrhagic areas in the uterus suggested that the fetuses died before the mother. Another apparently full-term female was autopsied shortly after death and found to contain several partially resorbed full-term embryos. Some of these had been released into the abdominal cavity following rupture of the uterus.

Upon palpation for pregnancy, more and more females were recorded as containing large hard masses in the abdomen. These sometimes reached a diameter of 90 mm. Usually death occurred before attainment of such size. A group of females with these abdominal masses were autopsied. The enlargements proved to be thick-walled dilatations of the uterus. Usually these dilatations contained a purulent mass. Partially decomposed fetuses were found in some of the rats in which these dilatations were still relatively small.

Eleven females with these masses, some from each of the three tiers, were autopsied by Dr. Katherine C. Snell of the National Cancer Institute. The general picture of the uterus was one of severe chronic suppurative endometritis, myometritis, and peritonitis with extension of the process to the fallopian tubule and ovary on one or both sides. Areas of focal inflammation of slight to moderate degree occurred in all kidneys.

The adrenal glands were normal in rats from the 3rd tier. Among 1st-tier rats all showed some degree of congestion of the adrenal glands with dilated vascular spaces in the cortex filled with red blood cells or fibrin or both. The adrenal of one 2nd-tier rat was normal. The other four 2nd-tier rats showed marked congestion of the reticular and fasicular zones of the cortex with dilated vessels filled with red blood cells, precipitated fibrin, or both.

Some of these 11 rats, as well as 4 others autopsied because of obvious mammary tumors, showed the following pathologic lesions in one or more females: (1) fibromyoma of a uterine horn; (2) fibrosarcoma of the mammary gland; (3) fibroadenoma of the mammary gland; (4) angiomatous adenoma of the adrenal cortex; (5) granulomas of the liver; (6) papillary cyst of the thyroid.

One 2nd-tier female was autopsied because a few days previously she was noted to be apparently near term, but she had considerable dark blood about the vagina. Upon autopsy the uterus was found to contain five healthy-appearing fetuses, four in the right horn and one in the left. The myometrium of the corpus and the cervix of this rat were inflamed, and the lumen of the horn near the cervix contained clotted blood that may have been associated with premature separation of the placenta.

From my own observations and the brief synopsis of Dr. Snell's findings, it appears that concomitant with the development of the behavioral sink females experienced difficulty in carrying young to term or if they carried to term they were sometimes unable to deliver. The extent to which the uterine infections preceded or followed failure to deliver is unknown.

Presence of tumors was from a highly selected sample. No conclusion is warranted concerning the influence of behavior upon incidence of the tumors. Dr. Snell pointed out another complicating factor. First-tier rats were marked with a black hair dye. Second-tier rats were marked with a red stamp-pad ink, and third-tier rats were marked with a combination of picric acid and a green oscillograph pen ink.

Known or suspected constituents of these dyes are known to be absorbed through the skin, to be toxic, and some possibly carcinogenic. That these dyes might have had some effect upon reproductive success and even upon behavior cannot be ruled out on the basis of present data. Evidence will be cited below why I suspect they were unimportant in producing abnormal behavior or in altering reproductive success.

MORTALITY OF FEMALES

By June, 1959, the populations in Rooms 1A, 2A and 2B had become predominately male in composition. Many females were known to have died following symptoms indicating complications with pregnancy or delivery. Others were too far decomposed when found dead to warrant autopsy. Comparative mortality for males and females to June, 1959, is shown in Table 22-2. Comparisons are based upon an original N of 48 rats in each of the six tier and sex categories.

Second-tier females despite their younger age experienced a much higher risk of death than did their older 1st-tier associates. Apparently attainment of sexual maturity under conditions of a developing behavioral sink predisposes rats to complications of pregnancy more acutely than among rats who matured in a more placid environment.

TABLE 22-2   MORTALITY

TIER	MONTHS OF AGE, JUNE, 1959	PROPORTION DEAD BY JUNE, 1959		FEMALES DYING FOR EACH MALE DYING
		MALES	FEMALES	
1st	15.5	.187	.582	3.1
2nd	12.0	.104	.562	5.4
3rd	9.5	.061	.125	2.1

The population in Room 1A was allowed to survive for several months beyond the termination of the populations in the other three rooms during July, 1959. Between June and September, 1959, only 0.140 of the 43 males alive in June died. In contrast 0.375 of the 32 females alive in June died.

POSSIBLE ROLE OF VITAMIN A

Complications with pregnancy, accentuation of frequency and severity of skin lesions, occasional abnormal appearance of eyes and surrounding membranes, blocked urethras, hemorrhagic bladders, and an occasional bladder or kidney stone suggested the possibilty of some dysfunction of Vitamin-A metabolism (Moore, 1957). Dr. Stanley R. Ames of the Distillation Products Industries consented to assay Vitamin A in the liver and sera of representative rats. This sample taken in July and August, 1959, from Rooms 1B, 2A, and 2B included both sexes, all three tiers, and brood-pen and nonbrood-pen rats. Total liver-storage levels ranged from 45,000 to 60,000 I.U. of Vitamin A. This contrasts with levels of 750 to 1,000 I.U. in year-old male rats on natural foods studied by Dr. Ames.

In December, 1959, livers from a second group of rats were sent to Dr. Ames. These included rats of several ages, from a wide range of size and complexity of social groups. Vitamin-A storage in the liver increased with age. No relationship existed between social background or size of group and Vitamin-A storage in the liver. The Purina Ralston Company informed Dr. Ames that the chow they had supplied me had a rating of 12 I.U. of Vitamin A per g. On the basis of an average intake of 15 g. of food per day and a 50 per cent storage of the Vitamin A consumed each day, Dr.

Ames concluded that the observed levels of Vitamin A with age would result.

The only rats which up to the termination of this study might have served as adequate controls for Vitamin-A assay were disposed of before I realized the necessity of a control group. Even so the history of these 18 females and 9 males does shed light on the problem. They were rats of the same age as the 3rd tier. In fact they were excess 3rd-tier rats born in Room 1A and removed before sexual maturity.

In contrast, they were housed in breeding cages containing two females and one male. All females reared several litters successfully, with no indication of complications with pregnancy. Nor were they characterized by abnormal nest building or transport behavior. They also were on a pure Purina Chow diet only supplemented by one orange per rat per week.

Complications relating to pregnancy characterizing my rats in the behavioral-sink environment resemble those observed in studies of Vitamin-A toxicity (Moore, 1957, Chapter 28). However, in most such experimental studies of Vitamin-A toxicity, liver-storage levels 10 times that seen in my rats were attained by administering very high levels in the diet. Since my rats in breeding cages failed to evince any difficulty with reproduction, even though they attained similar relatively high levels of Vitamin-A storage, Dr. Ames concluded that, if Vitamin A did play a role in the observed impairment of reproduction in my behavioral sink social colonies, it must mean that social stressors reduce the tolerance to Vitamin-A toxicity.

In conclusion, I can only say that complete uncertainty reigns as to the involvement of Vitamin A in the present study. It represents the type of previously unsuspected variables which inevitably arise when one attempts to gain insight into complex social systems. Only further studies can clarify their possible role.

FATE OF YOUNG

Detailed records were maintained for young born between December 25, 1958, and January 30, 1959. This group of young comprised the 5th tier of rats. Like all other tiers than the first three, they were removed prior to sexual maturity. These records provide insight into the relative impact of a developing behavioral sink upon survival and maturation. Relevant data are summarized in Table 22-3.

At this time each of the pens in the four rooms could be placed in one of three categories. *Brood pens* (1AI, 1BI, 2AI, 2BIII, and 2BIV) not only contained fewer resident adults, but the adults present were mostly females. Many young born here survived. Most of the residents ate elsewhere. *Major pens of feeding* (1AIII, 1BIII, 2AII, 2BII) *by adults* were those in which most of the adults, regardless of pen of residence, came and ate most frequently. The seven remaining pens, intermediate in their charactertistics, formed the third group, *other pens*.

This table includes data from all four rooms (1A, 1B, 2A, and 2B). Since each category of usage of pens includes a different number of pens, means of the raw data provide a more precise insight into the developed differential usage of the available environment. In some instances the raw data pertaining to the pens in each room were first converted into proportions of the total in that room for that item. Thus, in examining Table 22-3, if the proportion under each category of pen is multiplied by the number of pens in that category, the sum of these three products equals 4.00. Had the usage of all pens been

TABLE 22-3 CHARACTERISTICS OF 5TH-TIER RATS AND THEIR SOCIAL ENVIRONMENT OF ADULTS

	CATEGORY OF PEN			
	A	B	C	D
DATUM CATEGORY*	5 BROOD PENS	4 MAJOR PENS OF FEEDING BY ADULTS	7 OTHER PENS	TOTAL (OR $\bar{x}$)
I. Adults				
1. Resident rats				
a. Observed $\bar{x}$	9.7	24.5	23.0	307.5
b. Expected $\bar{x}$	17.9	22.4	18.4	307.9
c. Observed $\bar{x}$ proportion	.126	.319	.299	3.999
2. Proportion of residents males	.258	.556	.680	.591($\bar{x}$)
3. Food consumption				
a. Expected $\bar{x}$ proportion	.233	.292	.238	4.000
b. Observed $\bar{x}$ proportion	.049	.633	.175	4.002
4. Rats seen/3 hrs. ($\bar{x}$)	16.1	49.9	36.4	535
5. Contact index ($\bar{x}$)	41.7	170.8	102.9	1612
II. 5th-Tier Young				
6. $\bar{x}$ age in days when first seen	6.18	3.00	3.03	4.58($\bar{x}$)
7. $\bar{x}$ total observed for first time	51.30	28.20	25.60	558
8. $\bar{x}$ survived to marking	36.0	0.75	5.70	223
9. $\bar{x}$ marked which survived to March. 1959	26.2	0.25	1.60	143
10. $\bar{x}$ residents in March, 1959				
a. Male	7.00	5.25	1.86	69
b. Female	4.00	7.50	5.60	89
11. a. $\bar{x}$ feeding acts	5.4	158.5	31.7	883
b. $\bar{x}$ proportion of feeding acts	.025	.718	.143	
12. $\bar{x}$ size feeding groups	0.15	3.35	0.66	1.33($\bar{x}$)

* $\bar{x}$ = mean.

identical the mean proportion of usage under each category would have been 0.25.

The following comments will assist in evaluating the data in Table 22-3.

ROW 1 a and b. The observed number of residents was based upon two surveys, one conducted just prior to the weaning of 5th-tier young and a second during the first week in March, 1959, at the time the young were removed. The fewer number of adults in the brood pens comprises the most important facet of these data. Expected numbers were based upon the theoretical 3:4:3:2 ratio for Pens I:II:III:IV. This ratio did closely approximate the observed residence during the early history of these populations (Table 22-1). The pen where the rat stayed during the 12 hours of reduced activity is designated as its place of residence. The shift in residence accompanying the development of the behavioral sink entailed a decrease in what became the brood pens, with a corresponding increase elsewhere.

ROW 2. The low proportion of adult males in brood pens resulted in part from persistent antagonistic action by territorial males in excluding other males. Some of these excluded males settled in the major pen of feeding. However, the great increase in proportion of males in the "other pens" indicates that these males excluded from the brood pens were also largely excluded from the second category of favored type of location, the major pen of feeding.

ROW 3 a and b. The expected proportion of food consumption was based upon the theoretical 3:4:3:2 ratio for usage of Pens I:II:III:IV as discussed with reference to Figure 22-2. In other words, this ratio should have held if rats had eaten where they resided and no shift of residence had taken place during the development of the behavioral sink. However, the observed eating in the four feeding pens diverged markedly from the expected. Of particular note is the fact that rats resident in the brood pens were attracted over into the feeding pens much more so than were those living in the "other" pens. Comparison of Rows 1 *c* and 3 *b* indicates that .611 (i.e., .126 — .049/.126) of the eating by rats resident in the brood pens was in the major feeding pens; while only .415 (i.e., .299 — .175/.299) of the feeding by rats in the "other pens" was in the major feeding pens. These calculations refer to net changes. This forms perhaps the strongest evidence that all adults were in fact caught in the behavioral-sink phenomenon.

ROW 4. During February, 1959, Dr. Kyle R. Barbehenn and the author each observed each room for a total of three hours. The total number of different rats visiting each pen at least once during the three hours was recorded. Obviously many rats visited pens other than their place of residence. Nevertheless the greatest increase in visitation characterized the feeding pens.

ROW 5. Each above three-hour period was divided into four 45-minute periods. During each of these shorter periods a tally

was made for each rat that was seen on the floor or on the burrow in each pen. The sum of these for a three-hour period formed the contact index for each pen. At least in a rather crude way it reflects the probability of a rat's contacting another in a particular pen. Dividing the data in Row 5 by that in Row 4 produces quotients of 2.59, 3.42, and 2.83 respectively for the three columns. This means that not only do more rats visit the feeding pens but they spend longer times there.

These data in Part I of Table 22-3 reflect the profound changes which had taken place among adult rats during the development of the behavioral sink. They primarily concern the differential usage of space. In Part II of Table 22-3 is shown how this differential usage of space by the adults affected their progeny.

ROW 6. Mean age of 5th-tier litters when first seen: At intervals of less than two weeks the nest boxes in all burrows were examined for litters. At this time their age in days as judged by relative development was noted. Results are based upon 558 young observed during a five-week period. Since litters in the brood pens averaged twice as old as litters elsewhere, birth in the brood pen favored early survival. If there had been complete survival there should have been as many litters in the 1–4 day age range as in the 5–8 day range. For the 5 brood pens the number of young of these two ages was 115:91 whereas in the remaining 11 pens it was 235:51. Thus, no more than 0.217 of the young survived beyond four days if born outside the brood pens while 0.79 of the young in the brood pens survived past the first four days.

ROW 7. Mean total known to be born per pen: Approximately twice as many rats per pen survived to the survey dates in the brood pens as elsewhere.

ROW 8. Mean numbers per pen which

survived to age of marking: If the young survived to about 8–10 days of age, one or two toes were removed as a permanent identification. These few days witnessed a marked differential in mortality with the brood-pen young having by far the best chance for survival.

ROW 9. Mean numbers per pen which survived to March 2–6, 1959: At this time when all surviving marked young were removed they ranged in age from 40 to 70 days of age. Of the 142 survivors 130 were born in the five brood pens. In other words 0.51 of the 256 rats born in the five brood pens survived for at least 40 days, whereas only 0.04 of the 302 rats born outside of the brood pens survived to 40 days of age. Thus, if a rat was born in a brood pen its chances of being weaned were 12.75 times those of rats born outside of the brood pens where they were subject to the full impact of disturbances created by the behavioral sink.

ROW 10. Mean number of 5th-tier residents per pen: Residence refers to the pen of capture during the March 2–6, 1959, period when these young were removed. As may be seen by contrasting Row 9 with the sum of Rows 10 *a* and 10 *b*, 58 per cent of the surviving young which were born in the brood pens now lived elsewhere. Actually this change in residence resembled closely that exhibited by the original 1st-tier rats at about the same age during the period immediately following insertion of the ramps between pens at the start of the colonies. Of the 111 1st-tier young surviving to 11 weeks of age, 0.351 resided in the major feeding pens, whereas 0.359 of the 142 5th-tier young resided in these pens. Selection of place of residence by 5th-tier young must therefore be governed primarily by the two factors, height of burrows and endedness of the environment, in a similar manner as these factors affected selection

of residence by earlier generations. This means that the existing behavioral sink, including the marked differential residence by adults (Table 22-3, Rows 1 *a*, 1 *b*, and 1 *c*) in no way affected place of residence of the 5th-tier young. However, those 5th-tier young which did select the major feeding pens as a place of residence were exposed to a heightened association with adults during periods of rest. Furthermore, the differential sex ratio of adults (Table 22-3, row 2) seemed to affect selection of place of residence by these sexually immature 5th-tier young. Of the young males, 51 per cent remained in the five brood pens with their mothers, where also their resting contact with males was low. In contrast, 77 per cent of the females changed their residence to the remaining pens where their probability of associating with males during periods of rest was high.

ROWS 11 and 12. Feeding by 5th-tier young: During the six hours of observation of each room during February, 1959, periodic recordings were made of the number of 5th-tier young feeding in each of the four pens then being observed; 187 sets of such observations were tallied. A mean of 48 such observations per pen was recorded for each of the three classes of pens. A rat eating at a hopper was defined as a "feeding act." The great preponderance of these feeding acts was in the pen where the adults were also concentrating their feeding. Furthermore, in the major pen of feeding by adults the young usually ate in association with others of their age class, but this was rarely true elsewhere. Thus, despite a greater dispersal of place of residence, the young concentrated their feeding in those pens where contact with adults was greatest and where their behavior was most likely to be interrupted by other rats of all ages. Contrasting Row 11 *b* with Row 3 *b* suggests that a greater proportion of the eating by young 5th-tier rats took place in the major pen of eating than was true for adults.

EARLY GROWTH OF 1ST- AND 5TH-TIER MALES

Log-log graphic plots of the data in Table 22-4 reveal that at between 50 and 70 days of age the 5th-tier males averaged 35 g. less in weight than did the 1st-tier males who grew up in the absence of a behavioral sink. At all ages prior to weaning many of these 5th-tier young were characterized by various states of emaciation. Only a few were as plump as their 1st-tier predecessors at the same age. Failure of the mothers to nurse their scattered young frequently enough certainly contributed to this retardation before weaning. Even where litter size in a single nesting box continued large enough to provide adequate stimulation for a normal mother to nurse properly, such 5th-tier litters still were retarded in growth prior to weaning. In the absence of direct observation of nursing I can only suspect that both the perception of the litter as cues initiating nursing and the behavior of nursing itself were disrupted as were other behaviors under the influence of the behavioral sink. See the comments in the Discussion section with regard to the possibility of Billingham's "runt disease" having been

a contributing factor to the retarded development of these 5th-tier young.

DISCUSSION

Disruption of a sequential series of related perceptions or of a sequential series of similar or related responses formed a common characteristic in the development of all forms of abnormal behavior associated with the behavioral sink. We may then ask, "What was the origin of these disruptions?"

A relevant theoretical model of social interaction has already been presented (Calhoun, 1957, pp. 349–354). This model assumes that there are types of interaction between two individuals which lead to some satisfaction from the interaction. Such satisfaction places each individual in a refractory state during which time further interaction will fail to enhance the amount of satisfaction. By a refractory state I mean a period of inattentiveness, physiological unresponsiveness, or subthreshold motivation. At the end of the refractory period the individual again is in a responsive stage. However, if such a responsive individual interacts with another who is in the refractory state, the former individual will be thrown into a false refractory state during which time he no longer can add to a theta amount of total satiation from social interaction desired over some more extended period of time. Depending upon the intensity or duration of such social interaction there is some optimum group size assuring attainment of this theta amount of social satiation. Any reduction or increase in group size from the optimum with reference to a particular intensity or duration of interaction leads to a reduction in social satiation if the intensity of the response remains constant. As the group size increases, its members may continue to attain their desired level of social satiation provided

TABLE 22-4   EARLY GROWTH OF 1ST- AND 5TH-TIER MALES

	1ST TIER			5TH TIER	
N	$\bar{x}$ AGE IN DAYS	$\bar{x}$ WT. GRAMS	N	$\bar{x}$ AGE IN DAYS	$\bar{x}$ WT. GRAMS
62	49.2	178.0	19	50.2	142.3
62	88.1	322.0	16	58.7	174.0
			28	70.5	221.4

$\bar{x}$ = mean.

they continue to reduce the intensity or duration of interaction.

In the present study the over-all group size in each room did increase with time. Also due to the charactetristic of the feeding positive response situation in conjunction with certain factors biasing residence and movement between pens, the rats did develop the behavior of seeking proximity with other rats while eating. Each rat attempted to maximize the duration of total time of feeding during which it was in proximity with another rat similarly engaged in feeding. Concentration of feeding activity in a single pen increased the probability of engaging in such social interaction. However, this increase in animals in the major pen of eating has the curious consequence of requiring individuals to reduce the durations of each behavior, or otherwise the amount of eating side by side will actually become reduced. Full appreciation of this process requires examination of the mathematical model cited.

As pointed out earlier, no measurements were made of duration of feeding. However, following the above logic there should have arisen a gradual shortening of durations of feeding through the history of the colonies after June, 1958. Fewer long duration periods would be replaced by many shorter ones for each rat. Furthermore, it is most logical to assume that the changes in physiology permitting a reduction in the duration of feeding would serve as a governor reducing the duration of all other behaviors.

Feeding behavior happens to be one in which reduction of its duration and increase in its frequency can still lead to an animal's securing adequate satiation in the sense of sufficient nutrition. However, if behaviors including perception of sex partners, appropriate response to sex partners,

building nests, or transport of young are shortened, they culminate in inappropriate action or failure to complete some product of the behavior which is of value to survival.

The picture developed here is one of rapid shifting from one type of behavior to another, none of which persists for long before again changing to some other type. This presents the opportunity for a component of one type of behavior to be replaced by an inappropriate component from another.

Such confusion of parts of one behavior with another may be involved in the following:

A mother rat takes a pup from a nesting box and transports it down the spiral ramp to the floor where she drops and deserts it near the food hopper or the supply of nesting material. It is as if the behavior of transporting young had been shut off while she still had the pup in her mouth, and she just carried it part way during her initiation of an unrelated behavior.

Dropping nesting material halfway up the spiral ramp before getting to a nesting box seems to be a similar type.

I also cannot help but wonder if the infliction of wounds during sexual mounts and the tail biting really are insertions of a feeding act in the midst of the sexual mount or of the behavior of investigating another.

The attempt in this discussion represents an effort to construct a logical framework which might help in understanding the origin of the abnormal behavior arising as the behavioral sink developed. None of the observations form proof for the formulation.

Dr. Snell suggested that the utilization of dyes for marking the rats may have been a factor in the observed changes. Although they may have affected the likelihood of tumors developing, it appears to me un- likely that they were important in affecting behavior or maternal physiology. Regard- less of the dye used, representatives of all three tiers exhibited similar changes. Fur- thermore, despite use of these dyes the alterations in behavior and physiology did not appear until the development of the behavioral sink.

Alteration of maternal reproductive phys- iology represents an area of phenomenol- ogy associated with the behavioral sink concerning which observed data fail to per- mit adequate insight into its origins. All that can be said is that some set of circum- stances increased the prevalence of uterine hemorrhaging, death of fetuses before term, inability to deliver full-term fetuses, and extreme enlargement of some one segment of the uterus. No doubt social stressors con- tributed to an endocrine imbalance increas- ing the probability of these conditions. I also cannot help but wonder if the ob- served Vitamin-A levels of 45 to 60 thou- sand units per whole liver of adult rats might have been involved. If so, social stressor must have led to a lowered thresh- old to Vitamin-A toxicity. I am currently engaged in a series of studies in which both intensity of social stressors and Vitamin-A level of the diet form a matrix. Findings from these studies may throw light upon this puzzling set of phenomena.

In addition to behavioral disturbances among adults of both sexes and to impaired maternal reproductive physiology, fate of young born into an environment charac- terized by a behavioral sink forms an area of impact. Of the 558 young known to be born at the height of the behavioral sink, only one-fourth survived to weaning. Re- tarded growth characterized their later development. Poor maternal care un- doubtedly contributed to the poor survival.

Yet the recent account of experimentally induced "runt disease" described by Billing- ham (1959) suggests that histoincompat- ibility may also be a contributing factor.

Newborn mice, heterozygous for certain histocompatibility genes, if injected with leucocytes or macerated spleen from a homozygous donor develop runt disease. Their growth becomes markedly retarded, and their fur is sparse and matted. Donor lymphoid tissue invades the host's lym- phoid tissue and elaborates antibodies there which destroy the host's lymphoid tissue. Through lack of adequate lymphoid tissue to battle pathogenic invaders, the runts often die young. Billingham suggests that a similar phenomenon may account for certain hemolytic diseases in newborn children provided placental hemorrhaging prior to birth has made possible invasion of maternal leucocytes into the fetal cir- culation.

I wish, here, merely to point out that the scrawny Osborne-Mendel rats born during the behavioral sink stage of the colonies may well have been suffering from Billing- ham's runt disease. Uterine hemorrhaging did characterize many females prior to parturition. Furthermore, the stem mothers from which the populations started came from a random-bred stock known to be far from homozygous. Here again we en- counter a provocative set of observations which suggest an hypothesis incapable of substantiation from the recorded data.

This has been a study whose value lies not in rigorous validation of prior hypothe- ses but rather in its revelation of a striking phenomenon, the behavioral sink, and in the many hypotheses generated from the observations. In this connection, one can- not help but wonder concerning the impact of behavioral sinks upon the course of evolution.

Certainly many species have encountered situations leading to behavioral sinks. For example, consider a species for which several sources of water occurred within the home range of each individual. Following this phase in its evolution there arose a gradually developing xeric era. Previously members of this species had lived in small family groups or in local colonies averaging a dozen or so adults. However, as sources of water became sparser, members of adjoining families or colonies were more likely to arrive simultaneously at the same water hole. Although each family or colony might initially visit one or more water holes, one in particular would develop the character of an alpha positive response situation, since each individual's developing requirement for proximity with associates while drinking would more likely be achieved there.

Under these circumstances many young and many gravid females would die as a direct or indirect consequence of the incompatibility of maternal physiology with the abnormal aggregations accompanying a behavioral sink. Natural selection will favor survival of genotypes capable of tolerating continued association with many other individuals. By the same token, these survivors will now seek to avoid becoming isolated from their neighbors, since their physiology now no longer functions most effectively in the absence of frequent interactions with others. Such a sequence of circumstances and events forms a plausible path leading to the evolution of herd-type species. By a herd-type species I mean any species in which each individual has a fairly high probability of contacting at least 100 other individuals.

SUMMARY

Populations of domesticated albino rats were allowed to develop in rooms such that each population had access to four similar pens each 5×7 feet. Ramps over adjacent pens formed a linear communication system such that there were two end pens and two center pens. In one end pen and its adjoining center pen artificial "burrows" were placed on the wall 3 feet above the floor. In the other two pens these burrows were 6 feet above the floor.

The endedness of the row of four pens tended to make twice as many rats select the two central pens as places of living as selected the two end pens. On the other hand, the lower elevation of the burrows tended to make twice as many rats select the two pens on one end of the series as places of habitation as selected the two pens on the other end of the series. Operating together, these two biasing factors formed a theoretical biasing residence ratio of 3:4:3:2 along the series of four pens. Observed residence closely approximated the theoretical.

A large food hopper was located on the floor of each pen. Such spatially restricted structures are defined as *positive response situations*. Since more rats lived in one pen than in any of the other three, the chances were greatest there that when one rat was eating another would come and eat beside it. Once the number of rats in a room increased above a certain level, this frequency of contact while eating increased sufficiently that the rats developed a new definition of the feeding situation to include the presence of another rat. Gradually eating in the other three pens declined until 60–80 per cent of all food consumption was in this one of the four pens.

The development of this atypical aggregation under the influence of the several conditions and processes involved forms what I have termed a *behavioral sink*.

Concomitant with its development many abnormal behaviors and disturbances of reproduction began to appear. Females experienced difficulty in carrying fetuses to term, and if they carried to term they were sometimes unable to deliver young. Death frequently occurred at this time. If they survived, one region of the uterus enlarged until it was sometimes as large as the former size of the rat. Such affected rats always died. Females developed a mortality rate 3.5 times that for males.

On the behavioral side, males developed a pansexuality in which they would mount other rats regardless of their age, sex, or receptivity. Infliction of wounds during mounting developed. An abnormal response of biting the tails of other rats also developed. Nest-building behavior became completely disrupted. Transport of young by lactating rats became so disorganized that young became so scattered that they were no longer nursed.

A theoretical model for the origin of these abnormal behaviors is proposed. Briefly it points to reasons why the duration of each feeding behavior should become shortened. This change in rhythm of eating causes other behaviors to shorten with the end result that the behavior becomes inappropriate or incomplete. Thus the development of a behavioral sink leads to a state of sustained inordinate aggregation which may be called "pathological togetherness."

REFERENCES

BILLINGHAM, R. E. 1959. Reactions of grafts against their hosts. *Science. 130:* 947–953.

CALHOUN, J. B. 1957. Social welfare as a variable in population dynamics. *Symposia Quant. Biol.* (Cold Spring Harbor, N.Y.). *22:* 339–356.

MOORE, T. A. 1957. *Vitamin A.* New York, Elsevier, 645 pp.

23

AN INQUIRY INTO THE PHYLOGENY OF GANGS

David E. Davis

Since a knowledge of the biological origin or history of many human problems has often stimulated research and produced understanding, the present paper explores our curent knowledge of "gangs" among vertebrates to suggest lines of research that may lead to explanations. The phylogenetic viewpoint presents opportunities to apply generalizations about behavior of other animals to behavior of humans. It is assumed that the study of behavior, like anatomy, physiology, and other facets of general biology, may be used as an heuristic approach to human behavior.

The scope of this essay purposefully excludes all primates since the pertinent aspects of their behavior are described elsewhere in this symposium. A neglected task is the need to call attention to the behavior of "nonprimates" so that its heuristic value will be appreciated. In the space available it is possible merely to cite some of the major aspects of the vast store of knowledge about behavior of groups of vertebrates.

THE GANG DEFINED

Since we are focusing this discussion on gangs we should define the term, at least for present use. A gang is a few individuals of the same species, often all members of one sex, that regularly perform coordinated activities. Several aspects need clarification. The number must be small so that each can be individually recognized, thereby permitting social organization. For example, the members of a flock of 10 chickadees can know each individual, but the bison in a tremendous herd cannot identify each animal that it may meet. Thus the flock of chickadees may have a social organization while the bison may be merely an aggregation of individuals lacking social organization. Another characteristic of gangs is that, while the sex composition varies from species to species, even when both sexes occur together, a partial separation exists. "Regularly" means that certain activities are nearly always performed by the particular combination of individuals. "Joint activities" refers to behavior patterns performed by the group simultaneously with some degree of organization and reciprocal stimulation.

SOCIAL BEHAVIOR

The social behavior of vertebrates has been intensively studied both in the natural state and under experimental conditions. From this wealth of information some pertinent aspects of social behavior may be considered here. (For elaboration of these principles, see Scott, 1958; Tinbergen, 1951; Thorpe, 1956.)

Territorial Behavior and Social Rank

The first aspect of social behavior deals with the spatial arrangement of individuals. Many species possess a territory, which is usually defined as any defended area. Let us consider a typical territorial species such as the song sparrow which has been thoroughly studied by Nice (1943). This bird performs territorial behavior in a manner representative of many groups. The male arrives in a suitable breeding area in the early spring and promptly signals his presence by singing and by patrolling the area. Soon he sets boundaries to his territory with reference to adjacent males. Each bird defends his area by song, threats, or even fights. Sometimes an individual loses a contest and leaves the area to try to establish a territory in another place. When the females arrive, they select a location (which includes a male), and pairing and nesting begin. The defense of the territory gradually wanes during incubation and feeding periods; but if a new brood is started, the male again vigorously defends his territory. Most of the nesting and feeding activities take place within the territory.

The variations of this basic pattern seem almost infinite. In some resident species of birds the males defend a territory for many months. In others the male defends a territory only during courtship and copulation. In many species (colonial sea birds) both sexes defend a small area around the nest on a cliff. In a few species the females defend an area and the males incubate. Some fish defend a small spot in a stream for spawning. Some lizards secure a definite area and drive off other individuals. Species belonging to two distinct families of birds have developed territorial behavior as a group. Since this has some resemblance to a "gang," the behavior will be described briefly.

One family has been studied in detail (Davis, 1942) and suggests the possible phylogeny of the behavior. These birds, called Anis, live in Central and South America and belong to the cuckoo family which is notorious for aberrant breeding behavior. The most primitive species anatomically lives in Argentina and normally goes in pairs. The male defends a territory; but occasionally two pairs will join together, occupy one nest, and defend a territory simultaneously. A larger species lives in northern South America. Several pairs defend a territory, jointly build a nest, and act as a group, although still preserving the paired organization. A third species, which is abundant from Argentina to Mexico and Florida, has lost its paired organization and lives in groups of 10–15 birds. The group defends a territory from other groups; the individuals build a large nest; several females lay in it; various females incubate the eggs, and males and females feed the young. The group remains intact for many months. Strangers may force their way into the group by diligent fighting over a period of several days.

This brief summary of some aspects of territorial behavior illustrates several points. The defense of an area occurs in many kinds of vertebrates and clearly has survival value. By means of aggressive behavior, conditions are arranged so that certain needs are fulfilled. In some cases, widely separated taxonomically, a system of group defense has developed through definite stages.

The organization of a population into territories is one means of relating the needs of animals to the environment. Another rather different type of organization exists that also aids in the satisfaction of basic requirements. Individuals of many species arrange themselves in a social rank. The peck-order of roosters is the most widely observed example. In a flock of roosters one is boss and pecks all the others. Another is second and pecks all except the boss. The others arrange themselves in an order. The peck-order remains stable for long periods of time. A stranger usually is forced to the bottom place; generally the rank reflects vigor and seniority.

As was true in territorial behavior, social-rank organization shows many variations. Some mammals show a somewhat pyramidal rank; several individuals are located in each of the lowest ranks. In some species the males have a distinct series from that of the females, while in others the two sexes are interdigitated in an ordered series at least in the nonbreeding season. A further complication occurs in the species that maintain a group territory. Within the group a rank occurs so that both types of social organization are shown. This arrangement might be known as double security to ensure that some individuals will achieve their needs.

The function of these types of social organization seems to be to facilitate survival. When an excess of environmental necessities exist (food, water, mates, etc.), then there is enough for all, and no competition need occur. However, when a scarcity prevails, the individuals can make several choices: (1) If they divide the scarce food evenly, all may starve; (2) If no organization exists for distribution, they will spend their time squabbling and thus may starve; (3) But, when an organization exists, at least some individuals have enough to survive and to maintain the population through the period of scarcity. Thus both territorial and social-rank organization have survival value. Indeed, it seems impossible to maintain a species in an environment without some means to adjust behavior to a time of need, unless the population remains far below the average capacity. An important aspect to remember is that the social organization has been ingrained into the behavior of the species and is present whether or not there is a scarcity of environmental requisites. Thus one might say that the species is organized in readiness for a time of trouble.

Thus we see that species have developed behavior patterns that accommodate their numbers to the environment. It is now important to inquire into the phylogenetic origin to see whether evolution of social behavior is convergent or divergent. The distinction of these two terms may be remembered by a simple example. One hardly needs to mention that some anatomical structures have evolved from a very primitive source. The eye of vertebrates, for example, clearly developed from that of primitive fish and is fundamentally the same in all vertebrates. Other structures, however, have evolved convergently from different sources. The wings of birds, of bats, and of extinct reptiles developed independently from the forearm of terrestrial reptiles and mammals. Just as an anatomical structure has a history, so the evolution of a behavior pattern both social and individual also may proceed from one source or may develop convergently from many sources. For an understanding of social behavior it is important to ask how territorial behavior and social rank developed.

The evidence suggests that territorial behavior developed independently in many species or families. One fact is that defense of an area occurs in widely diverse species —such as fish, lizards, birds, and mammals —without any apparent phylogenetic connection. Furthermore, the primitive mammals (monotremes, insectivores) seem to lack territorial behavior, although more thorough study is needed. Similarly, the same arguments suggest that social-rank organization developed independently in many species rather than from a common source. Admittedly, the evidence is meager primarily because fossils do not reveal the social organization of their species.

The particular social organization adopted by a species presumably is related to its anatomical and physiological characteristics which determine the type of environment that will support the species. Concomitantly a set of behavior patterns develops that adjusts the population to the fluctuations in supply of necessities. The reproductive rate persistently pushes the population upward; but when adverse conditions occur, a means to permit survival of a few is necessary to maintain the population. Some species adopted territorial behavior; others adopted social rank; still others used both.

Aggressive Behavior

It is obvious that neither pattern of social organization could occur in the absence of some type of aggressive behavior. Animals that did not compete at a time of scarcity would fade out of the population. The aggressive individuals remain. A wide variety of observations suggests that fighting for rank or territory has innate features. Birds hatched and raised in isolation defend a territory or fight for rank. Mice kept in isolation after weaning fight at once when placed with another. Thus, contrary to the conclusions of some authors, it seems that aggression is heavily dependent on genetics. Probably only the means of fighting and the object of attack are learned.

HUMAN GANGS

This discussion of the phylogeny of group behavior suggests several thoughts about the behavior of human gangs. The aggressive impulses have genetic components, and the survival value of group organization is real. Furthermore, as a perusal of literature on primates shows, various nonhuman primates are organized into gangs. A contrast appears, however, between human gangs and groups of nonhumans. The human groups perform concerted and planned actions. Thus far no proof of such behavior among nonprimates is available. For example, birds attacking an owl apparently are reacting individually although simultaneously (Hinde 1954). Similarly, the territorial behavior of the Anis mentioned above appears to be individual. This problem has been neglected and merits much study.

The question of the extent of innateness of aggressive behavior also needs study. The experimental approach used in the study of sexual behavior (reported in this symposium and elsewhere) can serve as a model. Unfortunately, few data are available to discuss.

Presumably, among all vertebrates a number of manifestations of psychological principles occur. For example, extinction and reinforcement must play an essential role in the behavior of the individuals in the gang.

A few final comments may be made about the study of gangs of humans. First, their organization is typically primate. The gang has a social rank (Whyte, 1955) and frequently defends a territory (Block and Niederhoffer, 1958) by a "rumble." This type of organization appears in nonmammalian species, however, and thus it would appear to be a case of convergent evolution rather than to have a long phylogenetic history. On the other hand, the innateness of aggressive behavior seems to have a long history, and its manifestation among mature animals is widespread. On these bases, then, the origin of gang behavior is far more profound than merely a demonstration of adolescent male adjustment to society as suggested by Block and Niederhoffer who state (1958, p. 17):

When a society does not make adequate preparation, formal or otherwise, for the induction of its adolescents to the adult status, equivalent forms of behavior arise spontaneously among adolescents themselves, reinforced by their own group structure, which seemingly provides the same psychological content and function as the more formalized rituals found in other societies.

While it appears that there is a germ of truth in this hypothesis, namely that adjustment to adult society is difficult, nevertheless it seems from the comparative viewpoint that the source is more basic. A suggestion for investigation is that the aggressiveness is innate and is coupled with ecological needs in the environment. Thus the therapeutic approach would be to reduce the aggressive behavior by training and to provide the ecological necessities in the environment by vocations and activities.

REFERENCES

BLOCK, H. A., and NIEDERHOFFER, A. 1958. *The Gang*. New York, Philosophical Library, xv + 231 pp.

DAVIS, D. E. 1942. The phylogeny of social nesting habits in the crotophaginae. *Quart. Rev. Biol.* 17(2): 115–134.

HINDE, R. A. 1954. Factors governing the changes in strength of a partially inborn response, as shown by the mobbing behavior of the chaffinch (*Fringilla coelebs*). *Proc. Royal Soc. B142*(908): 306–331, 331–358.

NICE, M. M. 1943. Studies on the life history of the song sparrow II. *Tr. Linnean Soc.*, New York. 6: 1–328.

SCOTT, J. P. 1958. Aggression. Chicago, University of Chicago Press, x, + 149 pp.

THORPE, W. H. 1956. *Learning and Instinct in Animals*. Cambridge, Mass., Harvard University Press, 493 pp.

TINBERGEN, N. 1951. *The Study of Instinct*. London, Oxford University Press.

WHYTE, W. F. 1955. *Street Corner Society*. Chicago, University of Chicago Press.

INDEX